PEARSON
Physical Science
Concepts in Action
Part 1

Wysession • Frank • Yancopoulos

PEARSON

Boston, Massachusetts
Chandler, Arizona
Glenview, Illinois
Upper Saddle River, New Jersey

Cover Art: Courtesy of Tom Sanders/Image State.

Taken from:

Pearson Physical Science: Concepts in Action
By Michael Wysession, David Frank, and Sophia Yancopoulos
Copyright © 2011 by Pearson Education, Inc.
Published by Pearson Prentice Hall
Upper Saddle River, New Jersey 07458

This special edition published in cooperation with Pearson Learning Solutions.

Pearson Learning Solutions, 501 Boylston Street, Suite 900, Boston, MA 02116
A Pearson Education Company
www.pearsoned.com

Printed in the United States of America

1 2 3 4 5 6 7 8 9 10 V0ZN 16 15 14 13 12 11

000200010271276124

CT

PEARSON　　ISBN 10: 1-256-33216-x
ISBN 13: 978-1-256-33216-9

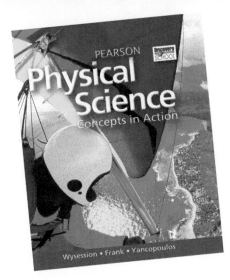

Pearson

Physical Science
Concepts in Action

The cover photograph of a hang glider shows chemistry and physics concepts in action.

Print Components
Student Edition
Progress Monitoring Assessments
Teacher's Edition
Easy Planner
Laboratory Manual
Laboratory Manual, Teacher's Edition
Reading and Study Workbook, Levels A and B
Reading and Study Workbook, Levels A and B,
    Teacher's Editions
Chapter and Unit Tests
Transparencies
Test-Taking Tips With Transparencies
Test Preparation Blackline Masters
Standardized Test Preparation Workbook
Math Skills and Problem Solving Workbook
Virtual Physical Science Lab Record Sheets Workbook

Technology
Interactive Textbook Online
StudentEXPRESS CD-ROM
PresentationEXPRESS CD-ROM
Probeware Lab Manual With CD-ROM
Virtual Physical Science CD-ROM
Discovery Channel Field Trips Videotapes
Discovery Channel Video Field Trips DVD
ExamView® Computer Test Bank CD-ROM
TeacherEXPRESS CD-ROM
Web site at PHSchool.com

Spanish Resources
Spanish Reading and Study Workbook
Spanish Chapter and Unit Tests
Spanish Section Summaries on Audio CD

Michael Wysession

Michael Wysession received his Ph.D. in geophysics from Northwestern University in 1991. He is an Associate Professor in Earth and Planetary Sciences at Washington University in St. Louis, Missouri. His area of specialization is using seismic waves to explore Earth's interior. Dr. Wysession is an author on more than 50 scientific publications. For his research, he was awarded a Packard Foundation Fellowship, and in 1996 was awarded a Presidential Faculty Fellowship at the White House. He also has created educational simulations to accurately show how seismic waves propagate. He currently chairs the Education & Outreach program for the Incorporated Research Institutions for Seismology (IRIS).

David Frank

David Frank completed his Ph.D. at Purdue University. For the last ten years he has been the head of the Physical Sciences Department at Ferris State University in Big Rapids, Michigan. He has taught general chemistry courses for science majors and for allied health students. With the assistance of his colleagues, he helped develop a new B.A. program in biochemistry. He has taught students in the university's Math/Science/Technology program, which enrolls gifted high school students. Recently he has worked with Michigan's "Connecting With the Learner" group, which produced a toolkit to help elementary and secondary teachers address diversity issues in the classroom.

Sophia Yancopoulos

Sophia Yancopoulos received her Ph.D. in physics from Columbia University. She has done postdoctoral research in astronomy at Yale University and in biophysics at the Mount Sinai School of Medicine. She considers teaching to be a vital and exciting part of her experience, having taught at Barnard College, Vassar College, the Stevens Institute of Technology, and Columbia University, as well as at Bronx High School of Science. She has worked on a neutrino oscillations experiment at Fermi National Laboratory, conducted experiments on acoustic modeling, and analyzed data on the extreme astrophysics of neutron stars. Currently she does research in genome evolution and works with a team of scientists at the Feinstein Institute for Medical Research trying to find a cure for a form of leukemia.

Contributing Writers

Steve Miller
Science Writer
State College,
Pennsylvania

Polly Weissman
Science Writer
New York, New York

T. Griffith Jones
P.K. Yonge Developmental
  Research School
College of Education—
University of Florida
Gainesville, Florida

Contributing Writers for DK

Robert Dinwiddie
M.A. M.Sc.
Science Writer
London, England

Susan Watt
M.A. M.Sc.
Science Writer
London, England

Reading Consultant

Bonnie Armbruster, Ph.D.
Department of Curriculum
  and Instruction
University of Illinois
Champaign, Illinois

Laboratory Activity Writers

Robert W. Arts
Associate Professor of
  Physics
Pikeville College
Pikeville, Kentucky

Hasan Fakhrudin
Physics Instructor
Indiana Academy for
  Science, Mathematics,
  and Humanities
Muncie, Indiana

Yvonne Favaro
Science Teacher (retired)
Englewood Cliffs,
New Jersey

JoAnne Mowczko, Ed.D.
Science Writer
Gaithersburg, Maryland

Brian Rohrig
Science Teacher
Columbus Public Schools
Columbus, Ohio

Safety Consultant

Dr. Kenneth R. Roy
Director, Science and
  Safety
Glastonbury Public
  Schools
Glastonbury, Connecticut

Content Reviewers

v

Contents

Labs and Activities

Inquiry Activity

Begin each chapter with an activity that sets a purpose for reading.

☰ Quick Lab

Introduce and reinforce key lesson content using simple materials.

Exploration › Lab — Practice and develop science methods.

Consumer › Lab — Make science concepts relevant by testing consumer products.

Forensics › Lab — Develop investigation skills in an engaging context.

Application › Lab — Apply concepts in a real-world context.

Design Your Own › Lab — Design and carry out open-ended experiments.

 Probe or sensor versions are available in the Probeware Lab Manual.

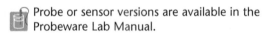 Go Online — PHSchool.com — Share data with students from across the country at phschool.com

Problem-Solving Activity

Apply science content in a new situation.

Math Skills

Develop math skills with sample problems and practice problems.

Data Analysis

Organize and analyze data to draw conclusions.

Features

CHAPTER

1

Science Skills

A technician tends a reactor that contains bacteria. The bacteria produce proteins that will be used in medicines.

21st Century Learning
Information and Media Literacy

How does curiosity lead to scientific discoveries?

Science begins with curiosity and often ends with discovery. Go online and search for articles about a scientific discovery that you have previously read about or heard about. Identify the types of questions that drove and guided the scientists' investigation. Create a timeline or flowchart that summarizes the progress of the investigation, and present it to your class.

How do science concepts apply to your world? Here are some questions you'll be able to answer after you read this chapter.

- **How do scientists plan to study Mars in the future?** *(Section 1.1)*

- **Which keeps you drier in the rain, walking or running?** *(Section 1.2)*

- **How do police investigators use scientific methods to solve a crime?** *(page 12)*

- **How many stars are there in the Milky Way galaxy?** *(Section 1.3)*

- **What is Earth's crust made of?** *(Section 1.4)*

DISCOVERY
CHANNEL
SCHOOL

Video Field Trip

Cracking the Case

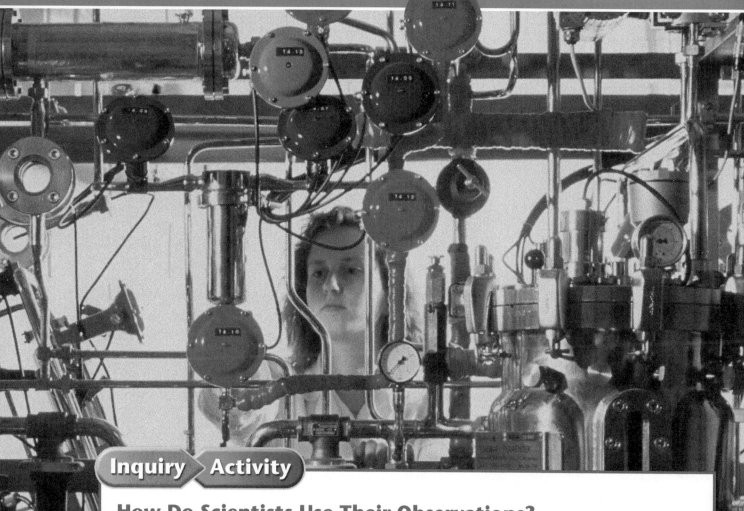

Inquiry ⟩ Activity

How Do Scientists Use Their Observations?

Procedure

1. Observe the liquid that your teacher gives you. Record your observations. **CAUTION** *Do not touch or drink the liquid.*

2. Use scissors and a metric ruler to cut a 5-cm square of aluminum foil. Loosely crumple the foil and drop it into the liquid.

3. Use a stirring rod to push the foil below the surface of the liquid. Observe and record any changes that occur in the liquid and foil.

Think About It

1. **Posing Questions** Write three questions about the materials or the changes that you observed.

2. **Designing Experiments** What could you do with the same or other materials to discover an answer to one of your questions?

3. **Communicating Results** Share your proposed experiments with your classmates. What results would you expect to observe?

What Is Science?

Key Concepts

- How does the process of science start and end?
- What is the relationship between science and technology?
- What are the branches of natural science?

Vocabulary

- science
- technology
- chemistry
- physics
- geology
- astronomy
- biology

Reading Strategy

Previewing Skim the section to find out what the main branches of natural science are. Copy the concept map below. As you read, complete the concept map based on what you have learned.

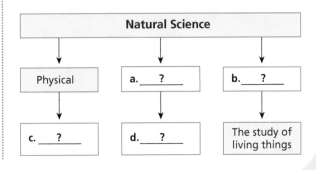

Natural Science		
Physical	a. ___?___	b. ___?___
c. ___?___	d. ___?___	The study of living things

Figure 1 In July 1997, the six-wheeled Sojourner rover became the first robot to explore planet Mars. The next generation of Mars rovers will help scientists further study the planet's geology, geography, and climate.

Suppose you could send a robot to another planet. What kinds of experiments would you program the robot to carry out? Before you programmed the robot, you would need to figure out what information you wanted it to gather. Scientists are currently developing robots, like the one in Figure 1, that they plan to send to Mars. These robots are being designed to examine the atmosphere, rocks, gravity, and magnetic fields of the planet.

Science involves asking questions about nature and then finding ways to answer them. This process doesn't happen by itself—it is driven by the curiosity of scientists.

Science From Curiosity

Throughout history, human beings have had a strong sense of curiosity. Human curiosity led to the use of fire, the building of tools, and the development of languages. Have you ever checked what was living at the bottom of a pond? Taken off the cover of a baseball to see what was inside? Tried putting more chocolate or less in your milk to find out how much would give the best flavor? These are all examples of curiosity, and curiosity is the basis of science.

Science is a system of knowledge and the methods you use to find that knowledge. Part of the excitement of science is that you never know what you will find. For instance, when you flip over a rock, will you see crawling insects, a snake, or nothing at all? You won't know until you look. ➤ **Science begins with curiosity and often ends with discovery.**

Curiosity provides questions but is seldom enough to achieve scientific results. Methods such as observing and measuring provide ways to find the answers. In some experiments, observations are qualitative, or descriptive. In others, they are quantitative, or numerical. Some experiments are impossible to do, such as observing what happened at the start of the universe. Scientists cannot go back in time to observe the creation of the universe. However, they can use the evidence of the universe around them to envision how this event occurred.

 What is science?

Science and Technology

As scientific knowledge is discovered, it can be applied in ways that improve the lives of people. **Technology** is the use of knowledge to solve practical problems. While the goal of science is to expand knowledge, the goal of technology is to apply that knowledge. Imagine living in the late 1700s, when there were no televisions, cars, antibiotics, or electricity. In a relatively small amount of time, people's lives changed dramatically. Perhaps your grandparents were born at a time when there were no televisions, and your parents were born at a time when there were no personal computers. Technology will have also changed your world dramatically by the time the generation following yours comes along.

Figure 2 illustrates the rapid evolution of the telephone, a technology invented in 1876. Within two years, the first telephone operators were connecting calls by hand. The first coin-operated phones appeared in 1889. By 1927, it was possible to make a phone call from New York to London. World War II saw the development of the first mobile telephones, which paved the way for modern cellular phones. Today, you can communicate by telephone between almost any two places in the world.

➤ **Science and technology are interdependent. Advances in one lead to advances in the other.** For example, advances in the study of physics led to the invention of the transistor. The use of transistors, in turn, led to advances in various other scientific fields, such as computer science and space science.

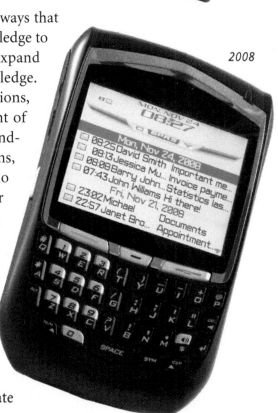

1876

1914

1955

2008

Figure 2 Telephones have quickly evolved from cumbersome, expensive machines to practical, cheap tools for communicating. **Classifying** *How is a telephone an example of both science and technology?*

Figure 3 Natural science covers a very broad range of knowledge. **Interpreting Diagrams** *How could you change this diagram to show how the branches of science can overlap?*

Branches of Science

The study of science is divided into social science and natural science. 🔑 **Natural science is generally divided into three branches: physical science, Earth and space science, and life science.** Each of these branches can be further divided, as shown in Figure 3.

Physical science covers a broad range of study that focuses on non-living things. The two main areas of physical science are chemistry and physics. **Chemistry** is the study of the composition, structure, properties, and reactions of matter. **Physics** is the study of matter and energy and the interactions between the two through forces and motion.

The application of physics and chemistry to the study of Earth is called Earth science. The foundation of Earth science is **geology,** the study of the origin, history, and structure of Earth. Geology has traditionally focused on the study of Earth's rocks. However, modern Earth science also involves the study of systems that may include living organisms. The foundation of space science is **astronomy,** the study of the universe beyond Earth, including the sun, moon, planets, and stars.

The study of living things is known as **biology,** or life science. Biology is not only the physics and chemistry of living things, but the study of the origin and behavior of living things. Biologists study the different ways that organisms grow, survive, and reproduce.

The problem with subdividing science into different areas is that there is often overlap between them. The boundary around each area of science is not always clear. For instance, much of biology is also chemistry, while much of chemistry is also physics. And a rapidly growing area of physics is biophysics, the application of physics to biology.

 Reading Checkpoint *What is physical science?*

The Big Ideas of Physical Science

What are the basic rules of nature? You can read this book to find out. As a sneak preview, some of these rules are summarized here. You can think of them as the big ideas of physical science. Keep in mind that there are also unknown rules of nature that are waiting to be discovered. In fact, you can take part in the search for these unknown laws if you become a scientist. Even though scientists have already discovered a great deal about the universe, there is still much to learn.

Space and Time The universe is both very old and very big. The age of the universe is about 13,700,000,000 (13.7 billion) years. The observable universe is about 700,000,000,000,000,000,000,000,000 (700 million billion billion) meters in diameter. The diameter of Earth is "only" 12,700,000 meters. To get an idea of how big this distance is, the diameter of a giant beach ball is about 1 meter.

Matter and Change A very small amount of the universe is matter. Matter has volume and mass, and on Earth usually takes the form of a solid, liquid, or gas. All matter that you are familiar with, from plants to stars to animals to humans, is made up of building blocks called atoms. Atoms consist of even smaller building blocks called electrons, protons, and neutrons.

Forces and Motion If you push on something that is sitting still, it starts to move. If you push on something that is already moving, you will change its motion. Forces cause changes in motion. As Figure 4 shows, your world is filled with motion and forces. Calculating these forces can sometimes be very challenging. For example, on a NASA mission to Mars, the Mars Exploration Rover must blast off from Earth on a rocket with enough speed to escape Earth's gravity. The rover must then travel a great distance through space on the rocket and land delicately on a planet that is moving very rapidly around the Sun. The laws of physics allow these movements to be calculated exactly so that the NASA robots get to where scientists want them to go.

For: Links on motion
Visit: www.SciLinks.org
Web Code: ccn-0011

Figure 4 The motion of cars on a city street is captured in this time-exposure photograph. Forces govern changes in the motion of each car.

Figure 5 Panels on a solar car convert energy from the sun into the mechanical energy of its moving parts.

Energy Energy exists in many forms. Moving objects have a kind of energy called kinetic energy. Objects moved against a force have another kind of energy called potential energy. Energy also exists in matter itself. When one form of matter changes into another form, energy is either absorbed or released. Matter itself can also be changed into energy.

Energy can be transferred from one form or object to another, but it can never be destroyed. If you push on a door and it swings open, you transfer energy from yourself to the door. Your cells are using the chemical energy stored in the food you have eaten to supply energy to your muscles, which then transfer energy to the door.

Science and Your Perspective

As you read this book, remember that science is both a process and a body of knowledge. The information in this book represents the best up-to-date models of how the universe works. However, like all models, some of these models will be rejected and replaced in the future. For instance, more moons revolving around Jupiter and Saturn will most likely be discovered as telescopes get better. It is therefore possible that by the time you read this book Saturn will be known to have more than the 62 moons currently identified. Be skeptical. Ask questions. Be aware that the scientific facts of today might change tomorrow. However, believe in the scientific process that has discovered them. And believe that you may be the one who makes the discoveries that will change scientific facts in the future.

Section 1.1 Assessment

Reviewing Concepts

1. ◠ How does the scientific process start and end?

2. ◠ How are science and technology related?

3. ◠ What are the branches of natural science?

4. Explain the advantages and disadvantages of subdividing science into many different areas.

5. Why do scientists seek to discover new laws of the universe?

Critical Thinking

6. **Evaluating** Why does the progress of science require both curiosity and methodology? Explain the role of each in scientific investigations.

7. **Making Judgments** Advances in science do not always immediately lead to advances in technology. Why are such scientific advances still valuable?

8. **Classifying** Is the study of the muscle movements in the human body an example of biology or of physics? Explain.

Writing in Science

Compare and Contrast Paragraph Write a paragraph comparing two branches of science. (*Hint:* Use an example that shows how these branches can overlap.)

1.2 Using a Scientific Approach

Reading Focus

Key Concepts

- What is the goal of a scientific method?
- How does a scientific law differ from a scientific theory?
- Why are scientific models useful?

Vocabulary

- scientific method
- observation
- hypothesis
- manipulated variable
- responding variable
- controlled experiment
- scientific theory
- scientific law
- model

Reading Strategy

Using Prior Knowledge Before you read, copy the web diagram below. Add to the web diagram what you already know about scientific methods. After you read, revise the diagram based on what you have learned.

If you've ever been caught in the rain without an umbrella, your first instinct was probably to start running. After all, the less time you spend in the rain, the less water there is falling down on you. So you might think that running in the rain keeps you drier than walking in the rain over a given distance. However, by running in the rain you run into more raindrops than by walking, thereby wetting more of your face, chest, and legs. Have your instincts been getting you wetter instead of keeping you drier?

You now have a question that you can try to answer with a scientific approach. Which keeps you drier in the rain—walking or running?

Scientific Methods

In order to answer questions about the world around them, scientists need to gather information. An organized plan for gathering, organizing, and communicating information is called a **scientific method.** Despite the name, a scientific method can be used by anyone, including yourself. All you need is a reason to use it. **The goal of any scientific method is to solve a problem or to better understand an observed event.**

Figure 6 To run, or not to run: that is the question. **Designing Experiments** *How can you test if running in the rain keeps you drier than walking in the rain over the same distance?*

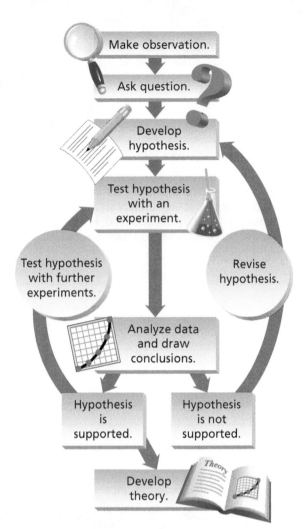

Figure 7 outlines an example of a scientific method. Each step in the method shown involves specific skills, some of which you will be learning as you read this book. It is important to note that scientific methods can vary from case to case. For example, one scientist might follow the steps shown in Figure 7 in a different order, or another might choose to skip one or more steps.

Making Observations Scientific investigations often begin with observations. An **observation** is information that you obtain through your senses. Repeatable observations are known as facts. For example, when you walk or run in the rain, you get wet. Standing in the rain leaves you much wetter than walking or running in the rain. You might combine these observations into a question: How does your speed affect how wet you get when you are caught in the rain?

Forming a Hypothesis A **hypothesis** is a proposed answer to a question. To answer the question raised by your observations about traveling in the rain, you might guess that the faster your speed, the drier you will stay in the rain. What can you do with your hypothesis? For a hypothesis to be useful, it must be testable.

 What is a hypothesis?

Figure 7 A scientific method provides a useful strategy for solving problems.
Inferring Is an observation required in order for you to arrive at a question? What does this tell you about the strictness of the scientific method?

Testing a Hypothesis Scientists perform experiments to test their hypotheses. In an experiment, any factor that can change is called a variable. Suppose you do an experiment to test if speed affects how wet you get in the rain. The variables will include your speed, your size, the rate of rainfall, and the amount of water that hits you.

Your hypothesis states that one variable, speed, causes a change in another variable, the amount of water that hits you. The speed with which you walk or run is the **manipulated variable,** or the variable that causes a change in another. The amount of water that you accumulate is the **responding variable,** or the variable that changes in response to the manipulated variable. To examine the relationship between a manipulated variable and a responding variable, scientists use controlled experiments. A **controlled experiment** is an experiment in which only one variable, the manipulated variable, is deliberately changed at a time. While the responding variable is observed for changes, all other variables are kept constant, or controlled.

In 1997, two meteorologists conducted a controlled experiment to determine if moving faster keeps you drier in the rain. In the experiment, both scientists traveled 100 yards by foot in the rain. One of them walked; the other ran. By measuring the mass of their clothes before and after traveling in the rain, the scientists were able to measure how much water each had accumulated. One of the controlled variables was size—the two scientists were about the same height and build. Another was the rate of rainfall—the scientists began traveling at the same time during the same rainstorm on the same path. A third was the ability to absorb water—the scientists wore identical sets of clothes.

Drawing Conclusions The scientists' rainy-day experiment produced some convincing data. The clothes of the walking scientist accumulated 217 grams of water, while the clothes of the running scientists accumulated 130 grams of water. Based on their data, the scientists concluded that running in the rain keeps you drier than walking—about 40 percent drier, in fact. Now you have scientific evidence to support the hypothesis stated earlier.

What happens if the data do not support the hypothesis? In such a case, a scientist can revise the hypothesis or propose a new one, based on the data from the experiment. A new experiment must then be designed to test the revised or new hypothesis.

Developing a Theory Once a hypothesis has been supported in repeated experiments, scientists can begin to develop a theory. A **scientific theory** is a well-tested explanation for a set of observations or experimental results. For example, according to the kinetic theory of matter, all particles of matter are in constant motion. Kinetic theory explains a wide range of observations, such as ice melting or the pressure of a gas.

Theories are never proved. Instead, they become stronger if the facts continue to support them. However, if an existing theory fails to explain new facts and discoveries, the theory may be revised or a new theory may replace it.

Scientific Laws

After repeated observations or experiments, scientists may arrive at a scientific law. A **scientific law** is a statement that summarizes a pattern found in nature. For example, Newton's law of gravity describes how two objects attract each other by means of a gravitational force. This law has been verified over and over. However, scientists have yet to agree on a theory that explains how gravity works. **A scientific law describes an observed pattern in nature without attempting to explain it. The explanation of such a pattern is provided by a scientific theory.**

Go Online
SCIENCE NEWS®

For: Articles on the nature of science
Visit: PHSchool.com
Web Code: cce-0011

Figure 8 An environmental scientist collects a sample for a water pollution study. After analyzing the sample, the scientist can draw conclusions about how the water became polluted.

Figure 9 Two engineers discuss a computer-aided design, or CAD, of an aircraft component.

Scientific Models

If you have ever been lost in a city, you know that a street map can help you find your location. A street map is a type of **model,** or representation, of an object or event. ⬤ **Scientific models make it easier to understand things that might be too difficult to observe directly.** For example, to understand how Earth rotates on its axis, you could look at a globe, which is a small-scale model of Earth. The computer model in Figure 9 represents the interior of an airplane. Other models help you visualize things that are too small to see, such as atoms. As long as a model lets you mentally picture what is supposed to be represented, then the model has done its job.

An example of a mental, rather than physical, model might be that comets are like giant snowballs, primarily made of ice. Scientists tested this model with observations and experiments. In 2006, a space probe collected samples from a comet. Tests on the samples confirmed that comets are made of ice, but the tests also showed that comets contain rocky material that is formed near the sun. So, a modified model of comets was adopted.

If new data show that a model is wrong, then it must either be changed or be replaced by a new model. If scientists never challenged old models, then nothing new would be learned, and we would still believe what we believed hundreds of years ago. Science works by making mistakes. The fact that newer models are continually replacing old models is a sign that new discoveries are continually occurring. As the knowledge that makes up science keeps changing, scientists develop a better and better understanding of the universe.

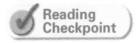 **Reading Checkpoint**   *What is a model?*

Working Safely in Science

Scientists working in the field, or in a laboratory, like those in Figure 10, are trained to use safe procedures when carrying out investigations. Laboratory work may involve flames or hot plates, electricity, chemicals, hot liquids, sharp instruments, and breakable glassware.

Whenever you work in your science laboratory, it's important for you to follow safety precautions at all times. Before performing any activity in this course, study the rules in the Science Safety section of the Skills Handbook. Before you start any activity, read all the steps. Make sure that you understand the entire procedure, especially any safety precautions that must be followed.

The single most important rule for your safety is simple: Always follow your teacher's instructions and the textbook directions exactly. If you are in doubt about any step in an activity, always ask your teacher for an explanation. Because you may be in contact with chemicals you cannot see, it is essential that you wash your hands thoroughly after every scientific activity. Remember, you share responsibility for your own safety and that of your teacher and classmates.

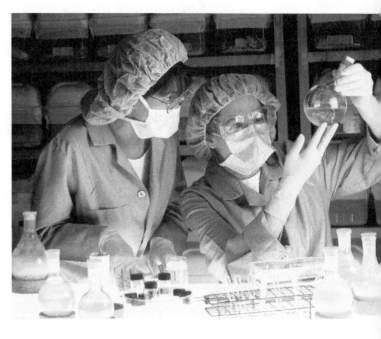

Figure 10 Safety plays an important role in science. Interpreting Photos *What safety measures are these scientists taking in their laboratory work?*

Section 1.2 Assessment

Reviewing Concepts

1. What is the goal of scientific methods?
2. How does a scientific law differ from a scientific theory?
3. Why are scientific models useful?
4. What are three types of variables in a controlled experiment?
5. Does every scientific method begin with an observation? Explain.

Critical Thinking

6. **Classifying** The scientists who tested the hypothesis on running in the rain performed only one controlled experiment that supported their hypothesis. Can their supported hypothesis be called a theory? Explain.

7. **Designing Experiments** Suppose you wanted to find out how running affects your pulse rate. What would your hypothesis be? Explain how you could test your hypothesis.

8. **Using Models** A scientific model can take the form of a physical object or a concept. List one example of each type of model. How does each one resemble what it is supposed to model?

Writing in Science

Descriptive Paragraph Write a paragraph describing two examples of pseudoscience. Use your examples to explain why pseudoscience is not actual science.

Forensic Science

The first job of police officers at a crime scene is to seal off the area so that potential evidence is not disturbed. Such evidence will be sent to a forensic science laboratory for examination.

Forensic science is the use of scientific methods, such as fingerprint matching or the analysis of clothing fibers, to solve crimes. As techniques in analytical chemistry have become more advanced, the amount of information that can be gleaned from tiny crime-scene samples has grown. Forensic science is becoming ever more powerful as a crime-solving tool.

Criminal investigators need to use several scientific techniques. They include making observations, establishing the problem to be solved, collecting evidence and gathering information, forming hypotheses, analyzing evidence, testing hypotheses, and drawing conclusions.

The crime scene
At the scene, the investigators make observations that may shed light on the nature of the crime. The investigators establish the problem to be solved—in this case, who committed the murder?

Collecting evidence and forming a hypothesis
Forensic scientists take photographs and collect materials from the crime scene. Investigators use all of the information gathered to formulate hypotheses about how and why the crime took place.

DNA evidence can be obtained from blood stains.

Analyzing the evidence

Much of the physical evidence must be analyzed in a laboratory. With a blood sample, for example, DNA is extracted and analyzed and the blood type is established.

Forensic blood sampling *Articles from a crime scene, such as the blood-stained clothing and the hatchet shown here, may match DNA to a suspect.*

Displaced objects can help determine a sequence of events.

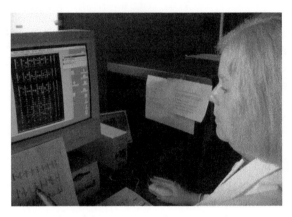

Testing hypotheses against the evidence

Investigators now test hypotheses on who committed the crime—looking for matches in DNA, fingerprints, or clothing fibers, for example. In some cases, this testing excludes a suspect. In other cases it strengthens the case against a particular person.

Drawing conclusions

To build a convincing case against a suspect, various pieces and types of evidence may be needed. Evidence might include a fingerprint match, a piece of clothing left at the crime scene, or a connection to the murder weapon.

Documents may provide evidence for a motive.

Fibers can link a suspect to a crime scene.

Going Further

- Describe how criminal investigators use scientific methods to solve their cases. (*Hint:* start by creating a flowchart of a scientific method. Then identify how criminal investigators carry out each step.)

- Take a Discovery Channel Video Field Trip by watching "Cracking the Case."

DISCOVERY CHANNEL SCHOOL™

Video Field Trip

1.3 Measurement

Reading Focus

Key Concepts

- Why is scientific notation useful?
- What units do scientists use for their measurements?
- How does the precision of measurements affect the precision of scientific calculations?

Vocabulary

- scientific notation
- length
- mass
- volume
- density
- conversion factor
- precision
- significant figures
- accuracy
- thermometer

Reading Strategy

Previewing Make a table like the one below. Before you read the section, rewrite the green and blue topic headings as questions. As you read, write answers to the questions.

Measurement
Why is scientific notation useful?
a. _____?_____
b. _____?_____

How old are you? How tall are you? The answers to these questions are measurements. Measurements are important in both science and everyday life. Hardly a day passes without the need for you to measure amounts of money or the passage of time. It would be difficult to imagine doing science without any measurements.

Figure 11 Scientists estimate that there are more than 200 billion stars in the Milky Way galaxy. **Applying Concepts** *What is this number in scientific notation?*

Using Scientific Notation

How many stars do you see in Figure 11? There are too many to count. Scientists often work with very large or very small numbers. For example, the speed of light is about 300,000,000 meters per second. On the other hand, an average snail has been clocked at a speed of only 0.00086 meter per second.

Instead of having to write out all the zeroes in these numbers, you can use a shortcut called scientific notation. **Scientific notation** is a way of expressing a value as the product of a number between 1 and 10 and a power of 10. For example, the number 300,000,000 written in scientific notation is 3.0×10^8. The exponent, 8, tells you that the decimal point is really 8 places to the right of the 3.

For numbers less than 1 that are written in scientific notation, the exponent is negative. For example, the number 0.00086 written in scientific notation is 8.6×10^{-4}. The negative exponent tells you how many decimals places there are to the *left* of the 8.6. **Scientific notation makes very large or very small numbers easier to work with.**

When multiplying numbers written in scientific notation, you multiply the numbers that appear before the multiplication signs and *add* the exponents. For example, to calculate how far light travels in 500 seconds, you multiply the speed of light by the number of seconds.

$$(3.0 \times 10^8 \text{ m/s}) \times (5.0 \times 10^2 \text{ s}) = 15 \times 10^{10} \text{ m} = 1.5 \times 10^{11} \text{ m}$$

This distance is about how far the sun is from Earth.

When dividing numbers written in scientific notation, you divide the numbers that appear before the exponential terms and *subtract* the exponents. For example, to calculate how long it takes for light from the sun to reach Earth, you would perform a division.

$$\frac{1.5 \times 10^{11} \text{ m}}{3.0 \times 10^8 \text{ m/s}} = \frac{1.5}{3.0} \times 10^{11-8} \text{ s} = 0.50 \times 10^3 \text{ s} = 5.0 \times 10^2 \text{ s}$$

For: Links on universal measurements

Visit: PHSchool.com

Web Code: ccc-0013

Using Scientific Notation

A rectangular parking lot has a length of 1.1×10^3 meters and a width of 2.4×10^3 meters. What is the area of the parking lot?

 Read and Understand

What information are you given?

Length (l) = 1.1×10^3 m

Width (w) = 2.4×10^3 m

2 **Plan and Solve**

What unknown are you trying to calculate?

Area (A) = ?

What formula contains the given quantities and the unknown?

$$A = l \times w$$

Replace each variable with its known value.

$$A = l \times w = (1.1 \times 10^3 \text{ m})(2.4 \times 10^3 \text{ m})$$
$$= (1.1 \times 2.4)\,(10^{3+3})(\text{m} \times \text{m})$$
$$= 2.6 \times 10^6 \text{ m}^2$$

 Look Back and Check

Is your answer reasonable?

Yes, the number calculated is the product of the numbers given, and the units (m^2) indicate area.

Math Practice

1. Perform the following calculations. Express your answers in scientific notation.

   a. $(7.6 \times 10^{-4} \text{ m}) \times (1.5 \times 10^7 \text{ m})$

   b. $0.00053 \div 29$

2. Calculate how far light travels in 8.64×10^4 seconds. (*Hint:* The speed of light is about 3.0×10^8 m/s.)

SI Units of Measurement

For a measurement to make sense, it requires both a number and a unit. For example, if you told one of your friends that you had finished a homework assignment "in five," what would your friend think? Would it be five minutes or five hours? Maybe it was a long assignment, and you actually meant five days. Or maybe you meant that you wrote five pages. You should always express measurements in numbers and units so that their meaning is clear. In Figure 12, students are measuring temperature in degrees Celsius.

Many of the units you are familiar with, such as inches, feet, and degrees Fahrenheit, are not units that are used in science. **Scientists use a set of measuring units called SI, or the International System of Units.** The abbreviation stands for the French name *Système International d'Unités.* SI is a revised version of the metric system, which was originally developed in France in 1791. By adhering to one system of units, scientists can readily interpret one another's measurements.

Figure 12 A measurement consists of a number and a unit. One of the units used to measure temperature is the degree Celsius.

Base Units and Derived Units SI is built upon seven metric units, known as base units, which are listed in Figure 13. In SI, the base unit for **length,** or the straight-line distance between two points, is the meter (m). The base unit for **mass,** or the quantity of matter in an object or sample, is the kilogram (kg).

Additional SI units, called derived units, are made from combinations of base units. Figure 14 lists some common derived units. For example, **volume** is the amount of space taken up by an object. The volume of a rectangular box equals its length times its width times its height. Each of these dimensions can be measured in meters, so you can derive the SI unit for volume by multiplying meters by meters by meters, which gives you cubic meters (m^3).

SI Base Units		
Quantity	Unit	Symbol
Length	meter	m
Mass	kilogram	kg
Temperature	kelvin	K
Time	second	s
Amount of substance	mole	mol
Electric current	ampere	A
Luminous intensity	candela	cd

Figure 13 Seven metric base units make up the foundation of SI.

Derived Units		
Quantity	Unit	Symbol
Area	square meter	m^2
Volume	cubic meter	m^3
Density	kilograms per cubic meter	kg/m^3
Pressure	pascal ($kg/m \cdot s^2$)	Pa
Energy	joule ($kg \cdot m^2/s^2$)	J
Frequency	hertz ($1/s$)	Hz
Electric charge	coulomb ($A \cdot s$)	C

Figure 14 Specific combinations of SI base units yield derived units.

SI Prefixes			
Prefix	Symbol	Meaning	Multiply Unit by
giga-	G	billion (10^9)	1,000,000,000
mega-	M	million (10^6)	1,000,000
kilo-	k	thousand (10^3)	1000
deci-	d	tenth (10^{-1})	0.1
centi-	c	hundredth (10^{-2})	0.01
milli-	m	thousandth (10^{-3})	0.001
micro-	μ	millionth (10^{-6})	0.000001
nano-	n	billionth (10^{-9})	0.000000001

Figure 15 Metric prefixes allow for more convenient ways to express SI base and derived units.

Another quantity that requires a derived unit is density. **Density** is the ratio of an object's mass to its volume.

$$\text{Density} = \frac{\text{Mass}}{\text{Volume}}$$

To derive the SI unit for density, you can divide the base unit for mass by the derived unit for volume. Dividing kilograms by cubic meters yields the SI unit for density, kilograms per cubic meter (kg/m^3).

 Reading Checkpoint   *What is the SI derived unit for density?*

Metric Prefixes The metric unit for a given quantity is not always a convenient one to use. For example, the time it takes for a computer hard drive to read or write data—also known as the seek time—is in the range of thousandths of a second. A typical seek time might be 0.009 second. This can be written in a more compact way by using a metric prefix. A metric prefix indicates how many times a unit should be multiplied or divided by 10. Figure 15 shows some common metric prefixes. Using the prefix *milli-* (m), you can write 0.009 second as 9 milliseconds, or 9 ms.

$$9 \text{ ms} = \frac{9}{1000} \text{ s} = 0.009 \text{ s}$$

Note that dividing by 1000 is the same as multiplying by 0.001.

Metric prefixes can also make a unit larger. For example, a distance of 12,000 meters can also be written as 12 kilometers.

$$12 \text{ km} = 12 \times 1000 \text{ m} = 12,000 \text{ m}$$

Metric prefixes turn up in non-metric units as well. If you have used a digital camera, you may know that a megapixel is 1,000,000 pixels. A kiloton is a unit of explosive force equal to 1,000 tons of TNT.

Figure 16 A bar of gold has more mass per unit volume than a feather. **Inferring** *Which takes up more space—one kilogram of gold or one kilogram of feathers?*

Nutrition Facts

Serving Size 1 oz (28g/about 18 chips)
Servings Per Container 7

Amount Per Serving

Calories 150   Calories from Fat 80

	% Daily Value*
Total Fat 9g	**14%**
Saturated Fat 1g	**5%**
Polyunsaturated Fat 1g	
Monounsaturated Fat 7g	
Cholesterol 0mg	**0%**
Sodium 160mg	**7%**

Figure 17 Nutrition labels often have some measurements listed in grams and milligrams.
Calculating **How many grams are in 160 milligrams?**

The easiest way to convert from one unit of measurement to another is to use conversion factors. A **conversion factor** is a ratio of equivalent measurements that is used to convert a quantity expressed in one unit to another unit. Suppose you want to convert the height of Mount Everest, 8848 meters, into kilometers. Based on the prefix *kilo-*, you know that 1 kilometer is 1000 meters. This ratio gives you two possible conversion factors.

$$\frac{1 \text{ km}}{1000 \text{ m}} \qquad \frac{1000 \text{ m}}{1 \text{ km}}$$

Since you are converting from meters to kilometers, the number should get smaller. Multiplying by the conversion factor on the left yields a smaller number.

$$8848 \text{ m} \times \frac{1 \text{ km}}{1000 \text{ m}} = 8.848 \text{ km}$$

Notice that the meter units cancel, leaving you with kilometers (the larger unit).

To convert 8.848 kilometers back into meters, multiply by the conversion factor on the right. Since you are converting from kilometers to meters, the number should get larger.

$$8.848 \text{ km} \times \frac{1000 \text{ m}}{1 \text{ km}} = 8848 \text{ m}$$

In this case, the kilometer units cancel, leaving you with meters.

≡Quick Lab

Comparing Precision

Materials

3 plastic bottles of different sizes, beaker, graduated cylinder

Procedure

1. Draw a data table with three rows and three columns. Label the columns Estimate, Beaker, and Graduated Cylinder.

2. Record your estimate of the volume of a plastic bottle in your data table. Then, fill the bottle with water and pour the water into the beaker. Read and record the volume of the water.

3. Pour the water from the beaker into the graduated cylinder. Read and record the volume of water.

4. Repeat Steps 2 and 3 with two other plastic bottles.

Analyze and Conclude

1. **Analyzing Data** Review your volume measurements for one of the bottles. How many significant figures does the volume measured with the beaker have? How many significant figures does the volume measured with the graduated cylinder have?

2. **Comparing and Contrasting** Which provided a more precise measurement—the beaker or the graduated cylinder?

3. **Inferring** How could you determine the accuracy of your measurements?

Limits of Measurement

Suppose you wanted to measure how much time it takes for you to eat your breakfast. Figure 18 shows two clocks you could use—an analog clock and a digital clock. The analog clock displays time to the nearest minute. The digital clock displays time to the nearest second (or one sixtieth of a minute). Which clock would you choose?

Precision The digital clock offers more precision. **Precision** is a gauge of how exact a measurement is. According to the analog clock, it might take you 5 minutes to eat your breakfast. Using the digital clock, however, you might measure 5 minutes and 15 seconds, or 5.25 minutes. The second measurement has more significant figures. **Significant figures** are all the digits that are known in a measurement, plus the last digit that is estimated. The time recorded as 5.25 minutes has three significant figures. The time recorded as 5 minutes has one significant figure. The fewer the significant figures, the less precise the measurement is.

When you make calculations with measurements, the uncertainty of the separate measurements must be correctly reflected in the final result. 🗝 **The precision of a calculated answer is limited by the least precise measurement used in the calculation.** So if the least precise measurement in your calculation has two significant figures, then your calculated answer can have at most two significant figures.

Suppose you measure the mass of a piece of iron to be 34.73 grams on an electronic balance. You then measure the volume to be 4.42 cubic centimeters. What is the density of the iron?

$$\text{Density} = \frac{34.73 \text{ g}}{4.42 \text{ cm}^3} = 7.857466 \text{ g/cm}^3$$

Your answer should have only three significant figures because the least precise measurement, the volume, has three significant figures. Rounding your answer to three significant figures gives you a density of 7.86 grams per cubic centimeter.

Accuracy Another important quality in a measurement is its accuracy. **Accuracy** is the closeness of a measurement to the actual value of what is being measured. For example, suppose the digital clock in Figure 18 is running 15 minutes slow. Although the clock would remain precise to the nearest second, the time displayed would not be accurate.

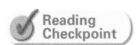 **Reading Checkpoint** *What is accuracy?*

Figure 18 A more precise time can be read from the digital clock than can be read from the analog clock. The digital clock is precise to the nearest second, while the analog clock is precise to the nearest minute.

Common Temperatures

	Fahrenheit (°F)	Celsius (°C)	Kelvin (K)
Water boils	212	100	373
Human body	98.6	37	310
Average room	68	20	293
Water freezes	32	0	273

Figure 19 Temperature can be expressed in degrees Fahrenheit, degrees Celsius, or kelvins.

Measuring Temperature

A **thermometer** is an instrument that measures temperature, or how hot an object is. The How It Works box on page 21 describes how a bulb thermometer measures temperature.

The two temperature scales that you are probably most familiar with are the Fahrenheit scale and the Celsius scale. On the Fahrenheit scale, water freezes at 32°F and boils at 212°F at sea level. On the Celsius (or centigrade) scale, water freezes at 0°C and boils at 100°C. A degree Celsius is almost twice as large as a degree Fahrenheit. There is also a difference of 32 degrees between the zero point of the Celsius scale and the zero point of the Fahrenheit scale. You can convert from one scale to the other by using one of the following formulas.

$$°C = \frac{5}{9}(°F - 32.0°) \qquad °F = \frac{9}{5}(°C) + 32.0°$$

The SI base unit for temperature is the kelvin (K). A temperature of 0 K, or 0 kelvin, refers to the lowest possible temperature that can be reached. In degrees Celsius, this temperature is $-273.15°C$. To convert between kelvins and degrees Celsius, use the following formula.

$$K = °C + 273$$

Figure 19 compares some common temperatures expressed in degrees Celsius, degrees Fahrenheit, and kelvins.

Section 1.3 Assessment

Reviewing Concepts

1. 🔵 Why do scientists use scientific notation?
2. 🔵 What system of units do scientists use for measurements?
3. 🔵 How does the precision of measurements affect the precision of scientific calculations?
4. List the SI units for mass, length, and temperature.

Critical Thinking

5. **Applying Concepts** A bulb thermometer gives an indoor temperature reading of 21°C. A digital thermometer in the same room gives a reading of 20.7°C. Which device is more precise? Explain.

6. **Calculating** Convert −11°F into degrees Celsius, and then into kelvins.

Math Practice

7. Write the following measurements in scientific notation. Then convert each measurement into SI base units.
   a. 0.0000000000372 g
   b. 45,000,000,000 km
8. The liquid in a bulb thermometer falls 1.1 cm. Calculate the liquid's change in volume if the inner radius of the tube is 6.5×10^{-3} cm.

Thermometer

A bulb thermometer consists of a sealed, narrow glass tube, called a capillary tube. It has a glass bulb at one end and is filled with colored alcohol or mercury. Because mercury is poisonous, mercury thermometers are rarely used in medicine. The thermometer works on the principle that the volume of a liquid changes when the temperature changes. When warmed, the liquid in the bulb takes up more space and moves up the capillary tube.

Interpreting Diagrams **Why is a thermometer with a narrow tube easier to read than one with a wide tube?**

Measuring temperature
Thermometers are useful scientific instruments. They can be used to measure the static temperature of a material, or to record the change in temperature of a substance being heated, as shown above.

Scale *The scale indicates the temperature according to how far up or down the capillary tube the liquid has moved.*

Celsius (centigrade) temperature scale

Fahrenheit scale

Capillary tube

Colored liquid *The liquid moves up and down the capillary tube as the temperature changes.*

Bulb *The bulb contains the reservoir of liquid.*

°C °F

Wide or narrow?
The volume of a tube is calculated using the formula $V = \pi r^2 l$, where r is the radius and l is the length. For a given volume, if the radius of a tube is decreased (as in a capillary tube), the length of the liquid column increases. Any change in volume is then easier to see.

Compressed scale

Liquid rises less in a wide tube for the same temperature change.

Liquid rises more in a narrow tube for the same temperature change.

Expanded, easy-to-read scale

1.4 Presenting Scientific Data

Reading Focus

Key Concepts
- How do scientists organize data?
- How can scientists communicate experimental data?

Vocabulary
- slope
- direct proportion
- inverse proportion

Reading Strategy

Comparing and Contrasting After you read this section, compare types of graphs by completing the table below.

Type of Graph	Description	Used For
Line	a. ___?___	b. ___?___
Bar	c. ___?___	d. ___?___
Circle	e. ___?___	f. ___?___

Much of the information you get every day comes from the news media. Newspapers, television, radio, and the Internet let you access a wealth of information about events going on in the world. But in order for news to be useful, it must be communicated. If a news reporter witnesses an event but doesn't report it, then he might as well not have seen it. If the event is reported, then it must be described in a clear, organized manner for it to be understood and appreciated. Like the news, scientific data become meaningful only when they are organized and communicated.

Organizing Data

Scientists accumulate vast amounts of data by observing events and making measurements. Interpreting these data can be a difficult task if they are not organized. **Scientists can organize their data by using data tables and graphs.** These tools make it easier to spot patterns or trends in the data that can support or disprove a hypothesis.

Data Tables The simplest way to organize data is to present them in a table. Figure 20 is a data table that shows the average annual precipitation for seven U.S. cities. The table relates two variables—a manipulated variable (location) and a responding variable (average annual precipitation).

Average Annual Precipitation for Selected U.S. Cities

City	Average Annual Precipitation (cm)
Buffalo, N.Y.	98.0
Chicago, Ill.	91.0
Colorado Springs, Colo.	41.2
Houston, Tex.	117.0
San Diego, Calif.	25.1
Tallahassee, Fla.	166.9
Tucson, Ariz.	30.5

Figure 20 Using a table is a simple way to present data visually.

Mass vs. Volume of Water

$$\text{Slope} = \frac{\text{Rise}}{\text{Run}} = \frac{5\text{ g}}{5\text{ cm}^3} = 1\text{ g/cm}^3$$

Rise = 5 g

Run = 5 cm^3

Mass (g)

Volume (cm^3)

Figure 21 Plotting the mass of water against the volume of water yields a straight line.
Using Graphs *What does the slope represent?*

Time to Fill a 1-gallon Pot With Water

Time (minutes)

Flow Rate (gallons per minute)

Figure 22 In an inverse proportion, the product of two variables remains constant. Each point on the graph above represents the same volume of water: 1 gallon.

Line Graphs A line graph is useful for showing changes that occur in related variables. In a line graph, the manipulated variable is generally plotted on the horizontal axis, or *x*-axis. The responding variable is plotted on the vertical axis, or *y*-axis, of the graph.

Figure 21 is a line graph that shows how the mass of water increases with volume. The data points yield a straight line. The steepness, or **slope,** of this line is the ratio of a vertical change to the corresponding horizontal change. The formula for the slope of a line is

$$\text{Slope} = \frac{\text{Rise}}{\text{Run}}$$

"Rise" represents the change in the *y*-variable. "Run" represents the corresponding change in the *x*-variable. Note that in Figure 21, because mass per unit volume is density, the slope represents the density of water.

The relationship between the mass and volume of water is an example of a direct proportion. A **direct proportion** is a relationship in which the ratio of two variables is constant. For example, suppose you have a 3-cubic-centimeter sample of water that has a mass of 3 grams. Doubling the volume of the sample to 6 cubic centimeters results in doubling the mass of the sample to 6 grams. Tripling the volume to 9 cubic centimeters results in tripling the mass to 9 grams.

Figure 22 shows how the flow rate of a water faucet affects the time required to fill a 1-gallon pot. Figure 22 illustrates an **inverse proportion,** a relationship in which the product of two variables is a constant. If you start with a flow rate of 0.5 gallon per minute, you will fill the pot in 2 minutes. If you double the flow rate to 1.0 gallon per minute, you reduce the time required to fill the pot to 1 minute, or one half of the original time.

Go **O**nline
active art

For: Activity on plotting line graphs
Visit: PHSchool.com
Web Code: ccp-0014

Science Skills **23**

Faster Than Speeding Data

A modem is a device used to send and receive data. For example, if you upload an image to a Web site, the modem in your computer converts the data of the image into a different format. The converted data are then sent through a telephone line or cable TV line. The smallest unit of data that can be read by a computer is a binary digit, or "bit." A bit is either a 0 or a 1. Computers process bits in larger units called bytes. A byte is a group of eight bits.

The table shows the data transfer rates for modems used in home computers. Data transfer rates are often measured in kilobits per second, or

Modem Speeds		
Type of Modem	Data Transfer Rate (kbps)	Upload Time for 1 MB (s)
56K dial-up	48	167
Cable (low-speed)	384	21
DSL (medium-speed)	512	16
DSL (high-speed)	768	10
Cable (high-speed)	2000	4

kbps. The time required to upload a 1-megabyte (MB) file is given for each rate listed.

1. **Using Graphs** Use the data in the table to create a line graph. Describe the relationship between data transfer rate and upload time.

2. **Inferring** How would doubling the data transfer rate affect the upload time?

Bar Graphs A bar graph is often used to compare a set of measurements, amounts, or changes. Figure 23 is a bar graph of the data from Figure 20. The bar graph makes it easy to see how the data for one city compare with the data for another.

Circle Graphs If you think of a pie cut into pieces, you have a mental model of a circle graph. A circle graph is a divided circle that shows how a part or share of something relates to the whole. Figure 24 is a circle graph that describes the composition of Earth's crust. The entire circle represents the mass of Earth's crust. Each "slice" of the circle represents a percentage of that mass corresponding to a specific substance.

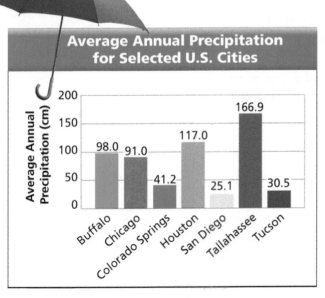

Figure 23 A bar graph is useful for comparing several measurements.

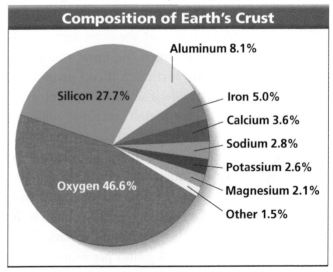

Figure 24 A circle graph is useful for showing how a part of something relates to the whole.

Communicating Data

A crucial part of any scientific investigation is reporting the results. **Scientists can communicate results by writing in scientific journals or speaking at conferences.** Scientists also exchange information through conversations, e-mails, and Web sites. Young scientists often present their research at science fairs like the one in Figure 25.

Different scientists may interpret the same data differently. This important notion is the basis for peer review, a process in which scientists examine other scientists' work. Not only do scientists share research with their peers, but they also invite feedback from those peers. Peer review encourages comments, suggestions, questions, and criticism from other scientists. Peer review can also help determine if data were reported accurately and honestly. Based on their peers' responses, the scientists who submitted their work for review can then reevaluate how to best interpret their data.

Figure 25 At a science fair, students communicate what knowledge they have gained by using scientific methods.

Section 1.4 Assessment

Reviewing Concepts

1. How do scientists organize data?

2. How can scientists communicate experimental results?

3. What does a given point represent on a line graph?

4. The density of copper is 8.92 g/cm³. If you plotted the mass of copper in grams versus the volume in cubic centimeters, what would the slope of the line be?

Critical Thinking

5. Comparing and Contrasting When would you choose a line graph to present data? When would you choose a bar graph?

6. Using Tables and Graphs Count the number of students in your class with blue eyes, brown eyes, and green eyes. Display these data in a table and bar graph.

Connecting Concepts

Scientific Methods Reread the description of scientific methods in Section 1.2. Then write a paragraph explaining which steps in a scientific method might require data to be organized. (*Hint:* You might use information diagrammed in Figure 7.)

Determining the Thickness of Aluminum Foil

Many products such as aluminum foil are too thin to measure easily. However, it is important for manufacturers to know how thick they are. They wouldn't be useful if they were made too thick or too thin. In this lab, you will use the same method that manufacturers use to determine the thickness of aluminum foil.

Problem
How can you determine the thickness of aluminum foil?

Materials
- metric ruler
- aluminum foil
- scissors
- balance
- graph paper

Skills
Measuring, Calculating, Using Graphs

Data Table				
Length (mm)	Area (mm²)	Mass (g)	Volume (mm³)	Thickness (mm)

Density of Alumnium = _____ g/mm³

Procedure

1. On a separate sheet of paper, make a copy of the data table shown. Include the information below the data table.

2. Cut out three squares of aluminum foil with sides of the following lengths: 50 mm, 100 mm, and 200 mm.

3. To determine the area of the 50-mm foil square, measure the length of one of its sides and then square it. Record the length and area in your data table.

4. Place the foil square on the balance to determine its mass. Record the mass of the foil square in your data table.

5. You will need the density of aluminum foil to calculate the volume of the foil square from its mass. The density of aluminum foil is 2.71 g/cm^3. Convert cm^3 to mm^3 and record the density of aluminum foil (in g/mm^3) on the line provided below your data table.

6. To determine the volume of the foil square, divide its mass by its density in g/mm^3. Record the volume in your data table.

7. To determine the thickness of the foil square, divide its volume by its area. Record this thickness in your data table.

8. Repeat Steps 3 through 7 using the 100-mm foil square.

9. Repeat Steps 3 through 7 using the 200-mm foil square.

10. Construct a graph of your data. Plot length on the horizontal axis and thickness on the vertical axis. Draw a straight line connecting all three points.

Analyze and Conclude

1. **Measuring** How many significant figures were there in your measurement of the length of each square of aluminum foil?

2. **Using Graphs** What effect, if any, did the length of the square have on your estimate of the thickness of the foil?

3. **Comparing** Which estimate of thickness was most precise? Explain your answer.

4. **Controlling Variables** What factors limited the precision of your measurements?

Go Further Aluminum is composed of small particles. Each particle has a diameter of 2.86×10^{-10} m. Calculate how many particles make up the thickness of the foil. Then, calculate the number of particles in the 50-mm square. Finally, determine the mass of one particle.

For: Data sharing
Visit: PHSchool.com
Web Code: ccd-0010

Study Guide

1.1 What is Science?

Key Concepts

- Science begins with curiosity and often ends with discovery.
- Science and technology are interdependent. Advances in one lead to advances in the other.
- Natural science is generally divided into three branches: physical science, Earth and space science, and life science.

Vocabulary

science, *p. 3*

technology, *p. 3*

chemistry, *p. 4*

physics, *p. 4*

geology, *p. 4*

astronomy, *p. 4*

biology, *p. 4*

1.2 Using a Scientific Approach

Key Concepts

- The goal of a scientific method is to solve a problem or to better understand an observed event.
- A scientific law describes an observed pattern in nature without attempting to explain it. The explanation of such a pattern is provided by a scientific theory.
- Scientific models make it easier to understand things that might be too difficult to observe directly.

Vocabulary

scientific method, *p. 7*

observation, *p. 8*

hypothesis, *p. 8*

manipulated variable, *p. 8*

responding variable, *p. 8*

controlled experiment, *p. 8*

scientific theory, *p. 9*

scientific law, *p. 9*

model, *p. 10*

1.3 Measurement

Key Concepts

- Scientific notation makes very large or very small numbers easier to work with.
- Scientists use a set of measuring units called SI.
- The precision of a calculation is limited by the least precise measurement used in the calculation.

Vocabulary

scientific notation, *p. 14*

length, *p. 16*

mass, *p. 16*

volume, *p. 16*

density, *p. 17*

conversion factor, *p. 18*

precision, *p. 19*

significant figures, *p. 19*

accuracy, *p. 19*

thermometer, *p. 20*

1.4 Presenting Scientific Data

Key Concepts

- Scientists can organize their data by using data tables and graphs.
- Scientists can communicate results by writing in journals or speaking at conferences.

Vocabulary

slope, *p. 23*

direct proportion, *p. 23*

inverse proportion, *p. 23*

Thinking Visually

Using Tables Use information from the chapter to complete the table below.

Type of Unit	Description	Example
Base	a. ____?____	b. ____?____
Derived	c. ____?____	d. ____?____

Reviewing Content

*Choose the letter that best answers the question or
completes the statement.*

1. The application of knowledge to solve practical
problems is known as
  a. science.   **b.** curiosity.
  c. technology.   **d.** experimentation.

2. Which is not a branch of natural science?
  a. physical science **b.** life science
  c. Earth science   **d.** social science

3. What is the purpose of an experiment?
  a. to communicate data
  b. to test a hypothesis
  c. to prove a scientific law
  d. none of the above

4. A representation of an object or event is called
  a. a scientific law. **b.** a model.
  c. a hypothesis.   **d.** a variable.

5. Which value is equivalent to 5×10^6?
  a. five thousand   **b.** fifty thousand
  c. five million   **d.** fifty million

6. What is the SI base unit of mass?
  a. gram   **b.** kilogram
  c. milligram   **d.** pound

7. An electric generator produces 10 megawatts.
This amount is equivalent to
  a. 10,000 watts.   **b.** 1,000,000 watts.
  c. 10,000,000 watts. **d.** 0.010 watt.

8. Which of the following is a ratio of equivalent
measurements that is used to convert a quantity
expressed in one unit to another unit?
  a. slope   **b.** conversion factor
  c. derived unit   **d.** density

9. When the ratio of two variables is constant, their
relationship can be described as
  a. inversely proportional.
  b. interdependent.
  c. directly proportional.
  d. parallel.

10. Which of the following would best suit data that
describe how a part relates to the whole?
  a. line graph   **b.** bar graph
  c. circle graph   **d.** scientific notation

Understanding Concepts

11. Give an example of a case where the branches of
natural science appear to overlap.

12. What is the goal of a scientific method?

13. How are controlled experiments useful?

14. Suppose you perform an experiment, and the
resulting data do not support your hypothesis.
What is the next step you might take?

15. What are some safety precautions that you
should follow when working in the laboratory?

16. What is scientific notation?

17. What are the SI base units for length
and temperature?

18. How do derived units differ from base units?

19. How is the precision of a calculated result related
to the precision of the measurements used in
the calculation?

20. How can you convert a temperature expressed in
degrees Celsius to kelvins?

21. Which of the following graphs describes a
direct proportion?

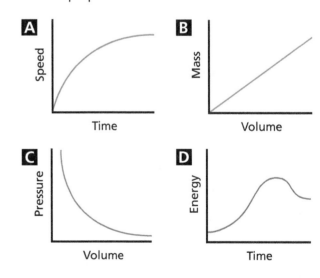

22. Why is it important for scientists to communicate
their results?

Critical Thinking

23. Formulating Hypotheses Suppose you want to know if objects with different masses fall to the ground at different rates. State a hypothesis about falling objects.

24. Designing Experiments Explain how you can test the hypothesis in Question 23. What will be the manipulated variable in your experiment? What will be the responding variable?

25. Calculating A triathlete enters a race in which he swims 500 meters, runs 3000 meters, and cycles 10.0 kilometers. What is the total distance of the race in kilometers?

26. Using Models Explain how a map of your town is an example of a model. How does this model help you plan a trip to an unfamiliar place?

27. Using Graphs Use the data in the table below to create a line graph. Plot distance on the vertical axis. Plot driving time on the horizontal axis. Calculate the slope of the line. If speed is the ratio of distance to time, what is the average driving speed of the trip?

Driving Distance and Time		
City	Distance From Start (km)	Driving Time From Start (h)
New York City, N.Y.	750	9.5
Cleveland, Ohio	1300	16.25
Chicago, Ill.	1900	23.25
Omaha, Nebr.	2100	26.25
Cheyenne, Wyo.	2900	36.25
Salt Lake City, Utah	3600	45
San Francisco, Calif.	4800	60

Math Skills

28. Calculating If a thermometer outside your classroom indicates a temperature of 61 degrees Fahrenheit, what is the temperature in degrees Celsius? In kelvins?

29. Problem Solving Suppose you have a large coffee can full of pennies. How can you estimate how much money the can contains without counting all the coins? (*Hint:* What is the relationship between the mass of pennies and the number of pennies?)

30. Calculating The Milky Way galaxy contains between 200 and 400 billion stars. Estimate the number of stars in a cluster of 30 galaxies similar in size to the Milky Way. Your answer should consist of a low estimate and a high estimate, both expressed in scientific notation.

Concepts in Action

31. Designing Experiments A zookeeper notices that elephants become restless shortly before an earthquake. The zookeeper forms a hypothesis that, just before an earthquake occurs, an elephant detects a sound that humans are unable to hear. How could this hypothesis be tested?

32. Making Judgments You see an advertisement on television for an over-the-counter medication that has been "scientifically proven to work." How could you find out if this claim is true?

33. Writing in Science Write a paragraph describing how advances in technology have affected your life. (*Hint:* The first sentence should state the paragraph's main idea.)

Performance-Based Assessment

Designing Experiments Grocery stores carry many brands of household detergents. Design an experiment to compare a more expensive brand of detergent with a less expensive one. Is one brand better for some purposes than the other?

For: Self-grading assessment
Visit: PHSchool.com
Web Code: cca-0015

Standardized Test Prep

Test-Taking Tip

Calculating
Checking units is a very important part of problem solving. Keep these tips in mind when solving problems involving unit conversions:

- A conversion factor is a ratio of equivalent measurements.

- Write horizontal fractions to help keep track of conversion factors. For example, write $\frac{32\ g}{cm^3}$ as opposed to 32 g/cm^3.

- Line up conversion factors so that the unit you are converting cancels.

- If you have to square or cube a unit, make sure you square or cube the entire conversion factor.

- Make a reality check of your answer. If the units are wrong, your calculations are probably wrong. Also, verify that the numerical answer is reasonable.

Practice using these tips in Questions 2 and 4.

Choose the letter that best answers the question or completes the statement.

1. In a controlled experiment,
 (A) there are multiple responding variables.
 (B) the responding variable is kept constant.
 (C) the manipulated variable is kept constant.
 (D) the responding variable is deliberately changed.
 (E) only one variable at a time is deliberately changed.

2. The speed of an object indicates how far it travels in a given amount of time. If an electron travels 2.42×10^8 meters in 2.00 seconds, what is the speed of this electron in cm/s?
 (A) 1.21×10^8 cm/s
 (B) 4.84×10^8 cm/s
 (C) 1.21×10^{10} cm/s
 (D) 2.42×10^{10} cm/s
 (E) 4.84×10^{10} cm/s

3. A doctor measures the temperature of a patient to be 101°F. What is this temperature in kelvins?
 (A) 38.3 K   (B) 73.8 K
 (C) 214 K   (D) 311 K
 (E) 346 K

4. The density of seawater is 1.024×10^3 kg/m^3. What is the density of seawater in g/cm^3?
 (A) 102.4 g/cm^3
 (B) 1.024×10^{-6} g/cm^3
 (C) 1.024 g/cm^3
 (D) 3.072×10^3 g/cm^3
 (E) 1.024×10^9 g/cm^3

5. A student conducts an experiment by dropping a basketball and a box of cereal of the same weight from the top of a building. The student measures the time it takes for each object to strike the ground. What was the student's hypothesis?

 (A) A basketball weighs more than cereal.
 (B) Curved objects travel through the air faster than flat objects.
 (C) Heavier objects travel through the air faster than lighter objects.
 (D) Gravity pulls on objects of the same weight with the same force.
 (E) Heavier objects strike the ground with a greater force than lighter objects.

6. If two variables are directly proportional, then
 (A) an increase in one variable causes a decrease in the other variable.
 (B) the product of the two variables is constant.
 (C) the ratio of the two variables is constant.
 (D) neither variable is the controlled variable.
 (E) both variables are constant.

**Fireworks Display in ▶
Sydney, Australia**
When fireworks explode, they produce colorful displays of light.

Chemistry

Focus ᵒⁿ the BIG Ideas

Chemistry is the study of the composition, structure, properties, and reactions of matter. Matter that always has exactly the same composition is classified as a substance. Elements are the simplest substances. The smallest particle of an element is an atom.

There are only about 100 elements. In the modern periodic table, elements are arranged by increasing atomic number (number of protons). Based on their chemical and physical properties, elements are classified as metals, nonmetals, and metalloids.

Unlike physical changes, chemical changes involve a change in the composition of matter. During a reaction, chemical bonds in the reactants are broken and chemical bonds in the products are formed. Mass is conserved in chemical reactions.

Nuclear changes (such as radioactivity) involve the conversion of atoms of one element to atoms of another. During nuclear reactions, mass can be created or destroyed, and it is the total sum of mass and energy that is conserved.

Careers in Chemistry

What do the people on these pages have in common? They all use chemistry on the job. From toxicologists to firefighters, there are many exciting chemistry careers to choose from.

Toxicologist

Toxicologists determine the effects natural and synthetic chemicals may have on people, other organisms, and the environment. Toxicologists conduct experiments to find out whether certain chemicals are dangerous or safe to use. They also determine how much of a given chemical could be harmful.

Educational requirements Four-year bachelor of science degree, majoring in chemistry

Forensic Chemist

Forensic chemists help law enforcement officials solve crimes. At a crime scene, a forensic chemist carefully gathers all the physical evidence and brings it back to the laboratory for analysis and identification. Physical evidence may include fibers, paints, glass, and stains.

Educational requirements Master's degree in chemistry

Food Science Technician

Food science technicians help to ensure that the food you eat is healthful, safe, and flavorful. They use their knowledge of chemistry to develop new or better ways of preserving, processing, packaging, and storing foods. Some food service technicians analyze food content to determine levels of vitamins, fat, carbohydrates, or protein.

Educational requirements
Four-year college degree, majoring in chemistry

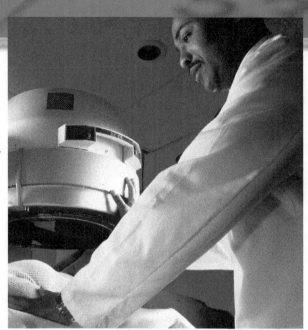

Nuclear Medicine Technologist

Nuclear medicine technologists apply their knowledge of nuclear chemistry to help diagnose diseases and disorders. They prepare and administer radioactive substances and use radiation detection devices to trace these substances in the body. Nuclear medicine technologists work directly with patients and closely with nuclear medicine physicians.
Educational requirements Two-year community or junior college degree, or a one-year certificate in nuclear medicine technology

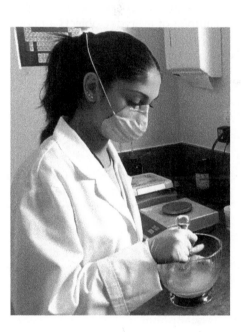

Firefighter

Firefighters are highly trained professionals who respond to fires, hazardous chemical spills, and medical emergencies. When responding to a fire or spill, firefighters have to know what effects different chemicals have in different situations.
Educational requirements
High-school diploma

Pharmacist

A pharmacist dispenses drugs prescribed by physicians and dentists and gives information to patients about the drugs and their uses. Pharmacists understand the uses, effects, and composition of drugs, including their chemical properties and biological side effects.
Educational requirements Two years of college, four-year college of pharmacy program, internship, and passage of a state board examination

Go Online
PHSchool.com

For: Career links
Visit: PHSchool.com
Web Code: ccb-1000

2 Properties of Matter

What factors influence the cost of metal?

Pots and pans, beverage cans, jewelry, the change in your pocket—these are just a few examples of everyday objects around you that are made of metal. Some metals, due to their properties, are more valuable than others. Select a particular metal and research its properties, uses, and price history. Digitally record a podcast that describes the metal, its current price per unit mass (or weight), and how its price has changed over the years.

How do science concepts apply to your world? Here are some questions you'll be able to answer after you read this chapter.

- **How do the properties of different materials affect the way clothes are cleaned?** *(Section 2.1)*

- **Why doesn't every batch of salsa taste equally "hot"?** *(Section 2.1)*

- **How does fog reduce a driver's ability to see the road ahead?** *(Section 2.1)*

- **Why does a cook use a wooden spoon to stir a pot of soup?** *(Section 2.2)*

- **What methods are used to purify water?** *(page 52)*

- **Why does a banana change color as it ripens?** *(Section 2.3)*

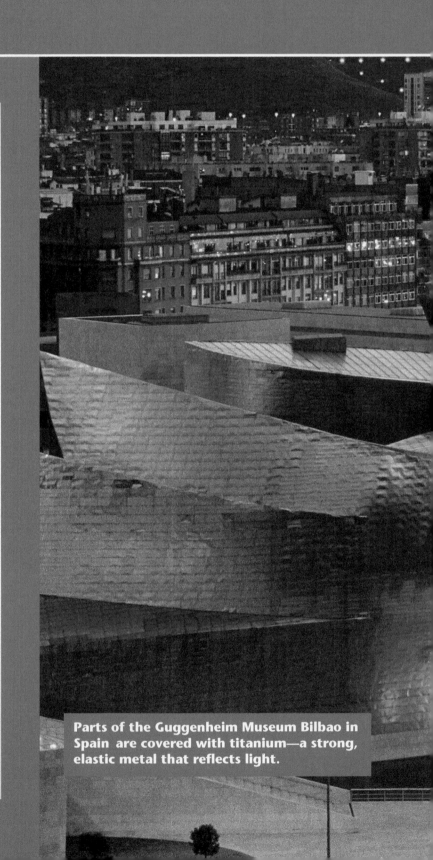

Parts of the Guggenheim Museum Bilbao in Spain are covered with titanium—a strong, elastic metal that reflects light.

Chapter Preview

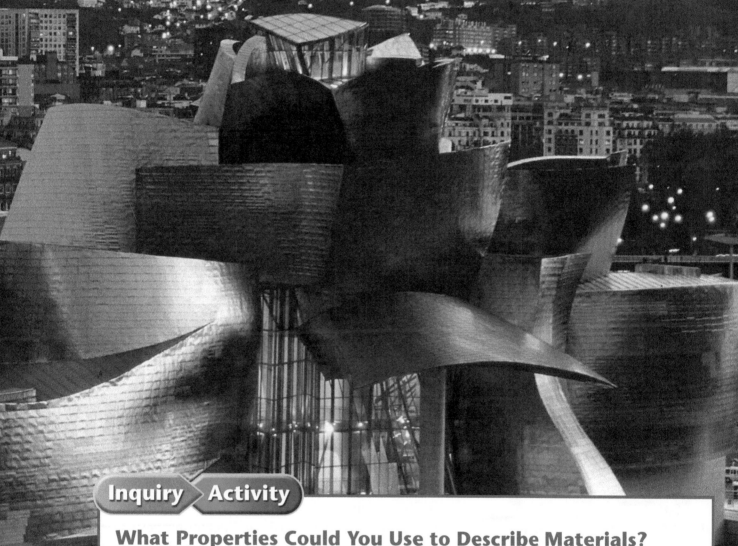

Inquiry ⟩ Activity

What Properties Could You Use to Describe Materials?

Procedure

1. Your teacher will provide you with samples of rubber, copper, steel, wood, and carbon. On a sheet of paper, list the materials, leaving room to write your description of each.

2. Determine and record the properties or characteristics of the materials by touching, manipulating, smelling, and looking at them.

Think About It

1. **Comparing and Contrasting** List one or more properties of each material that can be used to distinguish it from the others.

2. **Observing** Write a description of one of the materials that could be used to clearly identify it.

2.1 Classifying Matter

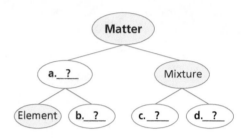

Reading Focus

Key Concepts

- Why are elements and compounds classified as pure substances?
- How do mixtures differ from pure substances?
- What is the main difference among solutions, suspensions, and colloids?

Vocabulary

- pure substance
- element
- atom
- compound
- heterogeneous mixture
- homogeneous mixture
- solution
- suspension
- colloid

Reading Strategy

Summarizing Copy the diagram below. As you read, complete the classification of matter.

```
                    Matter
                   /      \
              a._?_        Mixture
             /     \       /     \
        Element  b._?_  c._?_  d._?_
```

Each piece of clothing sold has a care label, which lists recommended cleaning methods for the clothing. For a sweater, the instructions might say to machine wash the sweater using a gentle cycle, and then tumble dry at a low temperature. They might say to hand wash the sweater in cold water and lay the sweater flat to dry. The label might even say, "Dry clean only."

Why is it necessary to put care instructions on a label? The same cleaning method will not work for all materials. For example, a shirt made from 100 percent cotton may need to be ironed after washing. But a shirt made from a cotton and polyester blend may come out of the dryer wrinkle free. A wool jacket often needs to be dry cleaned because wool can shrink when washed in water.

The tendency to wrinkle when washed is a property of cotton. The tendency not to wrinkle when washed is a property of polyester. The tendency to shrink when washed is a property of wool. Cotton, wool, and polyester have different properties because they have different compositions. The word *composition* comes from a Latin word meaning "a putting together," or the combining of parts into a whole. Based on their compositions, materials can be divided into pure substances and mixtures.

Figure 1 You can use the care labels on clothing to sort laundry into batches for cleaning. The care label shown is for a wool sweater that needs to be dry cleaned or washed by hand.

Pure Substances

Matter that always has exactly the same composition is classified as a **pure substance,** or simply a substance. Table salt and table sugar are two examples of pure substances. Every pinch of salt tastes equally salty. Every spoonful of sugar tastes equally sweet. 🔑 **Every sample of a given substance has the same properties because a substance has a fixed, uniform composition.** Substances can be classified into two categories—elements and compounds.

Elements

Although there are millions of known substances, there are only about 100 elements. An **element** is a substance that cannot be broken down into simpler substances. Imagine cutting a copper wire into smaller and smaller pieces. Eventually you would end up with extremely tiny particles called copper atoms. An **atom** is the smallest particle of an element. 🔑 **An element has a fixed composition because it contains only one type of atom.**

No two elements contain the same type of atom. In Chapter 4, you will find out more about atoms, including how the atoms of one element differ from the atoms of every other element.

Examples of Elements At room temperature (20°C, or 68°F), most elements are solids, including the elements aluminum and carbon. You have seen aluminum foil used to wrap food. Most soft drink cans are made from aluminum. Carbon is the main element in the marks you make with a pencil on a piece of paper. Some elements are gases at room temperature. The elements oxygen and nitrogen are the main gases in the air you breathe. Only two elements are liquids at room temperature, bromine and mercury, both of which are extremely poisonous. Figure 2 shows four elements and their symbols.

Figure 2 Aluminum, carbon, and gold are elements that you can see in common objects, such as cans, pencils, and rings. Mixtures containing iodine are used to prevent and treat infections.
Analyzing Data *Which of these elements has a symbol that is not related to its name in English?*

Iodine (I)

Aluminum (Al)

Gold (Au)

Carbon (C)

Silicon

Oxygen

Figure 3 Elements have different properties than their compounds. Silicon is a gray solid and oxygen is a colorless gas, which can be stored in a metal tank. Silicon and oxygen combine to form silicon dioxide—a colorless, transparent solid found in most grains of sand.

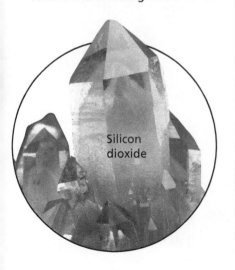

Silicon dioxide

Symbols for Elements In 1813, Jöns Berzelius, a Swedish chemist, suggested that chemists use symbols to represent elements. Many of the symbols he assigned to elements are still used. Each symbol has either one or two letters. The first letter is always capitalized. If there is a second letter, it is not capitalized.

It is easy to see why C and Al are used to represent carbon and aluminum. But why does gold have the symbol Au? The symbols that Berzelius chose were based on the Latin names of the elements. The Latin name for gold is *aurum.*

The symbols allow scientists who speak different languages to communicate without confusion. For example, nitrogen is known as *azote* in France, as *stickstoff* in Germany, and as *nitrógeno* in Mexico. But scientists who speak English, French, German, and Spanish all agree that the symbol for the element nitrogen is N.

Sometimes an element's name contains a clue to its properties. For example, the name hydrogen comes from the Greek words *hydro* and *genes,* meaning "water" and "forming."

Compounds

Water is composed of the elements hydrogen and oxygen. When electricity passes through water, bubbles of oxygen and hydrogen gas form and rise to the surface of the water. If the gases are collected in a container and a flame is brought near the mixture, the hydrogen and oxygen react and form water. Water is classified as a compound. A **compound** is a substance that is made from two or more simpler substances and can be broken down into those simpler substances. The simpler substances are either elements or other compounds.

The properties of a compound differ from those of the substances from which it is made. For example, oxygen and hydrogen are gases at room temperature, but water is a liquid. Hydrogen can fuel a fire, and oxygen can keep a fire burning, but water does not burn or help other substances to burn. In fact, water is one of the substances commonly used to put out fires.

Figure 3 shows another example of how properties change when elements join and form compounds. Silicon dioxide is a compound found in most light-colored grains of sand. It is a colorless, transparent solid. Yet, silicon dioxide is made from a colorless gas (oxygen) and a gray solid (silicon). Silicon is used to make chips for computers.

A compound always contains two or more elements joined in a fixed proportion. For example, in silicon dioxide, there are always two oxygen atoms for each silicon atom. (*Di-* means "two.") In water, there are always two hydrogen atoms for each oxygen atom.

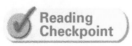

Reading Checkpoint *What happens if electricity passes through water?*

Figure 4 The ingredients shown are used to make one kind of salsa, which is an example of a heterogeneous mixture.

Salsa

- 4 or 5 plum tomatoes
- 3–5 fresh Serrano chili peppers
- 12 sprigs of cilantro
- large garlic clove
- small white onion
- 1½ teaspoons fresh lime juice
- ¾ teaspoon salt

Mixtures

Suppose you are making salsa using the ingredients shown in Figure 4. You have a choice. You can use exactly the amounts listed in the recipe, or you can adjust the ingredients according to your own taste. You might have to prepare the recipe a few times before deciding if you have just the right amount of each ingredient.

Mixtures tend to retain some of the properties of their individual substances. But the properties of a mixture are less constant than the properties of a substance. **The properties of a mixture can vary because the composition of a mixture is not fixed.** The type of pepper and the quantity of pepper used in a salsa recipe determine the "hotness" of a batch of salsa. Chili peppers contain a compound called capsaicin (kap SAY uh sin) that can cause a burning sensation in your mouth. The amount of capsaicin varies among types of peppers. Cayenne peppers, for example, contain more capsaicin than do jalapeño peppers.

No matter how well you stir a batch of salsa, the ingredients will not be evenly distributed. There may, for example, be more onion in one portion of the salsa than another. Mixtures can be classified by how well the parts of the mixture are distributed throughout the mixture.

Heterogeneous Mixtures If you look at a handful of sand from a beach, the sand appears to be all the same material. However, if you use a hand lens, you will notice that the sample of sand is not the same throughout. Figure 5 shows that grains of sand vary in size. Also, some grains are light in color and some are dark. Sand is an example of a heterogeneous mixture. Heterogeneous (het uh roh GEE nee us) comes from the Greek words *hetero* and *genus,* meaning "different" and "kind." In a **heterogeneous mixture,** the parts of the mixture are noticeably different from one another.

Figure 5 Sand is a heterogeneous mixture. The spoon is stainless steel, which is a homogeneous mixture. **Interpreting Photographs** *Explain how viewing sand through a hand lens helps show that sand is a heterogeneous mixture.*

Do the Contents of Two Cans of Mixed Nuts Meet FDA Regulations?

The Food and Drug Administration (FDA) has two main areas of concern about food. First, and most important, the FDA ensures that food sold in the United States is safe to eat. Second, the FDA ensures that the information on a food label accurately describes a food product.

What can you assume when you see the label "mixed nuts" on a can of nuts? According to the FDA regulations, a can labeled *mixed nuts* must contain at least four types of shelled nuts other than peanuts. The mass of each type of nut must be not less than 2 percent of the total mass and not more than 80 percent of the total mass.

Contents of Two Cans of Mixed Nuts		
Type of Nut	Mass in Brand A	Mass in Brand B
Peanut	152.39 g	191.96 g
Almond	47.02 g	31.18 g
Brazil nut	57.88 g	19.60 g
Cashew	46.20 g	73.78 g
Hazelnut	19.90 g	16.90 g
Pecan	21.40 g	16.90 g

1. **Comparing and Contrasting** How are the two brands of mixed nuts alike? How are they different?

2. **Calculating** What is the percent by mass of each type of nut in each can?

3. **Drawing Conclusions** Do the contents of each can meet the FDA regulations? Explain.

4. **Inferring** On the Brand A label, the nuts are listed in this order: peanuts, Brazil nuts, almonds, cashews, pecans, and hazelnuts. What do you think determines the order?

Go Online

NSTA SciLINKS

For: Links on mixtures
Visit: www.SciLinks.org
Web Code: ccn-1021

Homogeneous Mixtures If you collect water from both the shallow end and the deep end of a swimming pool, the water samples will appear the same. The water in a swimming pool is a homogeneous (hoh moh GEE nee us) mixture of water and substances that dissolve in water. In a **homogeneous mixture,** the substances are so evenly distributed that it is difficult to distinguish one substance in the mixture from another. A homogeneous mixture appears to contain only one substance. The serving spoon in Figure 5 is made of stainless steel—a homogeneous mixture of iron, chromium, and nickel.

Solutions, Suspensions, and Colloids

It isn't always easy to tell a homogeneous mixture from a heterogeneous mixture. You may need to observe the properties of a mixture before you decide. The size of the particles in a mixture has an effect on the properties of the mixture. **Based on the size of its largest particles, a mixture can be classified as a solution, a suspension, or a colloid.**

Solutions If you place a spoonful of sugar in a glass of hot water and stir, the sugar dissolves in the water. The result is a homogeneous mixture of sugar and water. When substances dissolve and form a homogeneous mixture, the mixture that forms is called a **solution.** The windshield wiper fluid in Figure 6 is a solution. So is tap water.

Figure 6 The liquids shown represent three categories of mixtures. **A** Windshield wiper fluid is a solution. **B** Muddy water collected from a swamp is a suspension. **C** Milk is a colloid.
Comparing and Contrasting *Based on appearance, how are a solution and a colloid similar?*

Liquid solutions are easy to recognize. They do not separate into distinct layers over time. If you pour a liquid solution through a filter, none of the substances in the solution are trapped in the filter. You can see through solutions that are liquids because light passes through them without being scattered in all directions. These three properties of liquid solutions can be traced to the size of the particles in a solution. The particles in a solution are too small to settle out of the solution, be trapped by a filter, or scatter light.

Suspensions Have you ever seen the instruction "Shake well before using" on a bottle? This instruction is a clue that the material in the bottle is a suspension. A **suspension** is a heterogeneous mixture that separates into layers over time. For example, if you shake up a container of sand and water, the sand mixes with the water and forms a suspension. Over time, the suspended particles of sand settle to the bottom of the container.

You could use a filter to separate the sand from the water. The water would pass through the filter, but the sand would remain in the filter paper. Suspended particles settle out of a mixture or are trapped by a filter because they are larger than the particles in a solution. The worker in Figure 7 is using a mask to filter out particles of plastic foam that are suspended in air. Because larger particles can scatter light in all directions, suspensions are cloudy.

 Reading Checkpoint   *What happens to suspended particles over time?*

Figure 7 When a surfboard is sanded, particles of plastic become suspended in air. The worker wears a mask to keep from breathing in the particles.

High beam

Low beam

Figure 8 The photograph shows how water droplets in fog scatter the light from high beams. The drawing compares the areas lit by high beams and low beams. **Interpreting Diagrams** *Which beams normally make a larger area of a road visible?*

Colloids Milk is a mixture of substances including water, sugar, proteins, and fats. When fresh cow's milk is allowed to stand, a layer of cream rises to the top. This layer contains much of the fat in the milk. In the milk you buy at the store, the cream does not form a separate layer. The milk has been processed so that the fat remains dispersed throughout the milk. The result is homogenized milk, which is a colloid.

A **colloid** contains some particles that are intermediate in size between the small particles in a solution and the larger particles in a suspension. Like solutions, colloids do not separate into layers. You cannot use a filter to separate the parts of a colloid.

Fog is a colloid of water droplets in air. Figure 8 shows how fog affects which headlights a driver uses. Automobiles have headlights with low beams for normal driving conditions and high beams for roads that are poorly lit. With the high beams, a driver can see a bend in the road or an obstacle sooner. But the high beams are not useful on a foggy night because the water droplets scatter light back toward the driver and reduce visibility. With the low beams, much less light is scattered. The scattering of light is a property that can be used to distinguish colloids and suspensions from solutions.

Section 2.1 Assessment

Reviewing Concepts

1. ⬤ Why does every sample of a given substance have the same properties?

2. ⬤ Explain why the composition of an element is fixed.

3. ⬤ Describe the composition of a compound.

4. ⬤ Why can the properties of a mixture vary?

5. ⬤ On what basis can mixtures be classified as solutions, suspensions, or colloids?

Critical Thinking

6. **Predicting** If you added salt instead of sugar to a pitcher of lemonade, how would this change the properties of the lemonade?

7. **Interpreting Visuals** Explain why silicon dioxide cannot be the only compound in the sample of sand shown in Figure 5.

8. **Inferring** Fresh milk is a suspension. After fresh milk is homogenized, it is a colloid. What happens to the size of the drops of fat in milk when milk is homogenized?

Writing in Science

Writing Instructions Pick a cereal that is an obvious mixture. Write rules that could be used to control the cereal's composition. Use the FDA rules for mixed nuts as a model.

2.2 Physical Properties

Reading Focus

Key Concepts
- What are some examples of physical properties?
- How can knowing the physical properties of matter be useful?
- What processes are used to separate mixtures?

Vocabulary
- physical property
- viscosity
- conductivity
- malleability
- melting point
- boiling point
- filtration
- distillation
- physical change

Reading Strategy
Building Vocabulary Copy the table. As you read, write a definition for each property.

Physical Property	Definition
Viscosity	a. ___?___
Malleability	b. ___?___
Melting point	c. ___?___

If there are pitchers of ice water and lemonade on a picnic table, how do you know which liquid is in each pitcher? It's easy! The lemonade is yellow. Lemonade also has a tart taste that is hard to miss. A yellow color and a tart taste are two properties of lemonade.

Examples of Physical Properties

A **physical property** is any characteristic of a material that can be observed or measured without changing the composition of the substances in the material. **Viscosity, conductivity, malleability, hardness, melting point, boiling point, and density are examples of physical properties.**

Viscosity Suppose you knock over an open bottle of vinegar and an open jar of honey at exactly the same time. In the time it takes for the vinegar bottle to empty, the honey will scarcely start to flow. The tendency of a liquid to keep from flowing—its resistance to flowing— is called its **viscosity**. The greater the viscosity, the slower the liquid moves. Thick liquids, such as corn syrup and the honey in Figure 9, have a high viscosity. Thin liquids, such as vinegar, have a low viscosity.

The viscosity of a liquid usually decreases when it is heated. For example, a spoonful of cooking oil will spread more quickly across the bottom of a heated frying pan than across the bottom of a cold pan.

Why is the viscosity of a liquid important? Consider the motor oil used to keep the parts of an automobile engine from wearing away as they move past one another. The motor oil must not be too thick in cold weather or too thin in hot weather.

Figure 9 The object in the photograph is called a honey dipper. Honey is an example of a liquid with a high viscosity.

Liquid crystal thermometer

°F
86
84
82
80
78
76
74
72
70
68
66
64

Metal rod
Wooden rod
Foam cups

☰Quick Lab

Comparing Heat Conductors

Materials

2 plastic foam cups, scissors, metric ruler, metal rod, wooden rod, 2 liquid crystal thermometers, hot water, clock or watch with second hand

Procedure

1. Make a data table with a column for time and a column to record the temperature of each rod.

2. Cut 3 cm off the top of one cup. Turn the cup upside down. Use the metal rod to make two holes about 3 cm apart in the bottom.

3. Attach a thermometer to each rod as shown.

4. Insert both rods so they will just touch the bottom of the second cup. Lay the cup with the rods on the table. Do not touch the rods and thermometers during the experiment.

5. Ask your teacher to add hot water to the intact cup until it is about three fourths full.

6. Hold the cup with the hot water firmly as you place the cup with the rods on top of it. **CAUTION** *Be careful not to overturn the cup.*

7. Observe and record the temperatures every minute for five minutes.

Analyze and Conclude

1. **Comparing and Contrasting** Is metal or wood a better conductor of heat? Explain.

2. **Applying Concepts** Is a metal cup a good container for keeping a drink hot for as long as possible? Give a reason for your answer.

3. **Evaluating** Describe any variables, other than the type of material, that were not controlled in this lab.

Conductivity Which spoon should you choose for stirring a pot of soup heating on the stove—a metal spoon or a wooden spoon? If one end of a metal object is heated, the other end will soon feel hot. A material's ability to allow heat to flow is called **conductivity.**

Materials that have a high conductivity, such as metals, are called conductors. If a material is a good conductor of heat, it is usually also a good conductor of electricity. Wood is not a good conductor of heat. You can stir hot soup with a wooden spoon without worrying about burning your hand because the wooden spoon stays cool to the touch.

Malleability The ancient gold objects in Figure 10 were found in a tomb in Greece. A goldsmith made the medallions by tapping gold with a small hammer and punch. Gold can be shaped in this way because it is malleable. **Malleability** (mal ee uh BIL uh tee) is the ability of a solid to be hammered without shattering. Most metals are malleable. By contrast, an ice cube breaks into small pieces when struck with a hammer. So does ordinary glass when hit by a fast-moving object such as a baseball. Solids that shatter when struck are brittle.

Figure 10 Because gold is both malleable and beautiful, it is often used to make jewelry. These ancient gold medallions were made to form a necklace.

✓ **Reading Checkpoint** *Why would a cook use a wooden spoon to stir hot soup?*

Hardness One way to compare the hardness of two materials is to see which of the materials can scratch the other. The blade of a typical kitchen knife, for example, can scratch a copper sheet because stainless steel is harder than copper. The stainless steel in a knife blade is a hard solid that can be shaped into a sharp cutting edge. The material used to sharpen the blade must be harder than stainless steel. Diamond is the hardest known material. Some of the grinding wheels used to sharpen steel contain small grains of diamond. The man in Figure 11 is carving a canoe from a soft wood—Western red cedar.

Figure 11 This Tlingit carver is using an adze to carve a canoe from Western red cedar. Red cedar is a relatively soft wood.

Melting and Boiling Points If you leave a tray of ice cubes on your kitchen counter, the ice cubes will melt. The temperature at which a substance changes from solid to liquid is its **melting point.** For water, this change normally occurs at 0°C. If you heat water to cook pasta at sea level, the water will start to boil at 100°C. The temperature at which a substance boils is its **boiling point.** Figure 12 shows the melting point and the boiling point for some substances.

Density Density can be used to test the purity of a substance. Recall that density is the ratio of the mass of a substance to its volume. At room temperature, silver has a density of 10.5 g/cm^3. If a coin has a density of 9.9 g/cm^3 at room temperature, either the coin is not made from silver or the coin contains substances in addition to silver.

Density can be used to test the purity of methanol. Methanol is a fuel burned in some racing motorcycles. The American Motorcycle Association (AMA) requires racers to use fuel that is at least 99.65 percent pure. Race officials may collect a sample of fuel and measure its temperature and density. Then they compare the measured density to the expected density of methanol at that temperature. These spot checks keep racers from adding substances to the fuel that will give them an unfair advantage in a race.

Melting and Boiling Points of Some Substances		
Substance	Melting Point	Boiling Point
Hydrogen	−259.3°C	−252.9°C
Nitrogen	−210.0°C	−195.8°C
Ammonia	−77.7°C	−33.3°C
Octane (found in gasoline)	−56.8°C	125.6°C
Water	0.0°C	100.0°C
Acetic acid (found in vinegar)	16.6°C	117.9°C
Table salt	800.7°C	1465°C
Gold	1064.2°C	2856°C

Figure 12 The table lists the melting points and boiling points for several substances.
Analyzing Data *Which of these substances are liquids at room temperature (20°C, or 68°F)?*

Using Physical Properties

People use data about physical properties to solve many different types of problems. ⊙ **Physical properties are used to identify a material, to choose a material for a specific purpose, or to separate the substances in a mixture.**

Using Properties to Identify Materials

The steps used to identify a material are similar to the steps used to test for purity. The first step is to decide which properties to test. The second step is to do tests on a sample of the unknown. The final step is to compare the results with the data reported for known materials.

The identification of a material can be a crucial step in solving a crime. A detective collects red paint chips from the scene of a hit-and-run accident. He asks a chemist at the crime lab to use the chips to identify the model of the missing vehicle. Because paint is a mixture of substances, the chemist can do tests that distinguish one type of red paint from another. The technician compares the data she collects to an FBI database. The database contains information about the paints used on different makes and models of cars. Once the detective knows the make and model, he uses a database of registered owners to create a list of possible suspects.

Using Properties to Choose Materials

Properties determine which materials are chosen for which uses. For example, you wouldn't want shoelaces made from wood. Shoelaces must be flexible, that is, they must be able to bend without breaking. They must also be durable, that is, they must be able to withstand repeated use. Laces in hiking boots like those in Figure 13 are usually nylon or leather.

People don't consider just one property when choosing a material for a particular application. They look at a set of properties. For example, the How It Works box on page 49 explains how the properties of wax are used when clay molds are made for casting metal sculptures.

Figure 13 Shoelaces for hiking boots are sometimes made from leather. So are some belts and shoes. **Making Generalizations** *What properties of leather would make it a suitable material for all three types of objects?*

Making a Sculpture

A process called lost-wax casting is used to make metal sculptures. Different stages of the process depend on physical properties of wax, clay, and metal. Wax can be carved and molded. Clay becomes brittle when baked at a high temperature. When melted, most metals form homogeneous mixtures, which can be poured into molds. Interpreting Diagrams *Why is it important that wax has a low melting point?*

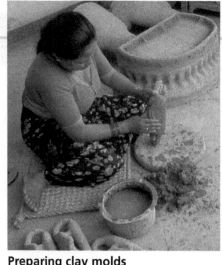

Preparing clay molds
This artist from Nepal in southern Asia is preparing molds for lost-wax casting. She is applying layers of clay to a wax model.

1 Wax model A wax model of the sculpture is built up around a clay core. Wax is used because it is soft enough for carving fine details, but hard enough to retain its shape at room temperature.

Wax model

Layers of clay applied to the wax model

Clay core

Wax model

Melting wax

Cast metal sculpture

Molten metal poured into mold

Broken clay

2 Clay mold Clay is applied to the wax model in layers of increasing coarseness, and left to dry. The inner, finer layers capture every detail of the sculpture in a smooth mold. The outer, coarser layers (clay mixed with sand) provide strength.

3 Melting wax The clay-covered wax model is then baked in a kiln. Because wax has a low melting point, the wax model melts away inside the clay, leaving a hardened shell mold. This clay mold is then used to make the final sculpture.

4 Molten metal Molten (liquid) metal is poured into the clay mold and left to cool and harden. For this sculpture of an African head, a mixture of copper, zinc, and lead was used.

5 Metal sculpture When the metal has cooled, the clay shell is broken open to reveal the finished metal sculpture.

Figure 14 These Americorps students are looking for artifacts at the San Diego Presidio—a fort that was built in 1769. As the students sift dirt through a screen, small objects buried in the dirt collect on the screen.
Applying Concepts How could changing the size of the holes in a screen change the number of objects found?

Using Properties to Separate Mixtures

Some properties can be used to separate mixtures. **Filtration and distillation are two common separation methods.**

Filtration One way to make a pot of tea is to pour hot water over loose tea leaves. Some compounds in the tea leaves, such as caffeine, dissolve in the water. You can separate the hot tea from the loose leaves by pouring the mixture through a strainer. Using a strainer is a type of filtration. **Filtration** is a process that separates materials based on the size of their particles. Particles of the compounds that dissolve are small enough to pass through the strainer, but the tea leaves themselves are too large to pass through the strainer. The drip method of brewing coffee also uses a filter to separate the brewed coffee from the coffee grounds.

The students in Figure 14 are using a wire screen to locate small objects buried in the sand at an archaeological site. Particles of dirt are small enough to pass through the holes in the screen, but objects such as broken bits of pottery are too large to pass through the screen.

Distillation How can you separate the parts of a solution when all the particles in a solution are small enough to pass through a filter? Sometimes distillation can work. **Distillation** is a process that separates the substances in a solution based on their boiling points.

One practical use of distillation is to provide fresh water for submarines. Most submarines can store only enough fresh water to last about ten days. Each submarine has equipment that can convert seawater into fresh water. The water is heated until it changes from a liquid to a gas. The gas is cooled until it changes back to a liquid, which is collected in a separate container. Boiling can separate fresh water from seawater because water has a much lower boiling point than the compounds dissolved in seawater. These compounds are left behind in the original container.

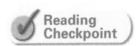 *How can loose tea leaves be removed from a pot of brewed tea?*

For: Articles on properties of matter
Visit: PHSchool.com
Web Code: cce-1022

Recognizing Physical Changes

The change of water from a liquid to a gas during boiling is a physical change. A **physical change** occurs when some of the properties of a material change, but the substances in the material remain the same. For example, if you slowly heat butter in a pan, it changes from a solid to a liquid, but the substances in the butter do not change. Two other examples of physical changes are crumpling a piece of paper and slicing a tomato. Crumpling and slicing are actions that change the size and shape of a material, but not its composition.

Some physical changes can be reversed. You can freeze water, melt the ice that forms, and then freeze the water again. You can use an iron to remove the wrinkles from a cotton shirt. You can braid hair, unbraid the hair, and then braid it again. Some physical changes cannot be reversed. You would not expect to reconstruct a whole tomato from tomato slices or to replace the peel on a peeled orange. Figure 15 shows one physical change that can be reversed and one that cannot be reversed.

Figure 15 Braiding hair and cutting hair are examples of physical changes. Braiding is a reversible change. Cutting cannot be reversed.

Section 2.2 Assessment

Reviewing Concepts

1. List seven examples of physical properties.
2. Describe three uses of physical properties.
3. Name two processes that are used to separate mixtures.
4. When you describe a liquid as thick, are you saying that it has a high or a low viscosity?
5. Explain why sharpening a pencil is an example of a physical change.
6. What allows a mixture to be separated by distillation?

Critical Thinking

7. **Designing Experiments** How could you find out whether copper is harder or softer than the plastic used in a plastic cup?

8. **Inferring** Why would you expect the materials used to make pot holders to be poor conductors of heat?
9. **Applying Concepts** Silicon dioxide is a solid at room temperature and methanol is a liquid. Which substance has the higher melting point?

Connecting Concepts

Organizing Data In what order are the substances arranged in Figure 12? Use what you studied about organizing data in Section 1.4 to explain why this order is useful. Explain why you might choose a different order if you had similar data for 500 substances.

Getting a Fresh Start

Water found in nature is never 100 percent pure. There are always substances dissolved in the water. Some of these substances, as well as bacteria and particles of dirt, must be removed before the water is fit to drink.

1 **Coarse filter** A screen prevents large items such as leaves from entering the water treatment plant.

Coarse filter screen

Outlet tower

Alum (aluminum sulfate) added

Aeration tank

Reservoir

2 **Aeration** During aeration, air may be bubbled into the water or water may be sprayed into the air. Aeration removes substances from water, such as iron compounds, that give water an unpleasant taste.

Colloid forms.

Layer of lumps

Cleaned water spills over into a trough.

3 **Forming a colloid** Alum is added to the mixing tank. Alum causes small particles in the water to form a type of colloid called a gel. Most of the bacteria in the water are trapped in the gel.

4 **Sedimentation** In the sedimentation tank, large lumps slowly settle to the bottom of the tank from where they can be removed.

Sedimentation tank

Water from the ground
About half of the drinking water in the United States comes from natural underground sources. Although this groundwater is filtered as it passes through rocks and sand, it sometimes contains high levels of dissolved minerals or chemical pollutants. So groundwater is purified using a modified version of surface water filtration.

6 Carbon filter The water is sometimes passed through a carbon filter. This filter removes tiny amounts of dissolved impurities, and improves the water's taste and color.

5 Sand and gravel filter
Next, the water trickles through sand and gravel filter beds, which trap the remaining suspended particles. Because the filter beds can become clogged, they are washed every 24 hours.

Water storage tank

Water softener added

Fluorine compound added

Chlorine added

Carbon filter

Filtered water

Gravel layer

Sand layer

7 Additives
The fluorine compound prevents tooth decay and the chlorine kills bacteria. The water softener removes some magnesium and calcium compounds.

8 Storage Finally, the water is held in storage tanks before passing into the public water supply.

Going Further

- Some people use a system to purify water at home. Research and write about one of these systems. What is the system designed to do? Compare the method used to the processes that occur at a water purification plant.

- Take a Discovery Channel Video Field Trip by watching "Fresh-Squeezed Water."

2.3 Chemical Properties

Reading Focus

Key Concepts

- When can chemical properties be observed?
- What observations might indicate that a chemical change has occurred?
- What is the difference between chemical and physical changes?

Vocabulary

- chemical property
- flammability
- reactivity
- chemical change
- precipitate

Reading Strategy

Relating Text and Visuals Copy the table. Find examples of the clues for recognizing chemical changes in Figures 19 and 20.

Clue	Example
Change in color	a.____?____
Production of gas	b.____?____
Formation of precipitate	c.____?____

How would you describe candles like the ones in Figure 16? You might describe their color or their hardness. Or, you might observe that the candles float on water, and conclude that the density of candle wax is less than that of water. Color, hardness, and density are physical properties. But there is something else about the candles that may seem even more obvious to you: the fact that the candles are burning. The ability to burn is not a physical property because you cannot observe burning without changing the composition of the material that is burning. As a candle burns, new substances form.

Observing Chemical Properties

Most candles are made from paraffin, which is a mixture of compounds containing carbon and hydrogen. As a candle burns, the compounds combine with oxygen in the air to form water and carbon dioxide. (Carbon dioxide is the gas that gives a carbonated beverage its fizz.) The ability to burn is a chemical property. A **chemical property** is any ability to produce a change in the composition of matter. Chemical properties can be observed only when the substances in a sample of matter are changing into different substances. Flammability and reactivity are two examples of chemical properties.

Flammability Materials that burn can be used as fuel. Sometimes, people use burning newspapers to start a fire in a fireplace. Gasoline is the fuel burned in most automobiles. The chemical property that paper and gasoline share is their flammability. **Flammability** is a material's ability to burn in the presence of oxygen.

Figure 16 When candles burn, new substances form. The ability to burn is a chemical property.

Sometimes flammability is not a desirable property. For example, there are laws that regulate the flammability of fabrics. The fabrics used in children's sleepwear must have a low flammability. These fabrics are described as flame-resistant because they are difficult to ignite. If they do ignite, they burn slowly.

Reactivity The property that describes how readily a substance combines chemically with other substances is **reactivity.** Nitrogen and oxygen are the main gases in air. Oxygen is a highly reactive element. Nitrogen has an extremely low reactivity.

Oxygen reacts easily with most other elements. Figure 17 shows the rust that forms when oxygen reacts with iron and water. Rust is a brittle, reddish-brown compound. A rusty chain or bolt is more likely to break than a new chain or bolt because rust is weaker than iron. Because iron is highly reactive, you would not choose iron to make decorative objects, such as jewelry or coins.

Many uses of nitrogen depend on its low reactivity. For example, seawater is often stored in steel tanks located below the lowest deck of a ship. The seawater helps to keep the ship stable in the water. Over time, rust forms in the tanks because iron in the steel reacts with oxygen dissolved in the water. Researchers in Japan have developed a way to reduce the amount of rust produced. They pump nitrogen gas into the tanks, and the nitrogen displaces the dissolved oxygen.

 Which element is more reactive—oxygen or nitrogen?

For: Links on chemical and physical changes
Visit: www.SciLinks.org
Web Code: ccn-1023

Figure 17 This automobile must have been exposed to air and water for many years.
Drawing Conclusions *What evidence is there that parts of the automobile contained iron?*

Identifying a Chemical Change

Materials

3 test tubes; test-tube rack; glass-marking pencil; 3 10-mL graduated cylinders; solutions of copper sulfate, calcium chloride, and sodium chloride

Procedure

1. Construct a data table with columns labeled Test Tube, Contents, and Observations.

2. Label the test tubes A, B, and C.

3. Pour 5 mL of copper sulfate solution into test tube A. Pour 5 mL of calcium chloride solution into test tube B. Pour 5 mL of sodium chloride solution into test tube C. **CAUTION** *Do not allow the solutions to touch your skin. They may cause irritation.*

4. Add 5 mL of calcium chloride solution to test tube A. Add 5 mL of sodium chloride solution to test tube B. Add 5 mL of copper sulfate solution to test tube C.

5. Examine the test tubes for evidence of a chemical change. Record your observations.

6. Pour the contents of the test tubes into the sink. Rinse out the test tubes and flush the contents down the drain. **CAUTION** *Wash your hands thoroughly with soap or detergent before leaving the laboratory.*

Analyze and Conclude

1. **Inferring** In which test tube(s) did a chemical change occur? Explain your answer.

2. **Evaluating** Can you be sure that a chemical change occurred? Explain your answer.

Figure 18 As a banana ripens, chemical changes cause the peel to change color from green to yellow. In a banana that is overly ripe, different chemical changes cause the peel to turn brown. Observing *Based on your experience, what other properties of a banana change as it ripens?*

Recognizing Chemical Changes

Figure 18 shows what happens to banana peels as bananas ripen. The color change in a banana peel is caused by chemical changes that are taking place in the cells of the banana. A **chemical change** occurs when a substance reacts and forms one or more new substances. Chemical changes occur when a cake bakes in an oven, leaves on trees change color, and food is digested in your stomach.

How can you recognize a chemical change? You have to look for clues. For example, when food spoils, it often gives off an unpleasant odor. 🔑 **Three common types of evidence for a chemical change are a change in color, the production of a gas, and the formation of a precipitate.**

A Change in Color Over time, a shiny silver bracelet that is exposed to air will darken. As a match burns, it shrivels up and turns black. The new copper roof and the old copper roof in Figure 19 have different colors. In each of these examples, a change in color is a clue that a chemical change has produced at least one new substance.

Production of a Gas Figure 20A shows what happens when you mix vinegar with baking soda. Bubbles of carbon dioxide form immediately. A similar chemical change happens when you use baking powder as an ingredient in a cake recipe. Baking powder is a mixture of baking soda and one or more acids that react when wet. As the cake bakes, the bubbles of carbon dioxide expand and cause the cake to rise.

Formation of a Precipitate Another chemical change you can observe in the kitchen is the curdling of milk. If you add lemon juice or vinegar to milk, small bits of white solid will separate from the liquid. Any solid that forms and separates from a liquid mixture is called a **precipitate.** When an acid is added to milk, proteins in the milk undergo a chemical change that alters their structure, causing them to stick together in clumps. They form the precipitate shown in Figure 20B.

Figure 19 When copper is exposed to moist air, it forms a thin coating called a patina. A new copper roof has a reddish color. The green patina on an old copper roof is a mixture of copper compounds.
Predicting *Would a patina form faster in a rainy climate or in a dry climate?*

> **Reading Checkpoint** *What happens when you add vinegar to baking soda?*

Figure 20 The formation of a gas or a precipitate can be a clue to chemical change. **A** Carbon dioxide gas forms when vinegar is mixed with baking soda. **B** The curds in cottage cheese form when an acid is added to milk.

Figure 21 A blacksmith uses a hammer to shape a horseshoe that has been heated. Although the color of the iron horseshoe changes, no chemical change is occurring. **Inferring** *Other than color, what physical property of iron is affected by heating?*

Is a Change Chemical or Physical?

It is not always easy to distinguish a chemical change from a physical change. Even if you observe a color change, a gas, or a precipitate, you cannot be sure that a chemical change has taken place. When the iron horseshoe in Figure 21 is heated, its color changes from gray to red. Despite this change in color, the iron is still iron. When water boils on a stove, the bubbles of gas that rise to the surface are still water.

Before you decide whether or not a chemical change has occurred, ask yourself this question: Are different substances present after the change takes place? If not, then the change is physical, not chemical. When matter undergoes a chemical change, the composition of the matter changes. When matter undergoes a physical change, the composition of the matter remains the same.

Section 2.3 Assessment

Reviewing Concepts

1. Under what conditions can chemical properties be observed?

2. List three common types of evidence for a chemical change.

3. How do chemical changes differ from physical changes?

4. Explain why the rusting of an iron bar decreases the strength of the bar.

5. A pat of butter melts and then burns in a hot frying pan. Which of these changes is physical and which is chemical?

Critical Thinking

6. **Comparing and Contrasting** Compare the properties of a raw egg to those of a hard-boiled egg.

7. **Classifying** If you spill household bleach on denim jeans, you will observe that the area of the spill no longer has a blue color. Is this change chemical or physical? Give a reason for your answer.

8. **Inferring** Gold and platinum are often used to make jewelry. What can you infer about the reactivity of these elements?

Connecting Concepts

Scientific Methods Section 1.2 listed typical steps scientists use. Which steps might you use to decide whether a change is physical or chemical? Explain.

issues in SCIENCE

What Should Be Done With Arsenic-Treated Wood?

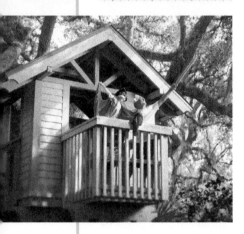

Termites are among the organisms that attack untreated wood. In 1950, United States suppliers of lumber began to treat wood with a mixture of copper, chromium, and arsenic (CCA). The mixture slows the damage to wood by poisoning the attacking organisms. Outdoor structures such as decks and porches were made from CCA-treated wood. By 2002, more than 95 percent of treated lumber sold for use outdoors contained CCA.

Arsenic is a poison that has been linked with certain types of cancer. Arsenic can be absorbed through the skin or ingested in water or food. Consumers were especially concerned about children touching CCA-treated wood and then placing their unwashed fingers in their mouths. Some consumers asked the Environmental Protection Agency (EPA) to ban the use of CCA. In 2002, the chemical and home-improvement industries agreed to stop producing CCA-treated wood for home use.

The Viewpoints

Old CCA-Treated Wood Does Not Need to Be Removed

The EPA did not recommend tearing down existing structures made from CCA-treated wood. A panel of Florida doctors reported that they found no studies linking cancer in children and exposure to CCA-treated wood. They concluded that the amount of arsenic that children could absorb from treated wood is small compared to the amount of arsenic that occurs naturally in soil.

There are risks associated with disposing of treated wood. Burning arsenic-treated wood produces ash with high levels of arsenic. The ash would poison a person who inhaled, ingested, or touched it. The only acceptable method of disposal is in landfills, which are rapidly filling. Also, arsenic from landfills can end up in groundwater.

Old CCA-Treated Wood Needs to Be Removed

A report produced by one state's Department of Environmental Protection concluded that there is a serious risk for children exposed to arsenic from treated wood. The level of arsenic remains high for 20 years in CCA-treated wood. The useful life of most treated wood products is about 20 years.

An area of CCA-treated wood the size of a four-year-old's hand contains about 120 times the amount of arsenic allowed in a 6-ounce glass of water. (The EPA limit for arsenic in drinking water is 10 parts per billion.) Rainwater penetrates wood and dissolves arsenic. The arsenic ends up on the surface of the wood or in the soil near the wood.

Research and Decide

1. **Defining the Issue** In your own words, describe the issue that needs to be resolved about existing structures made from CCA-treated wood.

2. **Analyzing the Viewpoints** List three arguments of those who don't think that existing structures made from CCA-treated wood need to be removed. List three arguments of those who want to remove existing structures made from CCA-treated wood.

3. **Forming Your Opinion** Should existing structures built from CCA-treated wood be removed? Which argument did you find most convincing?

For: More on this issue
Visit: PHSchool.com
Web Code: cch-1020

Using Properties to Identify Materials

Forensic chemists test the physical and chemical properties of materials found at a crime scene. They also do similar tests on the materials found on a suspect's skin or clothing. These materials are often complex mixtures, such as soil, which contain many substances. In this lab, you will compare the properties of three known materials with two samples of "evidence." These samples represent evidence from a crime scene and evidence from a suspect's shoe. Although your materials and equipment are less complex than those used by forensic chemists, your overall method will be similar to the methods they use.

Problem
Can the properties of materials that appear similar be used to tell them apart?

Materials
- 2 spot plates
- glass-marking pencil
- 5 laboratory spatulas
- cornstarch
- baking soda
- baking powder
- wash bottle of water
- vinegar
- iodine solution
- sample from crime scene
- sample from suspect's shoe

Skills
Observing, Inferring, Predicting

Procedure

Part A: Properties of Known Substances

1. On a separate sheet of paper, copy the data table shown.

2. Use a glass-marking pencil to label 15 wells A through O on the spot plates. Make a mark next to each well, not in the well.

3. Use a spatula to place a small amount of cornstarch in wells A, B, and C. Record any physical properties of the cornstarch that you observe.

4. Use a clean spatula to place a small amount of baking soda in wells D, E, and F. Record any physical properties of baking soda you observe.

5. Using a clean spatula, place a small amount of baking powder in wells G, H, and I. Record any physical properties of baking powder you observe.

6. Fill wells A, D, and G with water. Record any changes you observe.

Data Table				
Sample	Description	Result of Adding Water	Result of Adding Vinegar	Result of Adding Iodine
Cornstarch				
Baking soda				
Baking powder				
Crime scene sample				
Sample from suspect's shoe				

7. Fill wells B, E, and H with vinegar. Record any changes you observe.

8. Add one drop of iodine solution to wells C, F, and I. Record any changes you observe. **CAUTION** *Iodine solution is corrosive and poisonous. It can stain skin and clothing. Rinse any iodine spills with water.*

Part B: Properties of Unknown Substances

9. **Predicting** Look at the sample from the crime scene and the sample from the suspect's shoe. Based on your observations, predict whether testing will show that the samples are identical. Record your prediction.

10. Use a clean spatula to place a small amount of the sample from the crime scene in wells J, K, and L. Record any physical properties of the sample that you observe.

11. Use a clean laboratory spatula to place a small amount of the sample from the suspect's shoe in wells M, N, and O. Record any physical properties of the sample that you observe.

12. Fill wells J and M with water. Record your observations.

13. Fill wells K and N with vinegar. Record your observations.

14. Add one drop of iodine solution to wells L and O. Record your observations.

15. Rinse all materials off the spot plates and flush them down the drain with at least ten times as much water. Dispose of your plastic gloves as directed by your teacher. **CAUTION** *Wash your hands thoroughly with soap or detergent before leaving the laboratory.*

Analyze and Conclude

1. **Analyzing Data** Were you able to use the ability to dissolve in water to distinguish all three materials? Explain.

2. **Drawing Conclusions** Are the samples from the suspect and from the crime scene identical?

3. **Evaluating and Revising** Did the data you collected support your prediction? Explain your answer.

Go Further Design an experiment to determine the effect of heating on the materials you tested in this lab. With your teacher's approval and supervision, carry out your experiment and use the data you collect to identify a sample of an unknown material.

Study Guide

2.1 Classifying Matter

Key Concepts

- Every sample of a given substance has the same properties because a substance has a fixed, uniform composition.
- An element has a fixed composition because it contains only one type of atom.
- A compound always contains two or more elements joined in a fixed proportion.
- The properties of a mixture can vary because the composition of a mixture is not fixed.
- Based on the size of its largest particles, a mixture can be classified as a solution, a suspension, or a colloid.

Vocabulary

pure substance, *p. 39*

element, *p. 39*

atom, *p. 39*

compound, *p. 40*

heterogeneous
  mixture, *p. 41*

homogeneous
  mixture, *p. 42*

solution, *p. 42*

suspension, *p. 43*

colloid, *p. 44*

2.2 Physical Properties

Key Concepts

- Viscosity, conductivity, malleability, hardness, melting point, boiling point, and density are examples of physical properties.
- Physical properties are used to identify a material, to choose a material for a specific purpose, or to separate the substances in a mixture.
- Filtration and distillation are two common separation methods.

Vocabulary

physical property, *p. 45*

viscosity, *p. 45*

conductivity, *p. 46*

malleability, *p. 46*

melting point, *p. 47*

boiling point, *p. 47*

filtration, *p. 50*

distillation, *p. 50*

physical change, *p. 51*

2.3 Chemical Properties

Key Concepts

- Chemical properties can be observed only when the substances in a sample of matter are changing into different substances.
- Three common types of evidence for a chemical change are a change in color, the production of a gas, and the formation of a precipitate.
- When matter undergoes a chemical change, the composition of the matter changes. When matter undergoes a physical change, the composition of the matter remains the same.

Vocabulary

chemical property, *p. 54*

flammability, *p. 54*

reactivity, *p. 55*

chemical change, *p. 56*

precipitate, *p. 57*

Thinking Visually

Concept Map Use information from the chapter to complete the concept map below.

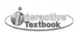
Reviewing Content

Choose the letter that best answers the question or completes the statement.

1. Which of these substances is not an element?
   a. water
   b. hydrogen
   c. aluminum
   d. iron

2. Tap water is
   a. an element.
   b. a compound.
   c. a substance.
   d. a mixture.

3. When a homemade oil-and-vinegar salad dressing is left standing, it separates into layers. The salad dressing is a
   a. solution.
   b. suspension.
   c. colloid.
   d. compound.

4. Which of the following is not an example of a physical property?
   a. density
   b. flammability
   c. hardness
   d. melting point

5. Which material is a poor conductor of heat?
   a. iron
   b. silver
   c. wood
   d. copper

6. A material that can be hit without shattering is
   a. viscous.
   b. flammable.
   c. malleable.
   d. hard.

7. At room temperature, a substance with a melting point of 40°C is a
   a. solid.
   b. liquid.
   c. gas.
   d. mixture.

8. Which action involves a chemical change?
   a. making ice cubes
   b. adding sugar to tea
   c. cutting wrapping paper
   d. baking a cake

9. A substance that has little tendency to change into other substances is said to have low
   a. reactivity.
   b. density.
   c. viscosity.
   d. conductivity.

10. Formation of a precipitate is usually evidence of
   a. the separation of a mixture.
   b. a chemical change.
   c. the formation of a mixture.
   d. a physical change.

Understanding Concepts

11. Explain why the properties of a pure substance do not vary from sample to sample.

12. What is the difference between an element and a compound?

13. How does the composition of a mixture of hydrogen and oxygen differ from the composition of a compound containing hydrogen and oxygen?

14. Suppose all the grains in a sample of sand were exactly the same size. Could the sample still be a heterogeneous mixture? Explain your answer.

15. What allows a mixture to be separated by filtration?

16. Explain why viscosity is classified as a physical property.

17. Based on these pieces of pottery found in Grand Canyon National Park, would you describe pottery as a malleable or brittle material?

18. A sample of copper can be drawn into a thin wire. Is this property of copper a physical property or a chemical property? Explain.

19. Name one physical property and one chemical property of wood.

20. Why is breaking down a compound into its elements considered a chemical change?

21. List one physical change and one chemical change that occur when a candle burns.

22. Suppose you need to identify the material in an object without changing the object in any way. Should you use physical or chemical properties to identify the material? Explain your choice.

Critical Thinking

23. Applying Concepts Ammonia is a compound of hydrogen and nitrogen that dissolves easily in water. Can you conclude that hydrogen and nitrogen dissolve in water? Explain your answer.

24. Posing Questions What information would you need to know about a sample of air before you could classify the sample as a solution, suspension, or colloid?

25. Applying Concepts Explain why you cannot use mass or volume alone to identify substances.

Use the table to answer questions 26 and 27.

Melting Points and Densities of Some Substances

Substance	Melting Point	Density
Aluminum	660.3°C	2.70 g/cm³
Table salt	800.7°C	2.17 g/cm³
Isopropyl alcohol	−89.5°C	0.78 g/cm³
Bromine	−7.2°C	3.10 g/cm³
Water	0.0°C	1.00 g/cm³
Gold	1064.2°C	19.3 g/cm³

26. Analyzing Data You have a solid with a density of 0.78 g/cm³. Is it possible that this solid is one of the substances listed in the table? Explain.

27. Using Tables A solid, rectangular block of material floats on water. Is it possible that the block is pure gold? Explain your answer.

28. Drawing Conclusions At room temperature, two white solids have the same density. With just this information, is it possible to conclude that the two solids are the same material? Explain.

29. Designing Experiments How could you use density to show that a gold bracelet contains elements other than gold?

30. Inferring Suppose you mix two colorless liquids together and a green solid settles to the bottom of the container. Explain why you might be confident that a chemical change has taken place.

Concepts in Action

31. Comparing and Contrasting The photo shows maple sap being collected in a bucket. The sap is about 97% water and 3% sugar with traces of other compounds. Cans of 100% pure maple syrup contain about 34% water and 66% sugar. Which would have the greater viscosity—the maple sap or the maple syrup? Give a reason for your answer.

32. Inferring One of the general safety instructions for working in a laboratory is to tie back long hair, especially when using a lab burner. From this instruction, what can you infer about the flammability of hair?

33. Applying Concepts Why might valuable documents be stored in pure nitrogen instead of in air? Recall that air is a mixture of gases, including nitrogen and oxygen.

34. Relating Cause and Effect Explain why painting an iron railing can slow down the rate at which the railing rusts.

35. Writing in Science Cheesecloth is a type of cotton cloth used by cooks. Write a paragraph explaining why a cook might wrap a lemon wedge in cheesecloth before squeezing juice from the lemon. What process for separating mixtures is the cook using?

Performance-Based Assessment

Writing in a Journal Keep a journal for a day. List five physical changes and five chemical changes that you observe. Be sure to describe why you think each change is physical or chemical.

Go Online
PHSchool.com

For: Self-grading assessment
Visit: PHSchool.com
Web Code: cca-1020

Standardized Test Prep

Test-Taking Tip

Using Models
For some test questions, you will be asked to decide what a visual model represents. Look at the model below. Notice that there are two types of particles shown and notice how the particles are distributed. Use what you observe to decide which answer is the best choice.

What type of matter does the model represent?
(A) a solution
(B) a colloid
(C) a suspension
(D) an element
(E) a homogeneous mixture

(Answer: C)

Choose the letter that best answers the question or completes the statement.

1. All pure substances
   (A) contain only one type of atom.
   (B) can be broken down into simpler substances.
   (C) cannot be broken down into simpler substances.
   (D) have a fixed composition.
   (E) have a variable composition.

2. Which property can be used to separate a mixture by distillation?
   (A) melting point
   (B) boiling point
   (C) density
   (D) viscosity
   (E) conductivity

3. During which of these events does a chemical change occur?
   (A) Ice cubes melt.
   (B) A pot of water boils.
   (C) A heated iron bar turns red.
   (D) A paper clip is bent.
   (E) A cake rises in the oven.

4. You can be certain that a change is a chemical change if
   (A) the change cannot be reversed.
   (B) new substances form.
   (C) bubbles are produced.
   (D) a precipitate forms.
   (E) there is a color change.

Use the drawings to answer Questions 5 and 6.

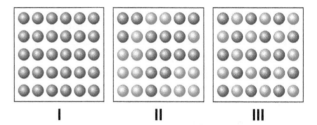

I   II   III

5. Which of the drawings could represent a homogeneous mixture?
   (A) drawing I
   (B) drawing II
   (C) drawing III
   (D) drawings I and III
   (E) drawings II and III

6. Which of the drawings could represent an element?
   (A) drawing I
   (B) drawing II
   (C) drawing III
   (D) drawings I and III
   (E) drawings II and III

3 States of Matter

21st Century Learning
Creativity and Intellectual Curiosity

What can you find out about plasma or Bose-Einstein condensates?

You are probably familiar with three common states of matter—solid, liquid, and gas. But scientists also recognize two states of matter that are more rare: plasma and Bose-Einstein condensate. Choose one of these for a research project. Find out how scientists define this particular state of matter and under what conditions it forms. Present your research to the class by posting on your class blog or wiki.

How do science concepts apply to your world? Here are some questions you'll be able to answer after you read this chapter.

- **How can balloons have many different shapes?** *(Section 3.1)*

- **Why should you check the air pressure of tires before you go for a long drive?** *(Section 3.2)*

- **What controls the movement of air into and out of your lungs as you breathe?** *(Section 3.2)*

- **How is the altitude of a hot-air balloon controlled?** *(page 82)*

- **Why does pasta take longer to cook in Denver than in New Orleans?** *(Section 3.3)*

When temperatures rise in the spring, the ice begins to melt on Bow Lake at Banff National Park in Alberta, Canada.

Chapter Preview

DISCOVERY CHANNEL
SCHOOL

Video Field Trip

Up, Up, and Away

Inquiry › Activity

How Easy Is It to Compress Air and Water?

Procedure

1. Insert a plunger into a syringe that is sealed at the narrow end. Push the plunger into the syringe as far as you can. Use the marks on the side of the syringe to read the volume of the air inside the syringe. Record this volume.

2. Remove the plunger. Fill the syringe with water by holding it under water in a large plastic container of water. **CAUTION** *Wipe up any spilled water right away to avoid slips and falls.*

3. While holding the syringe over the container, repeat Step 1. Record the volume of the water.

Think About It

1. **Comparing and Contrasting** Which was harder to compress, the air or the water? (To compress means to squeeze into a smaller volume.)

2. **Inferring** Based on your answer to Question 1, in which material are the particles closer together, in air or in water? Explain your answer.

3.1 Solids, Liquids, and Gases

Key Concepts

- How can shape and volume be used to classify materials?
- How can kinetic theory and forces of attraction be used to explain the behavior of gases, liquids, and solids?

Vocabulary

- solid
- liquid
- gas
- kinetic energy

Reading Strategy

Comparing and Contrasting Copy the diagram. As you read, replace each letter with one of these phrases: *definite volume, definite shape, variable volume,* or *variable shape.*

Solid   Liquid   Gas

a. ? b. ?   c. ? d. ?

Do you recognize the object in Figure 1? It is a carpenter's level. A level can be used to see whether a surface is perfectly horizontal. The level has one or more transparent tubes inside a metal or wooden frame. Inside each tube is a clear liquid, such as alcohol, and an air bubble. When a carpenter places the level on a surface that is perfectly horizontal, the air bubble stays in the middle of the horizontal tube. The bubble moves to the high end of the tube if the surface is slanted.

The metal, alcohol, and air in a carpenter's level represent three states of matter. At room temperature, most metals are solids, alcohol is a liquid, and air is a gas. In this chapter, you will learn why the appearance and behavior of solids, liquids, and gases are different.

Describing the States of Matter

If you were asked to classify some materials as solids, liquids, or gases, you would probably find the task fairly easy. But could you describe what method you used to classify the materials? You might notice that some materials have a definite shape and volume and some materials do not. **Materials can be classified as solids, liquids, or gases based on whether their shapes and volumes are definite or variable.** Shape and volume are clues to how the particles within a material are arranged.

Figure 1 Carpenters use a level to find out if a surface is perfectly horizontal. In the level shown, three clear plastic tubes are set into an aluminum frame. Each tube contains a liquid and a gas. **Classifying** *What property could you use to distinguish the liquid or gas from the solids in a level?*

Solids Think about these familiar objects: a pencil, a quarter, a book, and a cafeteria tray. What do these four objects have in common? They all have a recognizable shape and they all take up a certain amount of space. The materials in these objects are all in the solid state. **Solid** is the state of matter in which materials have a definite shape and a definite volume.

The term *definite* means that the shape and volume of a pencil won't change as you move the pencil from a desk drawer to a pencil case to a backpack. Changing the container doesn't change the shape or volume of a solid. However, the term *definite* doesn't mean that the shape or volume can never change. After all, you can change the shape of a pencil by sharpening it. You can change the shape of a copper wire by bending the wire.

Figure 2 shows the arrangement of atoms in a copper wire. The copper atoms are packed close together and are arranged in a regular pattern. Almost all solids have some type of orderly arrangement of particles at the atomic level.

Liquids How good are you at estimating whether the juice remaining in an almost-empty bottle will fit in a glass? If your estimate is not accurate, you will run out of space in the glass before you run out of juice in the bottle.

Appearances can be deceiving. Imagine a narrow glass and a wide bottle side by side. Each contains exactly 350 milliliters of juice (about three quarters of a pint). There will seem to be more juice in the glass because the juice rises almost to the rim of the glass. There will seem to be less juice in the bottle because the juice forms a shallow layer. What can you learn about liquids from this comparison?

A liquid always has the same shape as its container and can be poured from one container to another. **Liquid** is the state of matter in which a material has a definite volume but not a definite shape.

Mercury exists as a liquid at room temperature. The drawing in Figure 3 shows the arrangement of atoms in liquid mercury. Compare this arrangement to the arrangement of copper atoms in Figure 2. The mercury atoms are close together but their arrangement is more random than the arrangement of atoms in copper.

Figure 2 Samples of solid copper have definite volume. Copper atoms are packed close together in an orderly arrangement.

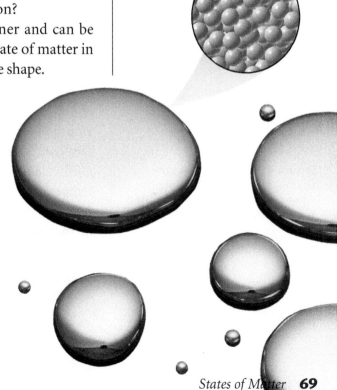

Figure 3 At room temperature, mercury is a liquid. Drops of mercury on a flat, clean surface have a round shape. Mercury in a container has the same shape as its container. *Comparing and Contrasting* **Compare the arrangement of atoms in copper and mercury.**

Gases If you were asked to name a gas, what would you say? Air, which is a mixture of gases, is probably the most obvious example. You might also mention natural gas, which is used as a fuel for heating homes. **Gas** is the state of matter in which a material has neither a definite shape nor a definite volume. (The adjective form of the word *gas* is *gaseous* (GAS e us), as in *gaseous state*.) A gas takes the shape and volume of its container.

The balloons in Figure 4 are filled with helium, a colorless gas that is less dense than air. Two of the balloons are teardrop-shaped and two are disk-shaped. The "shape" of the helium in a balloon is the same as the shape of the balloon itself. The volume of the helium in a balloon is equal to the volume of the balloon.

The helium atoms in a balloon are not arranged in a regular pattern, as shown in the drawing in Figure 4. They are at random locations throughout the balloon. There is more space between two helium atoms in a balloon than between two neighboring atoms in solid copper or liquid mercury.

Because of the space among helium atoms, a large amount of helium can be compressed into a metal cylinder. When helium flows from the cylinder into a balloon, the helium atoms spread out. If 200 balloons are filled from a single cylinder, the total volume of the balloons will be much larger than the volume of the cylinder.

Other States of Matter On Earth, almost all matter exists in a solid, liquid, or gaseous state. But ninety-nine percent of all the matter that can be observed in the universe exists in a state that is not as common on Earth. At extremely high temperatures, such as those found on the sun or other stars, matter exists as plasma. You will read more about the properties of plasmas in Chapter 10.

In the 1920s Satyendra Bose, a physicist from India, wrote a paper about the behavior of light. After Albert Einstein read the paper, he realized that the behavior described could apply to matter under certain conditions. Einstein made a bold prediction. He predicted that a fifth state of matter would exist at extremely low temperatures. At temperatures near −273°C, groups of atoms would behave as though they were a single particle. In 1995, scientists produced this fifth state of matter, which is called a Bose-Einstein condensate (or BEC). It behaved as Einstein had predicted decades before.

Figure 4 Helium gas takes the volume and shape of its container. **Observing** *Describe the shape of the helium in the blue balloon.*

Reading Checkpoint *How can atoms behave at temperatures near −273°C?*

Why Was Mercury Used in Thermometers?

Until recently, mercury thermometers were used in homes and schools. When a thermometer broke, people were exposed to mercury. When broken thermometers were thrown away, they ended up in landfills. Mercury is a toxic substance that can harm humans and other organisms. Schools no longer use mercury thermometers and people are encouraged to replace their fever thermometers.

So why did people continue to use mercury thermometers long after they knew the dangers of mercury? Look at the data table. It lists some densities over a temperature range from 0°C to 150°C. The temperatures are given at 30-degree intervals.

1. **Using Tables** How does the density of mercury change as the temperature increases?

2. **Relating Cause and Effect** How does a change in density affect the volume of a mercury sample?

Density of Mercury		
Temperature (°C)	Density (g/mL)	Volume of One Gram (mL)
0	13.60	0.07356
30	13.52	0.07396
60	13.45	0.07436
90	13.38	0.07476
120	13.30	0.07517
150	13.23	0.07558

3. **Calculating** If a thermometer contained a gram of mercury, how much would the volume of the mercury change when the temperature rose from 0°C to 30°C? From 30°C to 60°C? From 60°C to 90°C? From 90°C to 120°C?

4. **Drawing Conclusions** Why was mercury a better choice than water for the liquid in a thermometer? (*Hint:* Between 0°C and 30°C, the volume of a gram of water changes by 0.0042 mL. Between 30°C and 60°C, the volume changes by 0.0127 mL. Between 60°C and 90°C, the volume changes by 0.0188 mL.)

5. **Inferring** Why is the mercury in a thermometer stored in a narrow tube?

Kinetic Theory

Why, under ordinary conditions, is copper a solid, mercury a liquid, and helium a gas? To begin to answer that question, you need to know something about kinetic energy. An object that is moving has kinetic energy. The word *kinetic* comes from a Greek word meaning "to move." **Kinetic energy** is the energy an object has due to its motion.

The faster an object moves, the greater its kinetic energy is. A ball thrown at 85 miles (137 kilometers) per hour by the pitcher in Figure 5 has more kinetic energy than a ball thrown at 78 miles (125 kilometers) per hour. When a baseball is thrown, a batter can see that it is moving. But the batter cannot see that there is also motion occurring within the baseball. According to the kinetic theory of matter, particles inside the solid baseball are moving. Particles in the air that the baseball travels through are moving too.

👁 **The kinetic theory of matter says that all particles of matter are in constant motion.** The theory was developed in the mid-1800s to explain the behavior of gases. It can also help to explain the behavior of liquids and solids.

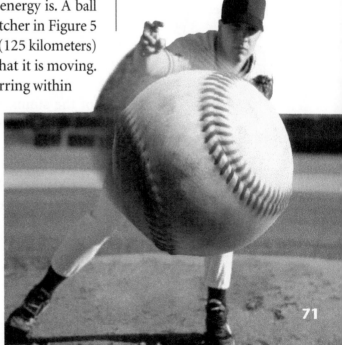

Figure 5 The kinetic energy of a baseball depends on the speed at which the pitcher throws the ball.

Figure 6 This photograph of billiard balls was taken just after the cue struck the white ball, which began to move. The white ball moved in a straight line until it collided with the dark blue ball. The collision caused the dark blue ball to start moving. The motion of billiard balls can be compared to the motion of particles in a gas.

Figure 7 A helium atom travels in a straight line until it collides with another helium atom or the side of its container.
Relating Cause and Effect *What can happen to the kinetic energy of two helium atoms when the atoms collide?*

Explaining the Behavior of Gases

You can compare the motion of the particles in a gas to the movement of balls during a game of billiards. When a cue strikes a billiard ball, as shown in Figure 6, the ball moves in a straight line until it strikes the side of the billiard table or another ball. When a moving ball strikes a ball at rest, the first ball slows down and the second ball begins to move. Kinetic energy is transferred during those collisions.

Motion in Gases Unlike billiard balls, the particles in a gas are never at rest. At room temperature, the average speed of the particles in a sample of gas is about 1600 kilometers per hour. The use of the term *average* is a clue that not all particles are moving at the same speed. Some are moving faster than the average speed and some are moving slower than the average speed.

Figure 7 shows the possible paths of two helium atoms in a container of helium gas. Notice that each atom moves in a straight line until it collides with the other atom or with a wall of the container. During a collision, one atom may lose kinetic energy and slow down while the other atom gains kinetic energy and speeds up. However, the total kinetic energy of the atoms remains the same.

The diagram in Figure 7 does not accurately compare the volumes of the atoms and the container. The volume of a helium atom is extremely small compared to the volume of its container. If there were a billion times a trillion helium atoms in a liter bottle, there would still be a large amount of space in the bottle.

Between collisions, why doesn't one particle in a gas affect the other particles in the gas? **There are forces of attraction among the particles in all matter.** If the particles are apart and moving fast, as in a gas, the attractions are too weak to have an effect. Under ordinary conditions, scientists can ignore the forces of attraction in a gas.

Kinetic Theory of Gases The kinetic theory explains the general properties of a gas. 🔑 **The constant motion of particles in a gas allows a gas to fill a container of any shape or size.** Think about air in a tire. The walls of the tire keep the air contained. What if there is a hole in the tire? Because the particles in the air are in constant motion, some of the particles would travel to the hole and move out of the tire. The kinetic theory as applied to gases has three main points.

- Particles in a gas are in constant, random motion.

- The motion of one particle is unaffected by the motion of other particles unless the particles collide.

- Forces of attraction among particles in a gas can be ignored under ordinary conditions.

Reading Checkpoint *Describe the motion of particles in a gas.*

Explaining the Behavior of Liquids

The particles in liquids also have kinetic energy. So why does a liquid such as mercury have a definite volume at room temperature instead of expanding to fill its container? The average speed of a mercury atom is much slower than the average speed of a helium atom at the same temperature. A mercury atom has about 50 times the mass of a helium atom. This greater mass is only partly responsible for the slower speed. What other factor is responsible?

The particles in a liquid are more closely packed than the particles in a gas. Therefore, attractions between the particles in a liquid do affect the movement of the particles. A mercury atom in liquid mercury is like a student in the crowded hallway in Figure 8. The student's path may be blocked by students moving in the other direction. The student's ability to move is affected by interactions with other students.

In a liquid, there is a kind of tug of war between the constant motion of particles and the attractions among particles. This tug of war explains the general behavior of liquids. 🔑 **A liquid takes the shape of its container because particles in a liquid can flow to new locations. The volume of a liquid is constant because forces of attraction keep the particles close together.** Because forces of attraction limit the motion of particles in a liquid, the particles in a liquid cannot spread out and fill a container.

For: Links on kinetic theory
Visit: www.SciLinks.org
Web Code: ccn-1031

For: Activity on mercury in the enviroment
Visit: PHSchool.com
Web Code: ccc-1031

Figure 8 Particles in a liquid behave like students moving through a crowded hallway.

Figure 9 These photographs of an audience in a movie theater were taken at different times on the same day. The behavior of the audience can be compared to the behavior of particles in a solid. *Observing What stayed the same and what changed between the photographs?*

Explaining the Behavior of Solids

You might compare the particles in a solid to a polite audience in a movie theater. While the movie is running, people stay in their seats. Although people move around in their seats, as shown in Figure 9, each person remains in essentially the same location during the movie. They have "fixed" locations in a total volume that does not change.

⬤ **Solids have a definite volume and shape because particles in a solid vibrate around fixed locations.** Vibration is a repetitive back-and-forth motion. Look back at the orderly arrangement of copper atoms in Figure 2. Strong attractions among the copper atoms restrict their motion and keep each atom in a fixed location relative to its neighbors. Each atom vibrates around its location but it does not exchange places with a neighboring atom.

Section 3.1 Assessment

Reviewing Concepts

1. ⬤ How are shape and volume used to classify solids, liquids, and gases?

2. ⬤ What does the kinetic theory say about the motion of atoms?

3. ⬤ How is a gas able to fill a container of any size or shape?

4. ⬤ Use kinetic theory and attractive forces to explain why a liquid has a definite volume and a shape that can vary.

5. ⬤ Explain why a solid has a definite shape and volume.

6. How does the arrangement of atoms in most solids differ from the arrangement of atoms in a liquid?

Critical Thinking

7. **Using Analogies** Explain how the behavior of popcorn in a popcorn popper can be used as an analogy for the motion of gas particles.

8. **Applying Concepts** A hazardous chemical is leaking from a tank truck. Rescue workers need to evacuate people who live near the accident. Why are more people likely to be affected if the chemical is a gas, rather than a liquid?

Connecting ⊂ Concepts

Viscosity Review the description of viscosity in Section 2.2. Use the tug of war between forces of attraction and kinetic energy to explain differences in viscosity among liquids at the same temperature.

3.2 The Gas Laws

Reading Focus

Key Concepts
- What causes gas pressure in a closed container?
- What factors affect gas pressure?
- How are the temperature, volume, and pressure of a gas related?

Vocabulary
- pressure
- absolute zero
- Charles's law
- Boyle's law

Reading Strategy
Identifying Cause and Effect Copy the diagram. As you read, identify the variables that affect gas pressure.

Gas pressure — is affected by

a. ?

b. ?

c. ?

The woman in Figure 10 is taking a deep breath. This action helps reduce her breathing rate and increase the volume of air she inhales. When you inhale, the volume of your chest cavity increases and air moves into your lungs. When you exhale, the volume of your chest cavity decreases and air is pushed out of your lungs.

After you read this section, you will understand how changing the volume of your chest cavity causes air to move into and out of your lungs. Changes in the volume, the temperature, the pressure, and the number of particles have predictable effects on the behavior of a gas.

Figure 10 Taking a deep breath increases the volume of your chest cavity, which causes air to move into your lungs.

Pressure

At many hockey rinks, a layer of shatterproof glass keeps the puck away from the spectators. The force with which the puck hits the glass depends on the speed of the puck. The faster the puck is traveling, the greater the force is. The smaller the area of impact is, the greater the pressure produced. **Pressure** is the result of a force distributed over an area. If the edge of the puck hits the glass, it exerts more pressure than if the face of the puck hits the glass at the same speed.

The SI unit of pressure is derived from SI units for force and area. Force is measured in newtons (N) and area in square meters (m^2). When a force in newtons is divided by an area in square meters, the unit of pressure is newtons per square meter (N/m^2). The SI unit for pressure, the pascal (Pa), is shorthand for newtons per square meter. One pascal is a small amount of pressure. Scientists often express larger amounts of pressure in kilopascals. One kilopascal (kPa) is equal to 1000 pascals.

An object does not need to be as large as a hockey puck to exert pressure when it collides with another object. Recall that the helium atoms in a balloon are constantly moving. The pressure produced by a single helium atom colliding with a wall is extremely small. However, there are more than 10^{22} helium atoms in a small balloon. When so many particles collide with the walls of a container at the same time, they produce a measurable pressure.

Collisions between particles of a gas and the walls of the container cause the pressure in a closed container of gas. The more frequent the collisions, the greater the pressure of the gas is. The speed of the particles and their mass also affect the pressure.

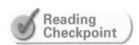
Reading Checkpoint *How does the frequency of collisions affect the pressure of a gas?*

Factors That Affect Gas Pressure

Think again about the collisions that produce gas pressure. What changes might affect the pressure of a gas in a container? The particles in the gas could move faster or slower. The gas could be moved into a larger or smaller container. You could add gas or remove gas from the container. **Factors that affect the pressure of an enclosed gas are its temperature, its volume, and the number of its particles.**

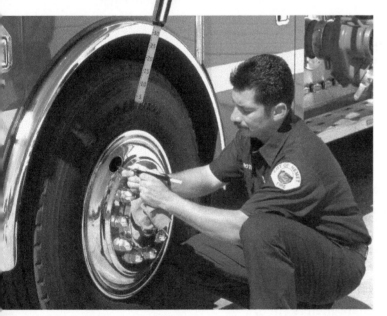

Figure 11 The fire-fighter is using a pressure gauge to check the air pressure in a tire on a firetruck. If the tires on the truck have a 44.5-inch diameter, the pressure on a front tire should be about 125 pounds per square inch (psi).

Temperature Suppose you are about to go on a long drive. The driver suspects that the air pressure in the automobile tires might be low. You check the pressure in each tire, using a pressure gauge like the one in Figure 11. You find that the measurements are well within the automobile manufacturer's guidelines. If you checked the tire pressures again after a few hours on the highway, would you be surprised to find that the pressure in the tires had increased?

The constant motion of tires on the highway causes the tires and the air in the tires to warm up. As the temperature rises, the average kinetic energy of the particles in the air increases. With increased kinetic energy, the particles move faster and collide more often with the inner walls of the tires. The faster-moving particles also hit the walls with greater force. The increase in the number of collisions along with the increase in the force of the collisions causes an increase in the pressure of the air in the tires. **Raising the temperature of a gas will increase its pressure if the volume of the gas and the number of particles are constant.**

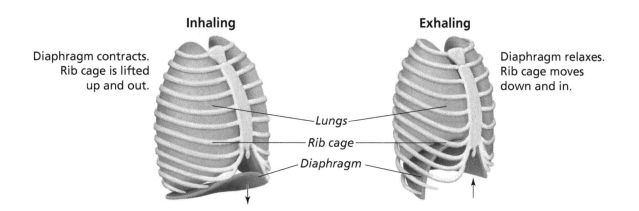

Inhaling

Diaphragm contracts.
Rib cage is lifted
up and out.

Lungs
Rib cage
Diaphragm

Exhaling

Diaphragm relaxes.
Rib cage moves
down and in.

Volume Imagine that you have a plastic bottle that appears empty. If you twist the cap onto the bottle and then squeeze the bottle, what will happen? At first, the plastic will give a little, reducing the volume of the bottle. But soon you will feel pressure from inside the bottle resisting your efforts to further reduce the volume. The pressure you feel is a result of the increased pressure of the air trapped inside the bottle. As the volume is decreased, particles of trapped air collide more often with the walls of the bottle. ➤ **Reducing the volume of a gas increases its pressure if the temperature of the gas and the number of particles are constant.**

Figure 12 shows how the relationship between volume and pressure explains what happens when you breathe. As you inhale, a muscle called the diaphragm (DY uh fram) contracts. The contraction causes your chest cavity to expand. This temporary increase in volume allows the particles in air to spread out, which lowers the pressure inside the chest cavity. Because the pressure of the air outside your body is now greater than the pressure inside your chest, air rushes into your lungs.

When you exhale, your diaphragm relaxes and the volume of your chest cavity decreases. The particles in the air are squeezed into a smaller volume and the pressure inside your lungs increases. Because the pressure of the air inside your chest is now greater than the pressure of the air outside your body, air is forced out of your lungs.

Number of Particles You can probably predict what will happen to the pressure when you add more gas to a container. Think about a tire. Once the tire is inflated, its volume is fairly constant. So adding more air will increase the pressure inside the tire. The more particles there are in the same volume, the greater the number of collisions and the greater the pressure. At some point the rubber from which the tire is made will not be strong enough to withstand the increased pressure and the tire will burst. ➤ **Increasing the number of particles will increase the pressure of a gas if the temperature and the volume are constant.**

Figure 12 Movement of a muscle called the diaphragm changes the volume of your chest cavity. The volume increases when you inhale and decreases when you exhale.
Interpreting Diagrams **How does the movement of your rib cage affect the volume of your chest cavity?**

For: Articles on properties of matter
Visit: PHSchool.com
Web Code: cce-1032

Charles's Law

Boyle's Law

Figure 13 These graphs compare the effects of temperature and volume on the pressure of a gas. Charles's law describes the direct relationship between the temperature and the volume. Boyle's law describes the inverse relationship between the volume and the pressure.
Controlling Variables For each graph, name the manipulated variable and the responding variable.

Charles's Law

During his lifetime, the French physicist Jacques Charles (1746–1823) was known for his inventions, including the hydrogen balloon. Today, Charles is best known for his investigations of the behavior of gases. Charles collected data on the relationship between the temperature and volume of gases. When he graphed the data, the graph was a straight line, as shown in Figure 13. The graph shows that the volume of a gas increases at the same rate as the temperature of the gas.

Charles extended the line on his graph beyond the measured data to see what the temperature would have to be to produce a volume of 0 L. The temperature at the point where the line crossed the x-axis was $-273.15°C$. This temperature is equal to 0 K on the Kelvin temperature scale. A temperature of 0 K is called **absolute zero.** No scientist has produced a temperature of absolute zero in a laboratory, but some have come extremely close. As a gas cools to temperatures near 0 K, the gas changes to a liquid, a solid, or sometimes a Bose-Einstein condensate.

Charles's law states that the volume of a gas is directly proportional to its temperature in kelvins if the pressure and the number of particles of the gas are constant. Charles's law can be written as a mathematical expression in which T_1 and V_1 represent the temperature and volume of a gas before a change occurs. T_2 and V_2 represent the temperature and volume after a change occurs.

Charles's Law
$$\frac{V_1}{T_1} = \frac{V_2}{T_2}$$

The temperatures must be expressed in kelvins. If temperatures in degrees Celsius are used in the expression, the volume will not be directly proportional to the temperature.

Boyle's Law

Robert Boyle, who was born in Ireland in 1627, was the first to describe the relationship between the pressure and volume of a gas. The graph in Figure 13 shows what happens when the volume of a cylinder containing a set amount of gas is decreased. What happens when the volume of the cylinder is reduced from 2.0 liters to 1.0 liter? The pressure of the gas in the cylinder doubles from 50 kilopascals to 100 kilopascals.

Boyle's Law

$$P_1V_1 = P_2V_2$$

Boyle's law states that the volume of a gas is inversely proportional to its pressure if the temperature and the number of particles are constant. Boyle's law can be expressed mathematically. P_1 and V_1 represent the pressure and volume of a gas before a change occurs. P_2 and V_2 represent the pressure and volume of a gas after a change occurs.

 Reading Checkpoint *How is Boyle's law expressed mathematically?*

Quick Lab

Observing the Effect of Temperature on Gas Pressure

Materials
pan, metric ruler, empty beverage can, masking tape, hot plate, clock, tongs

Procedure

1. Fill a pan with cold water to a depth of 3 cm.

2. Use masking tape to cover half the opening of the can. **CAUTION** *Do not cover the entire opening with tape.*

3. Place the can on the hot plate and turn the hot plate to a high setting. Heat the can for 5 minutes and then turn off the hot plate.

4. Use tongs to remove the can from the hot plate and place it upside down in the pan of water as shown. The opening should be below the surface of the water. Observe the can as it cools.

Analyze and Conclude

1. **Inferring** How did the temperature of the air inside the can change when you heated the can? How did it change when you put the can in the water?

2. **Drawing Conclusions** What happened to the pressure of the air inside the can when you put the can in the cold water?

3. **Inferring** Did the air pressure outside the can change during the experiment?

4. **Formulating Hypotheses** What caused the change you observed in Step 4?

The Combined Gas Law

The relationships described by Boyle's law and Charles's law can be described by a single law. The combined gas law describes the relationship among the temperature, volume, and pressure of a gas when the number of particles is constant.

Combined Gas Law

$$\frac{P_1 V_1}{T_1} = \frac{P_2 V_2}{T_2}$$

The combined gas law is used to solve many problems involving gases.

Math Skills

The Combined Gas Law

A cylinder that contains air at a pressure of 100 kPa has a volume of 0.75 L. The pressure is increased to 300 kPa. The temperature does not change. Find the new volume of air.

1 Read and Understand

What information are you given?

$$P_1 = 100 \text{ kPa} \qquad P_2 = 300 \text{ kPa} \qquad V_1 = 0.75 \text{ L}$$

2 Plan and Solve

What unknown are you trying to calculate?

$$V_2$$

What expression can you use?

$$\frac{P_1 V_1}{T_1} = \frac{P_2 V_2}{T_2}$$

Cancel out the variable that does not change and rearrange the expression to solve for V_2.

$$P_1 V_1 = P_2 V_2 \qquad V_2 = \frac{P_1 V_1}{P_2}$$

Replace each variable with its known value.

$$V_2 = 100 \text{ kPa} \times \frac{0.75 \text{ L}}{300 \text{ kPa}} = 0.25 \text{ L}$$

3 Look Back and Check

Is your answer reasonable?

Volume should decrease as pressure increases. The pressure tripled from 100 kPa to 300 kPa. The answer, 0.25 L, is one third the original volume, 0.75 L.

Math Practice

1. A gas has a volume of 5.0 L at a pressure of 50 kPa. What happens to the volume when the pressure is increased to 125 kPa? The temperature does not change.

2. Gas stored in a tank at 273 K has a pressure of 388 kPa. The safe limit for the pressure is 825 kPa. At what temperature will the gas reach this pressure?

3. At 10°C, the gas in a cylinder has a volume of 0.250 L. The gas is allowed to expand to 0.285 L. What must the final temperature be for the pressure to remain constant? (*Hint:* Convert from degrees Celsius to kelvins using the expression °C + 273 = K.)

It is harder for scientists to do a controlled experiment when they are studying events that occur in natural settings. Scientists need laws like the combined gas law to deal with situations in which multiple variables are changing. Balloons like the one in Figure 14 are used by scientists to gather data about Earth's atmosphere. The balloon is filled with hydrogen or helium. It carries a package of weather instruments up into the atmosphere. The instruments measure temperature, pressure, and water content at different levels in the atmosphere.

What will happen to the volume of the weather balloon as it rises through the atmosphere? Both pressure and temperature decrease as the altitude increases in Earth's atmosphere. A decrease in external pressure should cause the balloon to expand to a larger volume. A decrease in temperature should cause the balloon to contract to a smaller volume. Whether the balloon actually expands or contracts depends on the size of the changes in pressure and temperature.

Figure 14 These scientists are releasing a weather balloon into the atmosphere. The balloon is designed to burst when it reaches an altitude of about 27,400 meters.
Drawing Conclusions *What happens to the pressure inside a weather balloon as it rises?*

Section 3.2 Assessment

Reviewing Concepts

1. ⬡ How is the gas pressure produced in a closed container of gas?
2. ⬡ What three factors affect gas pressure?
3. ⬡ How does increasing the temperature affect the pressure of a contained gas?
4. ⬡ What happens to the pressure of a gas if its volume is reduced?
5. ⬡ How does increasing the number of particles of a contained gas affect its pressure?

Critical Thinking

6. **Predicting** What happens to the pressure in a tire if air is slowly leaking out of the tire? Explain your answer.
7. **Comparing and Contrasting** What do Boyle's law and Charles's law have in common? How are they different?

8. **Applying Concepts** Some liquid products are sold in aerosol cans. Gas is stored in a can under pressure and is used to propel the liquid out of the can. Explain why an aerosol can should never be thrown into a fireplace or incinerator.

Math ▷ Practice

9. Two liters of hydrogen gas are stored at a pressure of 100 kPa. If the temperature does not change, what will the volume of the gas be when the pressure is decreased to 25 kPa?
10. You know that a gas in a sealed container has a pressure of 111 kPa at 23°C. What will the pressure be if the temperature rises to 475°C?

Riding on Air

Warm air is less dense than cold air. So if enough warm air is confined to a lightweight container, the container can rise through the surrounding colder air. This is the principle that allows a hot-air balloon to get off and stay off the ground.

When air is heated, the particles in the air gain energy and move faster on average. The particles also move farther apart, so a given volume of hot air contains fewer particles and has less mass than the same volume of cold air. This difference in density produces an upward force. In a hot-air balloon, the force is very small, equivalent to lifting about one tenth of a gram for each liter of air. A large volume of air is needed to support the mass of the balloon and any passengers. That is why hot-air balloons need to be large.

To heat the air, the pilot burns propane gas, which is stored under pressure in tanks. The bottom of the balloon's envelope (the skirt) is treated so that it is not flammable.

As the balloon nears the chosen altitude, the pilot turns the burner off so that the balloon will stop rising. The pilot maintains the altitude of the balloon by turning the burner on and off and by opening a valve at the top of the balloon to let hot air escape.

The horizontal movement of the balloon is much harder to control. The wind speed and wind direction vary at different altitudes. The pilot uses the burner and the valve to change the altitude of the balloon and take advantage of favorable winds. A hot-air balloon cannot land at the same spot from which it took off. The ground crew must drive to the landing site to collect the balloon and the passengers.

Taking Off and Landing

Launching and piloting a hot-air balloon is an activity that takes skill and patience.

1 The crew uses fans to fill the envelope with cold air.

2 Gas burners are switched on to heat the air and inflate the balloon, which begins to rise.

Burner

3 Once up, the pilot maintains altitude by occasionally turning on the burner for a few seconds.

Valve

4 To lose altitude, the pilot opens a valve at the top of the envelope to let out some hot air.

Fast-moving
hot air
particles

Envelope
made from
tough nylon

Flame-resistant skirt

Jet of flame
from burner

Flexible, lightweight,
wicker basket

Slower-
moving
cold air
particles

Upward
force

Particle Pressure

Particles in hot air move faster
and are farther apart than those
in cold air, so hot air is less dense
than cold air. With lower density,
heated air rises over colder air.

Balloon Valve
The valve helps to control the balloon's altitude.
When the valve is opened, some hot air is
released from the top of the balloon. The hot air
is replaced by cold air flowing into the base of
the balloon. This exchange of cold air for hot air
increases the mass of the balloon, causing it to
descend until the pilot closes the valve.

5 The pilot selects a
suitable place to land
before opening the
valve all the way.

6 The balloon slowly
falls to the ground
and collapses.

7 The crew
gathers up the
envelope.

Going Further

- Write a paragraph comparing early hot-air
  balloons with modern balloons. Include the
  following information: the
  kind of materials used, the
  length of distances traveled,
  and the types of fuel used.

- Take a Discovery Channel
  Video Field Trip by watching
  "Up, Up, and Away."

3.3 Phase Changes

Reading Focus

Key Concepts

- What are six common phase changes?
- What happens to a substance's temperature and a system's energy during a phase change?
- How does the arrangement of water molecules change during melting and freezing?
- How are evaporation and boiling different?

Vocabulary

- phase change
- endothermic
- heat of fusion
- exothermic
- vaporization
- heat of vaporization
- evaporation
- vapor pressure
- condensation
- sublimation
- deposition

Reading Strategy

Summarizing Copy the diagram. As you read, complete the description of energy flow during phase changes.

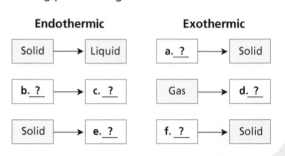

Massive chunks of frozen water called icebergs are a common sight off the continent of Antarctica. A large iceberg like the one in Figure 15 contains enough fresh water to supply millions of people with water for a year. During the summer in southern Australia, fresh water is a scarce resource. People have proposed towing icebergs to Australia from Antarctica. The plan has not been implemented because the trip could take months to complete and much of the iceberg would melt along the way. In this section, you will find out what happens when a substance, such as water, changes from one state to another.

Characteristics of Phase Changes

When at least two states of the same substance are present, scientists describe each different state as a phase. For example, if an iceberg is float-ing in the ocean, there are two phases of water present—a solid phase and a liquid phase. A **phase change** is the reversible physical change that occurs when a substance changes from one state of matter to another.

Figure 15 The solid and liquid phases of water are visible in this photograph of an iceberg in the Amundsen Sea near Antarctica.

In Figure 16, a state of matter is listed at each corner of the triangle. Each arrow in the diagram represents a different phase change. Each pair of arrows represents a set of reversible changes. For example, the arrow starting at the solid phase and ending at the liquid phase represents melting. The arrow starting at the liquid phase and ending at the solid phase represents freezing.

 Melting, freezing, vaporization, condensation, sublimation, and deposition are six common phase changes. All phase changes share certain characteristics related to energy and temperature.

Temperature and Phase Changes One way to recognize a phase change is by measuring the temperature of a substance as it is heated or cooled. **The temperature of a substance does not change during a phase change.**

Naphthalene (NAF thuh leen) is a compound that is sometimes used in mothballs. Figure 17 is a graph of the data collected when a solid piece of naphthalene is slowly heated. Temperature readings are taken at regular intervals. At first the temperature rises as the solid naphthalene warms up. But at 80°C, the temperature of the naphthalene stops rising. The temperature remains at 80°C, which is the melting point of naphthalene, until melting is complete.

If liquid naphthalene is placed in an ice-water bath, the temperature of the liquid will drop until it reaches 80°C. It will remain at 80°C until all the liquid freezes. The temperature at which the substance freezes—its freezing point—is identical to the temperature at which it melts. The freezing and melting points of naphthalene are both 80°C.

If naphthalene is heated after it has completely melted, its temperature begins to rise again. The temperature keeps rising until it reaches 218°C, which is the boiling point of naphthalene. Until boiling is complete, the temperature remains at 218°C.

Figure 16 This diagram lists six physical changes that can occur among the solid, liquid, and gaseous phases of a substance. Interpreting Diagrams *Explain why the changes are grouped into the pairs shown on the diagram.*

Go Online

NSTA *SciLINKS*

For: Links on phase diagrams
Visit: www.SciLinks.org
Web Code: ccn-1030

Heating Curve for Naphthalene

Figure 17 This graph shows what happens to the temperature of a solid sample of naphthalene as the sample is slowly heated. Using Graphs *What happened to the temperature in the interval between four and seven minutes?*

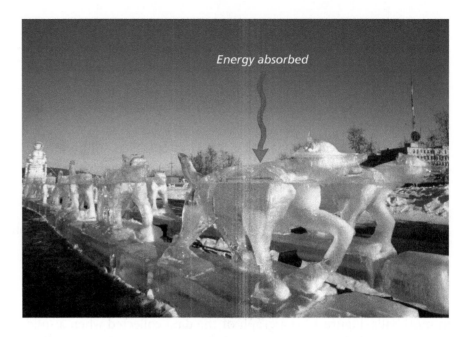

Energy absorbed

Figure 18 This ice sculpture of a dog sled was carved at a winter fair in Fairbanks, Alaska. The ice sculpture will start to melt if the temperature rises above 0°C or sunlight shines directly on the ice.

Energy released

Figure 19 Energy released as ice forms on these strawberry plants keeps the plants from freezing at temperatures slightly below 0°C. **Applying Concepts** *Explain why a farmer would need to keep spraying the plants with water while the temperature remains below freezing.*

Energy and Phase Changes During a phase change, energy is transferred between a substance and its surroundings. The direction of the transfer depends on the type of phase change. 🔑 **Energy is either absorbed or released during a phase change.**

The ice sculpture in Figure 18 isn't going to last forever. When the temperature of the air rises above 0°C or when sunlight shines directly on the ice, an ice sculpture begins to melt. Melting is an example of an endothermic change. During an **endothermic** change, the system absorbs energy from its surroundings.

The amount of energy absorbed depends on the substance. For example, one gram of ice absorbs 334 joules (J) of energy as it melts. This amount of energy is the **heat of fusion** for water. Fusion is another term for melting. The heat of fusion varies from substance to substance.

One gram of water releases 334 joules of energy to its surroundings as it freezes, the same amount of energy that is absorbed when one gram of ice melts. Farmers use this release of energy to protect their crops. When farmers expect temperatures to drop slightly below 0°C, they spray the crops with water as shown in Figure 19. As water freezes, it releases heat. The flow of heat slows the drop in temperature and helps protect the crops from damage. Freezing is an example of an exothermic change. During an **exothermic** change, the system releases energy to its surroundings.

An understanding of phase changes can be useful in many situations. The How It Works box explains how the design of an ice rink in Utah allows the manager of the rink to control the hardness of the ice.

 Reading Checkpoint *How much energy does one gram of ice absorb as it melts?*

Custom-Tailored Ice

At the Utah Olympic Oval the hardness of the ice can be controlled. The ice must be cold and hard for long speed-skating races, where the length of a skater's glide is important. For shorter races, the skaters need more traction, so the ice is made a little warmer and softer.

Interpreting Diagrams **What is the purpose of the sand layer?**

Speed Skater
This skater is racing at the Utah Olympic Oval, one of the world's most technically advanced ice rinks.

Lubricant

A **Skating surface** The surface is built up from thin layers of ice to a depth of less than 2 cm. The ice can be as cold as −8°C. The temperature and the hardness of the ice are controlled by tiny changes to the temperature of the underlying concrete layer.

B **Chilled concrete slab** The temperature is controlled by cold salt water, which is pumped through pipes embedded in the slab. The salt water remains liquid because its freezing point is lower than that of pure water.

C **Insulating layers** These layers prevent heat from rising up into the concrete slab from the warmer sand layer underneath.

D **Sand layer** To prevent the gravel layer from freezing, which could damage the rink structure, the sand layer is kept at a temperature above 0°C.

E **Gravel layer** This layer provides the foundation for the rink.

Paint layer with markings

Paint layer with logos

Paint layer with background color

Ice layers
The skating surface is formed with as many as 24 layers of ice and paint. Warm water is used for the top layers because it contains less dissolved air, and can produce a denser, harder, frozen surface.

Melting and Freezing

In water, hydrogen and oxygen atoms are combined in small units called molecules. Each water molecule contains two hydrogen atoms and one oxygen atom. 👁 **The arrangement of molecules in water becomes less orderly as water melts and more orderly as water freezes.**

Melting In ice, attractions between water molecules keep the molecules in fixed positions. When ice cubes are removed from a freezer and placed in an empty glass, heat flows from the air to the ice. As the ice gains energy, the molecules vibrate more quickly. At the melting point of water, 0°C, some molecules gain enough energy to overcome the attractions and move from their fixed positions. When all the molecules have enough energy to move, melting is complete. Any energy gained by the water after the phase change increases the average kinetic energy of the molecules, and the temperature rises.

Freezing When liquid water is placed in a freezer, energy flows from the water to the air in the freezer, and the water cools down. As the average kinetic energy of its molecules decreases, they move more slowly. At the freezing point of water, some molecules move slowly enough for the attractions between molecules to have an effect. When all the molecules have been drawn into an orderly arrangement, freezing is complete. Any energy removed from the ice after the phase change decreases the average kinetic energy of the molecules, and the temperature of the ice drops.

Often, people think of cold temperatures when they hear the term *freezing*. But substances that are solids at room temperature can freeze at temperatures that are quite high. For example, silicon freezes at 1412°C (2574°F). As a comparison, you can bake cookies at 177°C (350°F).

Vaporization and Condensation

Figure 20 shows how food cools and stays cold in a refrigerator. The process depends on a substance that changes from a liquid to a gas to a liquid over and over again. During these phase changes, energy flows from the inside of the refrigerator to the outside.

The phase change in which a substance changes from a liquid into a gas is **vaporization.** Vaporization is an endothermic process. That is, a substance must absorb energy in order to change from a liquid to a gas. One gram of water gains 2258 joules of energy when it vaporizes at 100°C. This amount of energy is the **heat of vaporization** for water. The heat of vaporization varies from substance to substance.

Figure 20 In a refrigerator, a pair of phase changes keep the food cold. Energy from inside the food compartment is used to change a liquid to a gas in the evaporator. This energy is released when the compressed gas changes back to a liquid in the condenser.

Evaporator

Energy removed from food compartment

Condenser

Compressor

Energy released to surroundings

Scientists distinguish two vaporization processes—boiling and evaporation. **Evaporation takes place at the surface of a liquid and occurs at temperatures below the boiling point.**

Evaporation If you go outside after a rain shower on a sunny, warm day, you may notice puddles of water. If you return to the same location after a few hours, the puddles may be gone. This disappearance of the puddles is due to evaporation. **Evaporation** is the process that changes a substance from a liquid to a gas at temperatures below the substance's boiling point.

Figure 21 shows what is happening as water evaporates from a small, shallow container. Some molecules near the surface are moving fast enough to escape the liquid and become water vapor. (A vapor is the gaseous phase of a substance that is normally a solid or liquid at room temperature.) The greater the surface area of the container, the faster the water evaporates.

What happens if the water is in a closed container? As the water evaporates, water vapor collects above the liquid. The pressure caused by the collisions of this vapor and the walls of the container is called **vapor pressure.** The vapor pressure of water increases as the temperature increases. At higher temperatures, more water molecules have enough kinetic energy to overcome the attractions of other molecules in the liquid.

Figure 21 Evaporation takes place at the surface of a liquid.

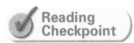 *How does the surface area of a liquid affect the rate of evaporation?*

Boiling As you heat a pot of water, both the temperature and the vapor pressure of the water increase. When the vapor pressure becomes equal to atmospheric pressure, the water boils. The temperature at which this happens is the boiling point of water.

The kinetic theory explains what happens when water boils. As the temperature increases, water molecules move faster and faster. When the temperature reaches 100°C, some molecules below the surface of the liquid have enough kinetic energy to overcome the attraction of neighboring molecules. Figure 22 shows that bubbles of water vapor form within the liquid. Because water vapor is less dense than liquid water, the bubbles quickly rise to the surface. When they reach the surface, the bubbles burst and release water vapor into the air.

Figure 22 Boiling takes place throughout a liquid. **Applying Concepts** *Explain why the temperature of water does not rise during boiling.*

Observing Phase Changes

Materials

250-mL Erlenmeyer flask, graduated cylinder, thermometer, dry ice

Procedure

1. Pour 150 milliliters of water into a 250-mL Erlenmeyer flask. Place a thermometer in the flask. **CAUTION** *Wipe up any spilled water right away to avoid slips and falls.*

2. Observe what happens after your teacher adds a small piece of dry ice to the flask. (Dry ice is solid carbon dioxide.) **CAUTION** *Dry ice can damage skin on contact. Do not touch the dry ice.*

3. Record the temperature of the water just after the dry ice is added and again after it is no longer visible.

Analyze and Conclude

1. **Observing** What happened when the dry ice was added to the water?

2. **Analyzing Data** Did adding the dry ice cause the water to boil? Explain your answer.

3. **Inferring** What was the source of the bubbles in the water?

4. **Formulating Hypotheses** What caused a cloud to form above the flask?

5. **Applying Concepts** What phase changes occurred in the flask?

The boiling point of a substance depends on the atmospheric pressure. The normal boiling point of water at sea level is 100°C. At higher elevations, the atmospheric pressure is lower. Do you know that Denver, Colorado, is called the mile-high city? This nickname is based on Denver's location at one mile above sea level. In Denver, the vapor pressure of water will equal atmospheric pressure at temperatures below 100°C. The boiling point of water in Denver can be as low as 95°C. Food does not cook as quickly at 95°C as it does at 100°C. Pasta takes longer to cook in Denver than in New Orleans, Louisiana, a city that is located near sea level.

Condensation Have you ever come out of a shower to find your bathroom mirror clouded over? The "cloud" on the mirror is caused by water vapor that cooled as it came in contact with the mirror. The water vapor transferred heat to the mirror and condensed into liquid water. **Condensation** is the phase change in which a substance changes from a gas or vapor to a liquid. This process is also responsible for the morning dew on the blades of grass in Figure 23. Condensation is an exothermic process.

Figure 23 Water vapor from the air condensed into drops of liquid water on these blades of grass.

Sublimation and Deposition

Directors of concerts and plays sometimes use dry ice to create a fog-like special effect. Dry ice is the common name for the solid form of carbon dioxide. At room temperature, dry ice can directly change from a solid to a colorless gas. **Sublimation** is the phase change in which a substance changes from a solid to a gas or vapor without changing to a liquid first. Sublimation is an endothermic change. As dry ice sublimes, the cold carbon dioxide vapor causes water vapor in the air to condense and form clouds.

Where does the name dry ice come from? Solid carbon dioxide does not form a liquid as its temperature rises. Suppose 100 steaks are shipped from Omaha, Nebraska, to a supermarket in Miami, Florida. The steaks will spoil unless they are kept cold during the trip. If regular ice is used, water collects in the shipping container as the ice melts. If the steaks are shipped in dry ice, the container and the steaks stay dry during the journey. Figure 24 shows another use of dry ice.

When a gas or vapor changes directly into a solid without first changing to a liquid, the phase change is called **deposition.** This exothermic phase change is the reverse of sublimation. Deposition causes frost to form on windows. When water vapor in the air comes in contact with cold window glass, the water vapor loses enough kinetic energy to change directly from a gas to a solid.

Figure 24 A technician at Tinker Air Force Base in Oklahoma hangs a mosquito trap. The trap is baited with dry ice because mosquitoes are attracted to carbon dioxide.

Section 3.3 Assessment

Reviewing Concepts

1. Name six common phase changes.

2. What happens to the temperature of a substance during a phase change?

3. How does the energy of a system change during a phase change?

4. What happens to the arrangement of water molecules as water melts and freezes?

5. What is the difference between evaporation and boiling?

6. Explain why sublimation and deposition are classified as physical changes.

Critical Thinking

7. **Applying Concepts** How can the mass of a pile of snow decrease on a sunny day when the air temperature does not rise above 0°C?

8. **Drawing Conclusions** At room temperature, table salt is a solid and acetone is a liquid. Acetone is the main ingredient in nail polish remover. What conclusion can you draw about the melting points of these materials?

Writing in Science

Steps in a Process Write a paragraph describing three steps that must occur for a water molecule to start on the surface of hot bath water and end up on the surface of a bathroom mirror. Note whether the phase changes that take place during the process are endothermic or exothermic. (*Hint:* Use words such as *first, next,* and *finally* to show the order of events.)

Investigating Changes in Temperature During Heating of Solids

Lauric acid is a solid that is found in coconuts and processed foods that are made with coconut oil. Lauric acid is also used to make some soaps and cosmetics. In this lab, you will measure the temperature of ice and of lauric acid as these solids are heated and melt. You will graph the data you collect and compare the heating curves for ice and lauric acid.

Problem
What happens to the temperature of a substance during a phase change?

Materials
- 500-mL beaker
- crushed ice
- thermometer
- hot plate
- clock with second hand
- test tube of lauric acid with thermometer
- glass stirring rod
- graph paper

 For the probeware version of this lab, see the Probeware Lab Manual, Lab 1.

Skills
Measuring, Using Graphs

Procedure

Part A: Heating Ice

1. On a sheet of paper, make a copy of the data table shown. Start with 11 blank rows, but leave space below your data table to add more rows, if necessary.

2. Fill a 500-mL beaker halfway with crushed ice.
   CAUTION *Use care when handling glassware to avoid breakage. Wipe up any spilled ice right away to avoid slips and falls.*

3. Place the beaker on a hot plate. Don't turn the hot plate on yet. Insert a thermometer into the ice. Because it takes several seconds for the thermometer to adjust to the temperature of its surroundings, wait 20 seconds and then measure the temperature of the ice. Record this temperature next to the 0 minutes entry in your data table.

4. Turn the hot plate to a low setting.
   CAUTION *Be careful not to touch the hot plate because contact with the hot plate could cause a burn.*

5. Observe and record the temperature at one-minute intervals until all the ice has changed to liquid water. Circle the temperature at which you first observe liquid water and the temperature at which all the ice has changed to liquid water.

Data Table		
Time (minutes)	Temperature of Water (°C)	Temperature of Lauric Acid (°C)
0		
1		

6. After all the ice has melted, make five more measurements of the temperature at one-minute intervals. Turn off the hot plate.

7. Graph your data with time on the horizontal axis and temperature on the vertical axis.

Part B: Heating Lauric Acid

8. Empty the water from the beaker into the sink. Fill the beaker halfway with cool tap water.

9. Place a test tube containing lauric acid and a thermometer into the beaker. If necessary, add or remove water from the beaker so that the surface of the water is above the surface of the lauric acid but below the opening of the test tube.

10. Place the beaker on the hot plate. After 20 seconds, measure the temperature of the lauric acid. Record this temperature next to the 0 minutes entry in your data table.

11. Repeat Steps 4 through 7 using the lauric acid instead of the ice. To keep the temperature the same throughout the water bath, use the glass stirring rod to stir the water after you take each temperature measurement.

Analyze and Conclude

1. **Using Graphs** Describe the shape of your graph for ice.

2. **Analyzing Data** What happened to the temperature of the ice-water mixture during the phase change?

3. **Drawing Conclusions** What happened to the energy that was transferred from the hot plate to the ice during the phase change?

4. **Comparing and Contrasting** Compare the shapes of the graphs for ice and for lauric acid. Compare the melting points of ice and lauric acid.

Go Online
PHSchool.com

For: Data sharing
Visit: PHSchool.com
Web Code: ccd-1030

3.1 Solids, Liquids, and Gases

Key Concepts

- Materials can be classified as solids, liquids, or gases based on whether their shapes and volumes are definite or variable.
- The kinetic theory of matter states that all particles of matter are in constant motion.
- There are forces of attraction among the particles in all matter.
- The constant motion of particles in a gas allows a gas to fill a container of any shape or size.
- A liquid takes the shape of its container because particles in a liquid can flow to new locations. The volume of a liquid is constant because forces of attraction keep the particles close together.
- Solids have a definite volume and shape because particles in a solid vibrate around fixed locations.

Vocabulary

solid, *p. 69;* liquid, *p. 69;* gas, *p. 70;* kinetic energy, *p. 71*

3.2 The Gas Laws

Key Concepts

- Collisions between particles of a gas and the walls of the container cause the pressure in a closed container of gas.
- Factors that affect the pressure of an enclosed gas are its temperature, its volume, and the number of its particles.
- Raising the temperature of a gas will increase its pressure if the volume of the gas and the number of particles are constant.
- Reducing the volume of a gas increases its pressure if the temperature of the gas and the number of particles are constant.
- Increasing the number of particles will increase the pressure of a gas if the temperature and the volume are constant.
- The combined gas law can be expressed as

$$\frac{P_1 V_1}{T_1} = \frac{P_2 V_2}{T_2}$$

Vocabulary

pressure, *p. 75;* absolute zero, *p. 78;*
Charles's law, *p. 78;* Boyle's law, *p. 79*

3.3 Phase Changes

Key Concepts

- Melting, freezing, vaporization, condensation, sublimation, and deposition are six common phase changes.
- The temperature of a substance does not change during a phase change.
- Energy is either absorbed or released during a phase change.
- The arrangement of molecules in water becomes less orderly as water melts, and more orderly as water freezes.
- Evaporation takes place at the surface of a liquid and occurs at temperatures below the boiling point.

Vocabulary

phase change, *p. 84;* endothermic, *p. 86;*
heat of fusion, *p. 86;* exothermic, *p. 86;*
vaporization, *p. 88;* heat of vaporization, *p. 88;*
evaporation, *p. 89;* vapor pressure, *p. 89;*
condensation, *p. 90;* sublimation, *p. 91;*
deposition, *p. 91;*

Thinking Visually

Web Diagram Use information from the chapter to complete the web diagram on phase changes.

Reviewing Content

Choose the letter that best answers the question or completes the statement.

1. Which state of matter has a definite volume but a variable shape?
   - **a.** solid
   - **b.** liquid
   - **c.** gas
   - **d.** vapor

2. In which state(s) of matter can materials take the shape of their containers?
   - **a.** solid and liquid
   - **b.** solid and gas
   - **c.** liquid and gas
   - **d.** liquid only

3. Which statement is true about the atoms in helium gas?
   - **a.** They travel in circular paths.
   - **b.** They have strong attractions to one another.
   - **c.** They are not closely packed.
   - **d.** They are arranged in an orderly pattern.

4. If the speed of an object increases, its kinetic energy
   - **a.** decreases.
   - **b.** increases.
   - **c.** stays the same.
   - **d.** is unpredictable.

5. The SI unit of pressure is the
   - **a.** pascal.
   - **b.** newton.
   - **c.** square meter.
   - **d.** psi.

6. Increasing which variable would decrease the pressure of a contained gas?
   - **a.** temperature
   - **b.** number of particles
   - **c.** boiling point
   - **d.** volume

7. Boyle's law relates pressure and
   - **a.** temperature.
   - **b.** number of particles.
   - **c.** volume.
   - **d.** mass.

8. Which of the following changes is exothermic?
   - **a.** evaporation
   - **b.** freezing
   - **c.** boiling
   - **d.** sublimation

9. The phase change that is the reverse of vaporization is
   - **a.** freezing.
   - **b.** melting.
   - **c.** condensation.
   - **d.** evaporation.

10. Which of these phase changes does NOT involve changing a liquid into a gas?
    - **a.** sublimation
    - **b.** vaporization
    - **c.** evaporation
    - **d.** boiling

Understanding Concepts

11. Provide an example of each of the three states of matter that exist at room temperature.

12. Compare and contrast liquid water and ice in terms of how definite their shapes and volumes are.

13. What three assumptions about particles in a gas are made by the kinetic theory?

14. Using the kinetic theory, explain why a liquid has a definite volume but a gas does not.

15. How do the way that atoms are arranged in liquid mercury and solid copper affect the movement of mercury and copper atoms?

16. Using the kinetic theory, explain what causes gas pressure.

17. What three factors affect the pressure of a gas in a closed container?

18. If a piston moves downward in a cylinder, what happens to the volume and pressure of the gas in the cylinder? The temperature remains constant.

19. What happens to the speed of the particles inside an air-filled balloon if the temperature of the balloon increases?

20. Using the kinetic theory, explain why the pressure of a gas increases when its temperature increases.

21. How are the pressure and volume of a gas related?

22. How does an endothermic phase change differ from an exothermic phase change?

23. Compare the vapor pressure of water at 10°C with its vapor pressure at 50°C.

24. Explain why water has a different boiling point at an elevation of 3000 meters than it does at sea level.

Critical Thinking

25. Classifying If you take a helium balloon from inside a warm house to outside on a snowy day, what will happen to the balloon? Could you classify this change as a phase change? Explain your answer.

26. Comparing and Contrasting Compare the melting and freezing of water in terms of (a) the temperature at which these processes take place and (b) how energy is involved in these processes.

Use the graphs to answer Questions 27–29.

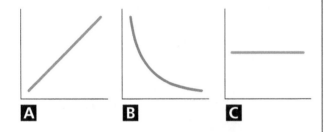

A   **B**   **C**

27. Using Graphs Which graph represents what happens to the pressure in a tire as air is added to the tire? Assume the temperature of the gas is constant.

28. Using Graphs Which graph represents what happens to the pressure in an aerosol can if the can is heated?

29. Applying Concepts Which graph represents temperature versus time during a phase change?

Math Skills

30. Making Generalizations The pressure of a gas is directly proportional to its temperature in kelvins. Using P_1, P_2, T_1, and T_2, write a mathematical equation that expresses this relationship.

31. Calculating An automobile tire has a pressure of 325 kPa when the temperature is 10°C. If the temperature of the tire rises to 50°C and its volume is constant, what is the new pressure?

32. Calculating A gas sample occupies 4.2 L at a pressure of 101 kPa. What volume will it occupy if the pressure is increased to 235 kPa?

Concepts in Action

33. Using Models If there is a gas leak in the basement of a building, you will soon notice an odor throughout the house. However, if there is a water leak in the basement, you will need to go to the basement to detect the leak. Use the kinetic theory to explain the differences.

34. Inferring A student examines a thermometer placed in a can containing a substance that is being heated. The temperature remains the same for several minutes, and then it starts to rise. Without looking in the can, how does the student know what is occurring in the can?

35. Relating Cause and Effect In Earth's atmosphere, pressure and temperature both decrease as altitude increases. Weather balloons expand as they rise. Which has more effect on the weather balloon, the decrease in pressure or the decrease in temperature? Explain your answer.

36. Drawing Conclusions In a car engine, air and gasoline vapors are mixed in a cylinder. A piston is pushed into the cylinder before a spark ignites the mixture of gases. When the piston is pushed into the cylinder, what happens to the pressure of the gases in the cylinder?

37. Writing in Science Unpopped popcorn kernels contain a small amount of water. Use what you know about vaporization and how gases behave to explain why popcorn pops when it is heated.

Performance-Based Assessment

Making a Poster The gas laws have many practical applications in cooking. Make a poster, including diagrams, that shows how two factors that affect gases affect cooking. Examples might include explaining why cakes rise while baking or why some recipes specify high-altitude temperatures and cooking times.

For: Self-grading assessment
Visit: PHSchool.com
Web Code: cca-1030

Standardized Test Prep

Watch For Qualifiers
The words *best* and *least* are examples of qualifiers. If a question contains a qualifier, more than one answer will contain correct information. However, only one answer will be complete and correct for the question asked. Look at the question below. Eliminate any answers that are clearly incorrect. Then choose the remaining answer that offers the best explanation for the question asked.

Choose the *best* explanation for why one particle in a gas does not affect other particles in a gas unless the particles collide.
(A) Particles in a gas are constantly moving.
(B) All the particles in a gas have the same kinetic energy.
(C) There are no forces of attraction among particles in a gas.
(D) There are billions of particles in a small sample of a gas.
(E) Particles in a gas are relatively far apart.

(Answer: E)

Choose the letter that best answers the question or completes the statement.

1. A material can be classified as a liquid if
(A) it has a definite shape and a definite volume.
(B) it has a definite shape and a variable volume.
(C) it has a variable shape and a definite volume.
(D) it has a variable shape and a variable volume.
(E) its particles vibrate around fixed locations.

2. Which statement *best* explains what must take place for water to boil?
(A) The water releases energy to its surroundings.
(B) Bubbles rise to the surface of the water.
(C) The vapor pressure of the water becomes equal to atmospheric pressure.
(D) Molecules at the surface of the water overcome the attractions of neighboring molecules.
(E) The temperature of the water increases.

3. Condensation is the phase change in which a substance changes from
(A) a solid to a gas.
(B) a solid to a liquid.
(C) a liquid to a solid.
(D) a liquid to a gas.
(E) a gas to a liquid.

4. Which of these statements about an enclosed gas is true? (Assume all quantities are constant except the two variables described in each statement.)
(A) Raising the temperature of a gas will increase its pressure.
(B) Increasing the volume of a gas will increase its pressure.
(C) Reducing the number of particles of a gas will increase its pressure.
(D) The volume of a gas is inversely proportional to its temperature in kelvins.
(E) The volume of a gas is directly proportional to its pressure.

Use the illustration to answer Question 5. Assume that the number of particles of gas in container A equals the number of particles of gas in container B.

5. If the temperature is constant, the pressure in container B is
(A) one half the pressure in container A.
(B) twice the pressure in container A.
(C) equal to the pressure in container A.
(D) five times the pressure in container A.
(E) one fifth the pressure in container A.

6. During an endothermic phase change,
(A) the temperature of a substance rises.
(B) the temperature of a substance decreases.
(C) energy is transferred from a substance to its surroundings.
(D) a substance absorbs energy from its surroundings.
(E) there is no transfer of energy.

Atomic Structure

21st Century Learning

Problem Identification, Formulation, and Solution

What are subatomic particles?

Atoms are too small to be seen, but scientists have learned much about their structure. Atoms are made of even smaller particles called subatomic particles. Make a slide-show presentation that describes the structure of an atom. Your presentation should include information about the size, mass, charge, and location of each type of subatomic particle. Show your presentation in class or post it to your class blog.

How do science concepts apply to your world? Here are some questions you'll be able to answer after you read this chapter.

- **What uses are there for objects that are not visible to the unaided eye?** *(page 106)*

- **Which subatomic particle produces the images on many television screens and computer monitors?** *(Section 4.2)*

- **How does the type of hydrogen atom in water affect the properties of water?** *(Section 4.2)*

- **How do fireworks produce the colors you see when the fireworks explode?** *(Section 4.3)*

These images of carbon were magnified as much as 20 million times. Color was added to the images to highlight features.

Chapter Preview

4.1 Studying Atoms

4.2 The Structure of an Atom

4.3 Modern Atomic Theory

DISCOVERY CHANNEL SCHOOL

Video Field Trip

Go For Gold

Inquiry Activity

How Can You Study Objects That Are Not Visible?

Procedure

1. Make and record observations about the contents of two sealed bags. Use your senses of touch, smell, and hearing to help you make your observations.

2. Predicting Based on your observations, make a prediction about what objects could be in each bag. Decide whether there is a single object or more than one object in each bag.

3. Your teacher will list on the chalkboard all of the predictions from the class.

Think About It

1. Inferring What evidence did you use to predict what objects were in the bags and how many objects were in the bags?

2. Evaluating and Revising Record one of the predictions listed that fits your observations as well as or better than your own prediction.

3. Designing Experiments Propose an experiment that would test the prediction.

4.1 Studying Atoms

Key Concepts
- What was Dalton's theory of the structure of matter?
- What contributions did Thomson and Rutherford make to the development of atomic theory?

Vocabulary
- nucleus

Reading Strategy

Summarizing Copy the table. As you read, complete the table about atomic models.

Scientist	Evidence	Model
a.____?____	Ratio of masses in compounds	b.____?____
c.____?____	Deflected beam	d.____?____
Rutherford	e.____?____	Positive, dense nucleus

Studying the structure of atoms is a little like studying wind. Because you cannot see air, you must use indirect evidence to tell the direction of the wind. You might notice which way fallen leaves move as they are pushed by the wind, and infer that the leaves and wind are moving in the same direction.

Atoms pose a similar problem because they are extremely small. Even with a microscope, scientists cannot see the structure of an atom. In this chapter, you will find out how John Dalton, J. J. Thomson, Ernest Rutherford, Niels Bohr, and other scientists used evidence from experiments to develop models of atoms.

Ancient Greek Models of Atoms

If you cut a piece of aluminum foil in half, you have two smaller pieces of the same shiny, flexible substance. You could cut the pieces again and again. Can you keep dividing the aluminum into smaller pieces? Greek philosophers debated a similar question about 2500 years ago.

The philosopher Democritus believed that all matter consisted of extremely small particles that could not be divided. He called these particles *atoms* from the Greek word *atomos*, which means "uncut" or "indivisible." He thought there were different types of atoms with specific sets of properties. The atoms in liquids, for example, were round and smooth, but the atoms in solids were rough and prickly.

Aristotle did not think there was a limit to the number of times matter could be divided. Figure 1 shows the model Aristotle used to describe matter. For many centuries, most people accepted Aristotle's views on the structure of matter. But by the 1800s, scientists had enough data from experiments to support an atomic model of matter.

Figure 1 Aristotle thought that all substances were built up from only four elements—earth, air, fire, and water. These elements were a combination of four qualities—hot, cold, dry, and wet. Fire was a combination of hot and dry. Water was a combination of cold and wet.

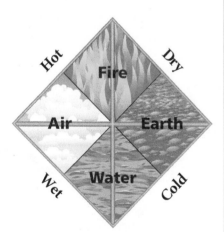

Dalton's Atomic Theory

John Dalton was born in England in 1766. He was a teacher who spent his spare time doing scientific experiments. Because of his interest in predicting the weather, Dalton studied the behavior of gases in air. Based on the way gases exert pressure, Dalton correctly concluded that a gas consists of individual particles.

Evidence for Atoms Dalton gathered evidence for the existence of atoms by measuring the masses of elements that combine when compounds form. He noticed that all compounds have something in common. No matter how large or small the sample, the ratio of the masses of the elements in the compound is always the same. In other words, compounds have a fixed composition.

For example, when magnesium burns, as shown in Figure 2, it combines with oxygen. The product of this change is a white solid called magnesium oxide. A 100-gram sample of magnesium combines with 65.8 grams of oxygen. A 10-gram sample of magnesium combines with 6.58 grams of oxygen. The ratio of the mass of magnesium to the mass of oxygen is constant in magnesium oxide.

Dalton's Theory Dalton developed a theory to explain why the elements in a compound always join in the same way. 🔑 **Dalton proposed the theory that all matter is made up of individual particles called atoms, which cannot be divided.** The main points of Dalton's theory are as follows.

- All elements are composed of atoms.

- All atoms of the same element have the same mass, and atoms of different elements have different masses.

- Compounds contain atoms of more than one element.

- In a particular compound, atoms of different elements always combine in the same way.

In the model of atoms based on Dalton's theory, the elements are pictured as solid spheres like those in Figure 3. Each type of atom is represented by a tiny, solid sphere with a different mass.

Recall that a theory must explain the data from many experiments. Because Dalton's atomic theory met that goal, the theory became widely accepted. Over time, scientists found that not all of Dalton's ideas about atoms were completely correct. But this did not cause later scientists to discard the atomic theory. Instead, they revised the theory to take into account new discoveries.

 Reading Checkpoint *What did Dalton notice that all compounds have in common?*

Figure 2 Magnesium reacts with oxygen to form the compound magnesium oxide. The ratio of magnesium to oxygen, by mass, in magnesium oxide is always about 3 : 2. **Observing** *What color is magnesium oxide?*

Figure 3 Dalton made these wooden spheres to represent the atoms of different elements.

Sticky sides down

Investigating Charged Objects

Materials

transparent tape, metric ruler, scissors

Procedure

1. Cut two 10-cm pieces of tape. Fold over 1 cm of tape at one end of each piece of tape to form a "handle."

2. Hold the pieces of tape by their folded ends so that they are hanging straight down. Then, without letting the pieces of tape touch, slowly bring their sticky sides close together. Record your observations.

3. Place one piece of tape on a clean surface with the sticky side facing down.

4. Place the second piece, sticky side down, directly over the first piece, as shown. Press down firmly so the pieces stick together.

5. Remove the joined strips from the table. Slowly peel the strips apart.

6. Bring the separated strips close together without touching. Record your observations.

Analyze and Conclude

1. **Drawing Conclusions** What can you conclude about the charges on the two pieces of tape after they are separated?

2. **Inferring** What other objects have you observed that became charged?

Figure 4 Amber is the hardened form of a sticky, viscous liquid that protects trees from insects and disease. If amber is rubbed with wool, it becomes charged and can attract a feather. Predicting *What will happen to the feather if the amber loses its charge?*

Thomson's Model of the Atom

When some materials are rubbed, they gain the ability to attract or repel other materials. Glass and the amber in Figure 4 have this property. Based on their behavior, such materials are said to have either a positive or a negative electric charge. Objects with like charges repel, or push apart. Objects with opposite charges attract, or pull together.

Some charged particles can flow from one location to another. A flow of charged particles is called an electric current. When you turn on an appliance such as a hair dryer, a current flows from the wall socket through the appliance. Joseph John Thomson (1856–1940), better known as J. J. Thomson, used an electric current to learn more about atoms.

Thomson's Experiments Thomson used a device like the one shown in Figure 5A. At the center of the device is a sealed glass tube from which most of the air has been removed. There is a metal disk at each end of the tube. Wires connect the metal disks to a source of electric current. When the current is turned on, one disk becomes negatively charged and the other disk becomes positively charged. A glowing beam appears in the space between the disks.

Thomson hypothesized that the beam was a stream of charged particles that interacted with the air in the tube and caused the air to glow. In one experiment Thomson did to test his hypothesis, he placed a pair of charged metal plates on either side of the glass tube, as shown in Figure 5B. The plates caused the beam to deflect, or bend, from its straight path. Thomson observed that the beam was repelled by the negatively charged plate and attracted by the positively charged plate.

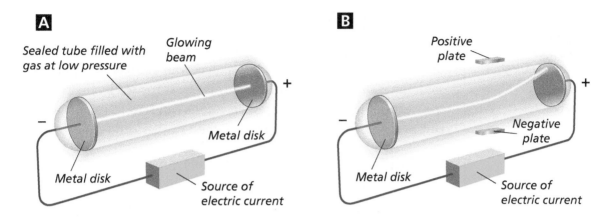

A

Sealed tube filled with gas at low pressure

Glowing beam

Metal disk

+

−

Metal disk

Source of electric current

B

Positive plate

+

Negative plate

Metal disk

Source of electric current

Figure 5 Thomson used a sealed tube of gas in his experiments. **A** When the current was on, the disks became charged and a glowing beam appeared in the tube. **B** The beam bent toward a positively charged plate placed outside the tube.
Inferring *What was the charge on the particles in the beam?*

Evidence for Subatomic Particles Thomson concluded that the particles in the beam had a negative charge because they were attracted to the positive plate. He hypothesized that the particles came from inside atoms. He had two pieces of evidence to support his hypothesis. No matter what metal Thomson used for the disk, the particles produced were identical. The particles had about $\frac{1}{2000}$ the mass of a hydrogen atom, the lightest atom.

Thomson's discovery changed how scientists thought about atoms. Before his experiments, the accepted model of the atom was a solid ball of matter that could not be divided into smaller parts. ⚷ **Thomson's experiments provided the first evidence that atoms are made of even smaller particles.** Thomson revised Dalton's model to account for these subatomic particles.

Thomson's Model An atom is neutral, meaning it has neither a negative nor a positive charge. How can an atom contain negative particles and still be neutral? There must be some positive charge in the atom. In Thomson's model of the atom, the negative charges were evenly scattered throughout an atom filled with a positively charged mass of matter. The model is called the "plum pudding" model, after a traditional English dessert.

You might prefer to think of Thomson's model as the "chocolate chip ice cream" model. Think of the chocolate chips in Figure 6 as the negative particles and the vanilla ice cream as the positively charged mass of matter. When the chocolate chips are spread evenly throughout the ice cream, their "negative charges" balance out the "positive charge" of the vanilla ice cream.

Figure 6 A scoop of chocolate chip ice cream can represent Thomson's model of the atom. The chips represent negatively charged particles, which are spread evenly through a mass of positively charged matter—the vanilla ice cream.

Reading Checkpoint

How do objects with the same charge behave when they come close to one another?

Go Online

ⓃⓈⓉⒶ SC*i*LINKS

For: Links on atomic theory
Visit: www.SciLinks.org
Web Code: ccn-1041

Rutherford's Atomic Theory

When you try something new, you may have expectations about the outcome. Does the outcome always meet your expectations or are you sometimes surprised? Scientists can also be surprised by the results of their experiments, but unexpected results can lead to important discoveries. This is what happened to Ernest Rutherford (1871–1937).

Rutherford's Hypothesis In 1899, Ernest Rutherford discovered that uranium emits fast-moving particles that have a positive charge. He named them alpha particles. In 1909, Rutherford asked one of his students, Ernest Marsden, to find out what happens to alpha particles when they pass through a thin sheet of gold.

Recall that in Thomson's model of the atom, the mass and positive charge are evenly spread throughout an atom. Based on this model, Rutherford hypothesized that the mass and charge at any location in the gold would be too small to change the path of an alpha particle. He predicted that most particles would travel in a straight path from their source to a screen that lit up when struck. Those few that did not pass straight through would be deflected only slightly.

The Gold Foil Experiment Marsden used the equipment shown in Figure 7. He aimed a narrow beam of alpha particles at the gold. The screen around the gold was made of a material that produced a flash of light when struck by a fast-moving alpha particle. By observing the flash, Marsden could figure out the path of an alpha particle after it passed through the gold.

Some of the locations of the flashes on the screen did not support Rutherford's prediction. More particles were deflected than he expected. About one out of every 20,000 was deflected by more than 90 degrees. Some of the alpha particles behaved as though they had struck an object and bounced straight back.

Figure 7 The path of an alpha particle can be detected by the location of a flash on a screen. Rutherford expected the paths of the positively charged alpha particles that were aimed at the thin gold foil to be affected only slightly by the gold atoms. But more particles were deflected than expected and some particles bounced straight back.

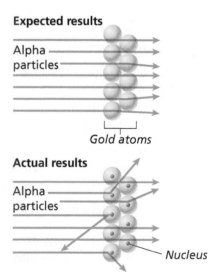

Discovery of the Nucleus The alpha particles whose paths were deflected must have come close to another charged object. The closer they came, the greater the deflection was. But many alpha particles passed through the gold without being deflected. From these results, Rutherford concluded that the positive charge of an atom is not evenly spread throughout the atom. It is concentrated in a very small, central area that Rutherford called the nucleus. The **nucleus** is a dense, positively charged mass located in the center of the atom. (The plural of *nucleus* is *nuclei*.)

Because Thomson's model no longer explained all the evidence, Rutherford proposed a new model. **According to Rutherford's model, all of an atom's positive charge is concentrated in its nucleus.** The alpha particles whose paths were deflected by more than 90 degrees came very close to a nucleus. The alpha particles whose paths were not bent moved through the space surrounding the nuclei without coming very close to any nucleus.

Figure 8 shows the inside of the Astrodome, a domed stadium in Houston, Texas. The roof of the stadium rises to a height of 202 feet above the center of the field. If an atom had the same volume as the stadium, its nucleus would have the volume of a marble. The total volume of an atom is about a trillion (10^{12}) times the volume of its nucleus.

Figure 8 The Houston Astrodome occupies more than nine acres and seats 60,000 people. If the stadium were a model for an atom, a marble could represent its nucleus. Using Analogies *In the model, where would the marble have to be located in the stadium to represent the nucleus?*

Section 4.1 Assessment

Reviewing Concepts

1. What theory did Dalton propose about the structure of matter?

2. What evidence did J. J. Thomson provide about the structure of an atom?

3. What did Rutherford discover about the structure of an atom?

4. What evidence did Thomson have that his glowing beam contained negative particles?

5. Why was Dalton's model of the atom changed after Thomson's experiment?

Critical Thinking

6. **Comparing and Contrasting** Explain why scientists accepted Dalton's atomic theory but not the idea of an atom proposed by the Greek philosophers.

7. **Drawing Conclusions** If you observed a beam of particles being bent toward a negatively charged plate, what might you conclude?

8. **Relating Cause and Effect** In the Rutherford experiment, why weren't all the alpha particles deflected?

Writing in Science

Writing to Persuade Imagine you live in ancient Greece. Assume all you know about matter is what you can observe with your five senses. You have heard the views of both Democritus and Aristotle about matter. Write a paragraph supporting one of their views.

Small-Scale Construction

Some scientists and engineers think of atoms and molecules as construction materials for building very small objects.

The field of science called nanotechnology is named for a unit of measurement—the nanometer. A billion nanometers (10^9 nm) can fit in one meter. The diameter of a human hair is about 80,000 nm. Scientists and engineers who use nanometers as measuring units are building miniature versions of objects such as motors.

There are two general methods for building any object. You can start with more material than you need and shape the object by removing matter or you can build up the object from smaller pieces. When you shape your nails with an emery board, you are using a top-down construction method. When you see "some assembly required" on the side of a box, the manufacturer expects you to use a bottom-up method of construction.

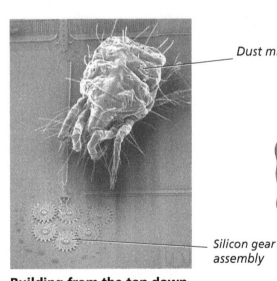

Dust mite

Silicon gear assembly

Building from the top down
Gears are toothed disks that are designed to fit together so that the motion of one gear controls the motion of another. These silicon gears are among the smallest objects ever made from the top down.

Building from the bottom up
With a scanning tunneling microscope, it is possible to move individual atoms or molecules. This figure, made of linked carbon monoxide molecules, is just five nanometers (0.000005 mm) tall. In 1990, scientists built this figure to demonstrate bottom-up construction methods.

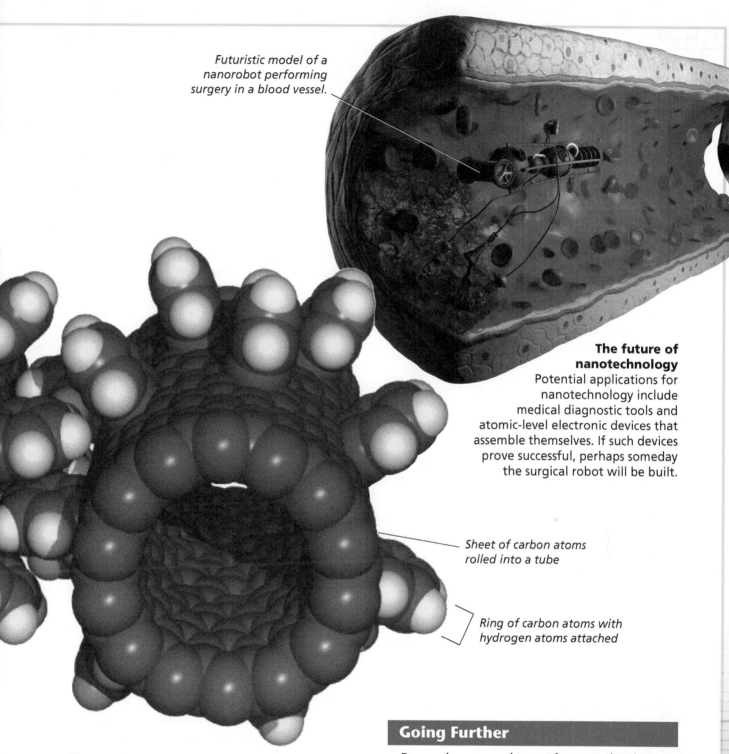

Futuristic model of a nanorobot performing surgery in a blood vessel.

The future of nanotechnology
Potential applications for nanotechnology include medical diagnostic tools and atomic-level electronic devices that assemble themselves. If such devices prove successful, perhaps someday the surgical robot will be built.

Sheet of carbon atoms rolled into a tube

Ring of carbon atoms with hydrogen atoms attached

Nanogears
This image of nanogears was produced with a computer program designed to make models of molecules. Hollow tubes (nanotubes) made from sheets of carbon atoms do exist. So do the rings containing carbon and hydrogen atoms, which are used for the "teeth" of the gears. But researchers need to figure out how to get the "teeth" to attach to the tubes.

Going Further

- Research proposed uses of nanotechnology. Make a poster describing one proposed use. Explain the advantage of using small objects in this application. What problems must be solved before the application can be used?

- Take a Discovery Channel Video Field Trip by watching "Go For Gold."

DISCOVERY
CHANNEL
SCHOOL
Video Field Trip

Figure 9 This 45-foot-tall steel sculpture of a clothespin is in Philadelphia, Pennsylvania. Claes Oldenburg made the clothespin in 1976 from 10 tons of steel. If a proton had a mass of 10 tons, then an electron would have a mass of about 5 kilograms.

Beams like the ones Thomson produced create the images on many television screens. When a beam sweeps across the screen, spots on the screen light up in the same way the screen in the gold-foil experiment lit up when struck by an alpha particle. In a color television, there are three beams, one for each primary color of light—red, green, and blue. The particles in these beams are subatomic particles.

Properties of Subatomic Particles

By 1920, Rutherford had seen evidence for the existence of two subatomic particles and had predicted the existence of a third particle. ◦ **Protons, electrons, and neutrons are subatomic particles.**

Protons Based on experiments with elements other than gold, Rutherford concluded that the amount of positive charge varies among elements. Each nucleus must contain at least one particle with a positive charge. Rutherford called these particles protons. A **proton** is a positively charged subatomic particle that is found in the nucleus of an atom. Each proton is assigned a charge of 1+. Some nuclei contain more than 100 protons.

Electrons The particles that Thomson detected were later named electrons. *Electron* comes from a Greek word meaning "amber." An **electron** is a negatively charged subatomic particle that is found in the space outside the nucleus. Each electron has a charge of 1−.

Properties of Subatomic Particles					
Particle	Symbol	Relative Charge	Relative Mass (proton = 1)	Actual Mass (g)	Model
Electron	e⁻	1−	$\frac{1}{1836}$	9.11×10^{-28}	
Proton	p⁺	1+	1	1.674×10^{-24}	
Neutron	n	0	1	1.675×10^{-24}	

Figure 10 This table lists the symbol, the relative charge, the relative mass, and the actual mass of an electron, a proton, and a neutron. The Model column shows the colors used in this book to represent the subatomic particles. **Calculating** *What is the difference in actual mass between a proton and a neutron?*

Neutrons In 1932, the English physicist James Chadwick designed an experiment to show that neutrons exist. Chadwick concluded that the particles he produced were neutral because a charged object did not deflect their paths. A **neutron** is a neutral subatomic particle that is found in the nucleus of an atom. It has a mass almost exactly equal to that of a proton.

Comparing Subatomic Particles

Figure 10 summarizes some properties of protons, electrons, and neutrons. 🔵 **Protons, electrons, and neutrons can be distinguished by mass, charge, and location in an atom.** Protons and neutrons have almost the same mass. But the data in Figure 10 show that it would take about 2000 electrons to equal the mass of one proton. Electrons have a charge that is equal in size to, but the opposite of, the charge of a proton. Neutrons have no charge. Protons and neutrons are found in the nucleus, but electrons are found in the space outside the nucleus.

Go Online
SCIENCE NEWS

For: Articles on atomic chemistry
Visit: PHSchool.com
Web Code: cce-1042

Problem-Solving Activity

Designing an Atomic Exhibit

You work as a volunteer at the local science museum. You are asked to design an exhibit that compares the size of a lithium atom to the size of its nucleus. A lithium atom has a diameter of about 3×10^2 picometers. The nucleus of a lithium atom has a diameter of about 5×10^{-3} picometers. There are a trillion (10^{12}) picometers in a meter.

Defining the Problem State the problem in your own words. What decisions will you need to make before you can proceed?

Organizing Information How many times larger is the lithium atom than its nucleus? Find several objects that could represent the nucleus in your exhibit and measure their diameters.

Creating a Solution Pick one of the objects you measured to represent the nucleus in your atomic exhibit. Figure out how far away from the object you would have to place a marker so that people could visualize the relative sizes of the atom and the nucleus.

Presenting Your Plan Write a proposal to present to the committee that approves projects. Tell them where you would place the nucleus and where you would have to place the marker. Be prepared to explain why your exhibit needs the space you are requesting.

Everything scientists know about the nucleus and subatomic particles is based on how the particles behave. Scientists still do not have an instrument that can show the inside of an atom. But they do have microscopes that can show how atoms are arranged on the surface of a material. The How It Works box on page 111 describes one of those microscopes.

 Reading Checkpoint *Which scientist demonstrated the existence of neutrons?*

Atomic Number and Mass Number

Dalton predicted that the atoms of any element are different from the atoms of all other elements. With the discovery of subatomic particles, scientists were able to describe those differences.

Atomic Number The atoms of any given element always have the same number of protons. For example, there is one proton in the nucleus of each and every hydrogen atom. Therefore, hydrogen is assigned the atomic number 1. The **atomic number** of an element equals the number of protons in an atom of that element.

Hydrogen atoms are the only atoms with a single proton. ☞ **Atoms of different elements have different numbers of protons.** The sulfur shown in Figure 11A is assigned atomic number 16 because a sulfur atom has 16 protons. You can use atomic numbers to refer to elements, like names and symbols, because each element has a unique atomic number.

Each positive charge in an atom is balanced by a negative charge because atoms are neutral. So the atomic number of an element also equals the number of electrons in an atom. Each hydrogen atom has one electron. Each sulfur atom has 16.

Mass Number The atomic number tells you the number of protons in an atom's nucleus. It does not give you any information about the number of neutrons in an atom. For that information, you need to know the atom's mass number. The **mass number** of an atom is the sum of the protons and neutrons in the nucleus of that atom. An atom of aluminum with 13 protons and 14 neutrons has a mass number of 27. If you know the atomic number and the mass number of an atom, you can find the number of neutrons by subtracting.

Figure 11 Each element has a different atomic number. **A** The atomic number of sulfur (S) is 16. **B** The atomic number of iron (Fe) is 26. **C** The atomic number of silver (Ag) is 47.
Applying Concepts How many protons are there in each atom of sulfur, iron, and silver?

Number of Neutrons

Number of neutrons = Mass number − Atomic number

Scanning Tunneling Microscope

A probe is moved back and forth across the surface of a sample. When electrons jump, or tunnel, across the gap between the sample and the probe, an electric current is produced. A computer uses data about changes in the probe's position to produce an image of the sample's surface. **Interpreting Diagrams** *How is the distance between the probe tip and the sample kept constant?*

Scanning tunneling microscope
Modern scanning tunneling microscopes produce images of metal samples or biological specimens such as DNA.

A **Scanning probe**
As the probe is moved over the sample, current flows between the probe tip and the sample. The processor holds the tip at a constant distance from the sample by keeping the electric current constant. Thus, changes in the vertical position of the probe will follow the contours of the sample's surface.

Electrical signal from processor

Electrical signal from probe

B **Processor**
The processor sends, receives, and records information about the movement of the probe.

Scanning device *This device raises and lowers the probe.*

Electron flow
Electrons flow across a gap of about one nanometer (0.000001 mm) between the probe tip and the sample, producing an electric current.

Gold sample

C **Computer** A computer assembles a map of the sample's surface, using data received from the processor. Color was added to the image shown on the computer screen.

Probe tip *The tip of the probe is only one or two atoms in width.*

Comparing Ordinary Water and Heavy Water		
Property	Ordinary Water	Heavy Water
Melting point	0.00°C	3.81°C
Boiling point	100.00°C	101.42°C
Density (at 25°C)	0.99701 g/cm³	1.1044 g/cm³

Figure 12 Heavy water contains hydrogen-2 atoms, which have twice the mass of hydrogen-1 atoms. **Using Tables** *At what temperature would a sample of heavy water freeze?*

Isotopes

In Dalton's atomic theory, all the atoms of a given element are identical. Every atom of a given element *does* have the same number of protons and electrons. But every atom of a given element *does not* have the same number of neutrons. **Isotopes are atoms of the same element that have different numbers of neutrons and different mass numbers.** ⬭ **Isotopes of an element have the same atomic number but different mass numbers because they have different numbers of neutrons.**

For example, every atom of oxygen has 8 protons. Some oxygen atoms have 8 neutrons and a mass number of 16. Some oxygen atoms have 9 neutrons and a mass number of 17. Some oxygen atoms have 10 neutrons and a mass number of 18. When it is important to distinguish one oxygen isotope from another, the isotopes are referred to as oxygen-16, oxygen-17, and oxygen-18. All three oxygen isotopes can react with hydrogen to form water or combine with iron to form rust.

With most elements, it is hard to notice any differences in the physical or chemical properties of their isotopes. Hydrogen is an exception. Hydrogen-1 has no neutrons. (Almost all hydrogen is hydrogen-1.) Hydrogen-2 has one neutron, and hydrogen-3 has two neutrons. Because a hydrogen-1 atom has only one proton, adding a neutron doubles its mass. Water that contains hydrogen-2 atoms in place of hydrogen-1 atoms is called heavy water. Figure 12 compares some physical properties of ordinary water and heavy water.

Section 4.2 Assessment

Reviewing Concepts

1. ⬭ Name three subatomic particles.

2. ⬭ Name three properties you could use to distinguish a proton from an electron.

3. ⬭ Which characteristic of an atom always varies among atoms of different elements?

4. ⬭ How are the isotopes of an element different from one another?

5. What do neutrons and protons have in common? How are they different?

6. How can atoms be neutral if they contain charged particles?

7. What is the difference between atoms of oxygen-16 and oxygen-17?

Critical Thinking

8. **Comparing and Contrasting** What property do protons and electrons have that neutrons do not?

9. **Applying Concepts** Explain why it isn't possible for an atom to have a mass number of 10 and an atomic number of 12.

Connecting ⊂ Concepts

Elements In Section 2.1, you were told that elements contain only one type of atom. How would you define "type of atom" to account for the existence of isotopes?

4.3 Modern Atomic Theory

Reading Focus

Key Concepts
- What can happen to electrons when atoms gain or lose energy?
- What model do scientists use to describe how electrons behave in atoms?
- What is the most stable configuration of electrons in an atom?

Vocabulary
- energy levels
- electron cloud
- orbital
- electron configuration
- ground state

Reading Strategy
Sequencing Copy the flowchart. After you read, complete the description of how a gain or loss of energy affects atoms.

Electrons and Energy Levels

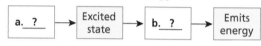

a. ? → Excited state → b. ? → Emits energy

Have you ever wondered what produces the different colors in a fireworks display? Why does one explosion produce red light and another explosion produce green light? The people who make fireworks know that certain compounds will produce certain colors of light when they are heated. For example, compounds containing the element strontium produce red light when they are heated. Compounds containing barium produce green light.

You have seen two things that can happen when atoms absorb energy—an increase in kinetic energy or a phase change. But there is another possibility. The energy may be temporarily absorbed by the atom and then emitted as light. The colors in a fireworks display are a clue to how electrons are arranged in atoms.

Bohr's Model of the Atom

You may have seen diagrams of an atom that look like a solar system with planets revolving around a sun. These diagrams are based on a model of the atom that was developed by Niels Bohr (1885–1962), a Danish physicist who worked for a while with Rutherford. Bohr agreed with Rutherford's model of a nucleus surrounded by a large volume of space. But Bohr's model did something that Rutherford's model did not do. It focused on the electrons. A description of the arrangement of electrons in an atom is the centerpiece of the modern atomic model.

Figure 13 Fireworks are often displayed above the Lincoln Memorial in Washington, D.C. The red light was produced by a strontium compound.

Energy Levels In Bohr's model, electrons move with constant speed in fixed orbits around the nucleus, like planets around a sun. Each electron in an atom has a specific amount of energy. If an atom gains or loses energy, the energy of an electron can change. The possible energies that electrons in an atom can have are called **energy levels.**

To understand energy levels, picture them as steps in a staircase. As you move up or down the staircase, you can measure how your position changes by counting the number of steps you take. You might take one step up, or you might jump two steps down. Whether you are going up or down, you can move only in whole-step increments. Just as you cannot stand between steps on a staircase, an electron cannot exist between energy levels.

DK SCIENCE and History

Models of the Atom

The development of scientific ideas on the structure of atoms has passed several key milestones during the last 200 years.

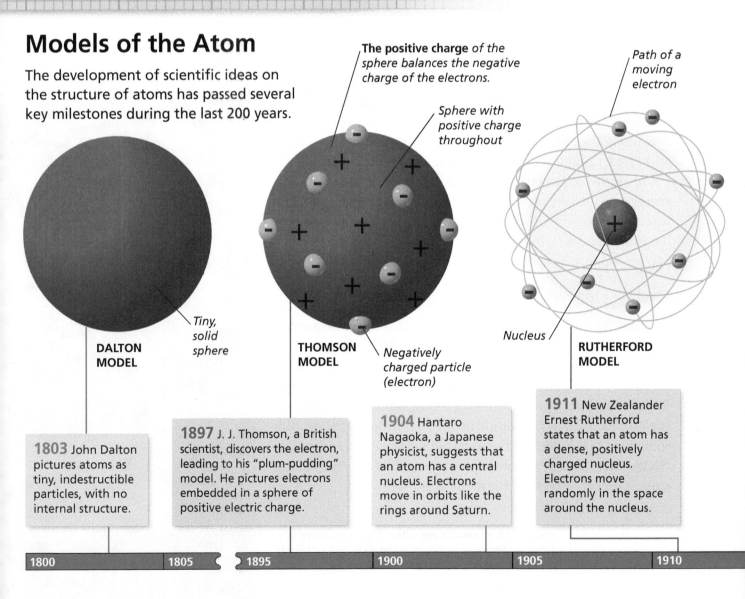

The positive charge of the sphere balances the negative charge of the electrons.

Sphere with positive charge throughout

Path of a moving electron

Tiny, solid sphere

DALTON MODEL

THOMSON MODEL

Negatively charged particle (electron)

Nucleus

RUTHERFORD MODEL

1803 John Dalton pictures atoms as tiny, indestructible particles, with no internal structure.

1897 J. J. Thomson, a British scientist, discovers the electron, leading to his "plum-pudding" model. He pictures electrons embedded in a sphere of positive electric charge.

1904 Hantaro Nagaoka, a Japanese physicist, suggests that an atom has a central nucleus. Electrons move in orbits like the rings around Saturn.

1911 New Zealander Ernest Rutherford states that an atom has a dense, positively charged nucleus. Electrons move randomly in the space around the nucleus.

| 1800 | 1805 | 1895 | 1900 | 1905 | 1910 |

The landing at the bottom of the staircase is like the lowest energy level in an atom. Each step up represents a higher energy level. The distance between two steps represents the difference in energy between two energy levels. To continue the analogy, there would need to be a different staircase for each element because no two elements have the same set of energy levels.

🔑 **An electron in an atom can move from one energy level to another when the atom gains or loses energy.** An electron may move up two energy levels if it gains the right amount of energy. An electron in a higher energy level may move down two energy levels if it loses the right amount of energy. The size of the jump between energy levels determines the amount of energy gained or lost.

Writing in Science

Summary Select a scientist mentioned on the time line. Research and write a paragraph about the scientist's early years. What experiences led to his interest in science? Was he the first in his family to be interested in science? What subjects did he study at school?

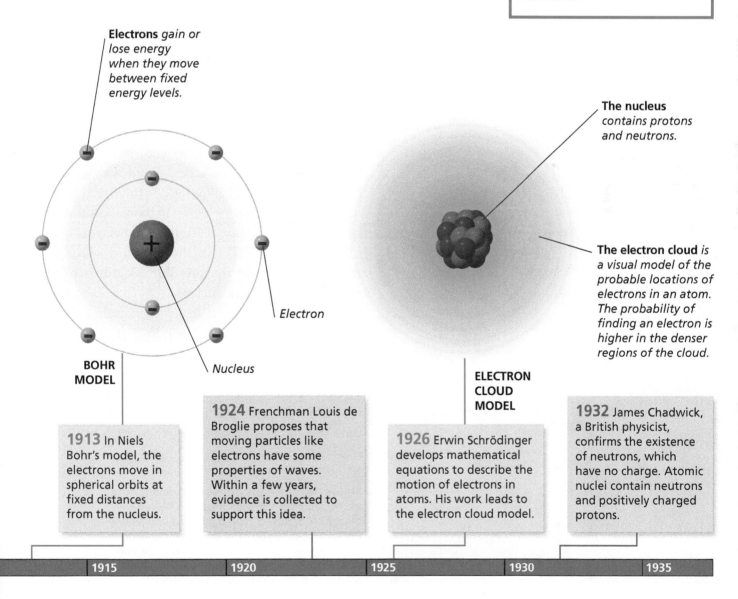

Electrons *gain or lose energy when they move between fixed energy levels.*

The nucleus *contains protons and neutrons.*

The electron cloud *is a visual model of the probable locations of electrons in an atom. The probability of finding an electron is higher in the denser regions of the cloud.*

Electron

BOHR MODEL

Nucleus

ELECTRON CLOUD MODEL

1913 In Niels Bohr's model, the electrons move in spherical orbits at fixed distances from the nucleus.

1924 Frenchman Louis de Broglie proposes that moving particles like electrons have some properties of waves. Within a few years, evidence is collected to support this idea.

1926 Erwin Schrödinger develops mathematical equations to describe the motion of electrons in atoms. His work leads to the electron cloud model.

1932 James Chadwick, a British physicist, confirms the existence of neutrons, which have no charge. Atomic nuclei contain neutrons and positively charged protons.

| 1915 | 1920 | 1925 | 1930 | 1935 |

Evidence for Energy Levels What evidence is there that electrons can move from one energy level to another? Scientists can measure the energy gained when electrons absorb energy and move to a higher energy level. They can measure the energy released when the electron returns to a lower energy level.

The movement of electrons between energy levels explains the light you see when fireworks explode. Light is a form of energy. Heat produced by the explosion causes some electrons to move to higher energy levels. When those electrons move back to lower energy levels, they emit energy. Some of that energy is released as visible light. Because no two elements have the same set of energy levels, different elements emit different colors of light.

 Reading Checkpoint *What determines the amount of energy gained or lost when an electron moves between energy levels?*

Electron Cloud Model

Like earlier models, Bohr's model was improved as scientists made further discoveries. Bohr was correct in assigning energy levels to electrons. But he was incorrect in assuming that electrons moved like planets in a solar system. Today, scientists know that electrons move in a less predictable way.

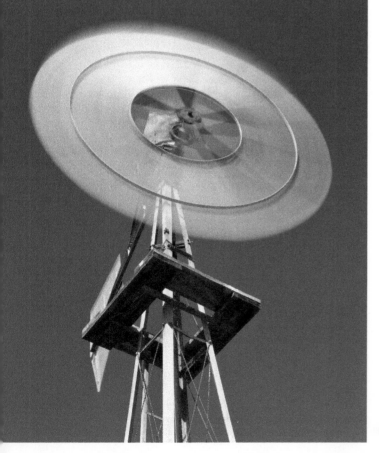

Scientists must deal with probability when trying to predict the locations and motions of electrons in atoms. An **electron cloud** is a visual model of the most likely locations for electrons in an atom. The cloud is denser at those locations where the probability of finding an electron is high. ⬤ **Scientists use the electron cloud model to describe the possible locations of electrons around the nucleus.**

Figure 14 provides an analogy for an electron cloud. When the blades of a windmill are at rest, you can count the number of blades. When they are moving, the blades spin so fast that you see only a blur. You know that the blades are located somewhere in the blur, but at any specific moment in time you can't be exactly sure where each blade is located.

Figure 14 When the blades of a windmill are at rest, you can see their locations. When the blades are spinning, you see only a blur that is similar to a drawing of an electron cloud. **Comparing and Contrasting** *Describe one difference between the motion of windmill blades and the motion of an electron.*

Comparing Excited States

Materials

fluorescent ("neon") markers, glow-in-the-dark toy, ultraviolet (UV) lamp

Procedure

1. Use the fluorescent markers to draw a picture on a piece of paper.

2. With the room darkened, observe your drawing under a UV lamp. **CAUTION** *Do not look directly at the light.* Remove the drawing from under the UV light and observe it again. Record your observations.

3. Observe the glow-in-the-dark toy under the UV light. Remove the toy from the light and observe it again. Record your observations.

Analyze and Conclude

1. **Observing** How did the glow of the toy differ from the glow of your drawing?

2. **Formulating Hypotheses** Use the concepts of ground and excited states to explain how UV light caused your drawing and the toy to glow.

3. **Drawing Conclusions** In which object, your drawing or the toy, do the atoms have excited states that are more stable, or less likely to change? Explain your answer.

Atomic Orbitals

The electron cloud represents all the orbitals in an atom. An **orbital** is a region of space around the nucleus where an electron is likely to be found. To understand the concept of an orbital, imagine a map of your school. Suppose you mark your exact location with a dot once every 10 minutes over a period of one week. The places you visit the most—such as your classrooms, the cafeteria, and the area near your locker—would have the highest concentration of dots. The places you visit the least would have the lowest concentration of dots.

The dots on your map are a model of your "orbital." They describe your most likely locations. There are some locations in your orbital that you may not visit every week—such as the principal's office or the auditorium. These locations may not be represented by a dot on your map. Despite such omissions, the dots on your map are a good model of how you usually behave in your orbital. 🔑 **An electron cloud is a good approximation of how electrons behave in their orbitals.**

The level in which an electron has the least energy—the lowest energy level—has only one orbital. Higher energy levels have more than one orbital. Figure 15 shows the number of orbitals in the first four energy levels of an atom. Notice that the maximum number of electrons in an energy level is twice the number of orbitals. Each orbital can contain two electrons at most.

Figure 15 The table lists the number of orbitals in the first four energy levels of an atom. It also lists the maximum number of electrons in each energy level. *Inferring* ***How many electrons can be in each orbital?***

Energy Levels, Orbitals, and Electrons		
Energy Level	Number of Orbitals	Maximum Number of Electrons
1	1	2
2	4	8
3	9	18
4	16	32

Figure 16 A gymnast on a balance beam is like an atom in an excited state—not very stable.

Electron Configurations

How are the seats in your classroom arranged? Are they lined up neatly in rows, or are they grouped in clusters? A configuration is an arrangement of objects in a given space. Some configurations are more stable than others, meaning that they are less likely to change. The position of the gymnast on the balance beam in Figure 16 is not very stable because the beam is only 10 centimeters wide.

An **electron configuration** is the arrangement of electrons in the orbitals of an atom. 🔑 **The most stable electron configuration is the one in which the electrons are in orbitals with the lowest possible energies.** When all the electrons in an atom have the lowest possible energies, the atom is said to be in its **ground state.**

For example, lithium is a silvery-white metal with an atomic number of 3, which means that a lithium atom has three electrons. In the ground state, two of the lithium electrons are in the orbital of the first energy level. The third electron is in an orbital of the second energy level.

If a lithium atom absorbs enough energy, one of its electrons can move to an orbital with a higher energy. This configuration is referred to as an excited state. An excited state is less stable than the ground state. Eventually, the electron that was promoted to a higher energy level loses energy, and the atom returns to the ground state. Helium, neon, argon, krypton, and xenon atoms returning from excited states to the ground state emit the light you see in "neon" lights.

Section 4.3 Assessment

Reviewing Concepts

1. 🔑 When is an electron in an atom likely to move from one energy level to another?

2. 🔑 What model do scientists use to describe how electrons move around the nucleus?

3. 🔑 Describe the most stable configuration of the electrons in an atom.

4. What did Bohr contribute to modern atomic theory?

5. What does an electron cloud represent?

Critical Thinking

6. **Comparing and Contrasting** A boron atom has two electrons in the first energy level and three in the second energy level. Compare the relative energies of the electrons in these two energy levels.

7. **Making Judgments** Was Rutherford's model of an atom incorrect or incomplete? Explain your answer.

8. **Posing Questions** Apply what you know about charged particles to the modern model of the atom. Is there anything about the behavior of electrons in atoms that is unexpected? Explain your answer.

Writing in Science

Describing Energy Levels Use a bookcase as an analogy for the energy levels in an atom. Use the analogy to write a paragraph about electrons and energy levels. (*Hint:* Reread the staircase analogy on pages 114 and 115.)

Forensics Lab

Using Flame Tests

Forensic scientists use various approaches to distinguish different substances. In this lab, you will observe the flame colors of several substances and use the data to determine the identity of an unknown substance.

Problem
How can the color of a flame be used to distinguish substances?

Materials
- solutions of calcium chloride, boric acid, potassium chloride, copper(II) sulfate, sodium chloride, and an unknown
- Bunsen burner
- nichrome wire loop
- dilute solution of hydrochloric acid
- wash bottle with distilled water

Skills
Observing, Predicting, Using Data Tables

Procedure

Part A: Observing Flame Colors

1. Make a copy of the data table shown.

Data Table	
Solution	Flame Color
Calcium chloride	
Potassium chloride	
Boric acid	
Copper(II) sulfate	
Sodium chloride	
Unknown	
Identity of Unknown	

2. Light the Bunsen burner. **CAUTION** *Put on safety goggles and a lab apron. Tie back loose hair and clothing before working with a flame.*

3. Dip the wire loop into the calcium chloride solution and then place the loop in the flame as shown. Observe and record the color of the flame.

4. Clean the loop by dipping it into hydrochloric acid. Then, while holding the loop over a sink, rinse away the acid with distilled water. **CAUTION** *Keep hydrochloric acid away from your skin and clothing. Do not breathe in its vapor.*

5. Repeat Steps 3 and 4 with each of the other solutions. Be careful not to transfer any solution from one container to another. **CAUTION** *These chemicals are poisonous. Do not let them get on your skin.*

Part B: Examining an Unknown Solution

6. Obtain the unknown solution from your teacher.

7. Repeat Steps 3 and 4 using the unknown solution. Compare your observations with the other data you recorded to identify the unknown. **CAUTION** *Wash your hands thoroughly before leaving the laboratory.*

Analyze and Conclude

1. **Comparing and Contrasting** Is there a relationship between the color of the flame and the color of the solution?

2. **Formulating Hypotheses** How do these substances produce light of different colors?

3. **Drawing Conclusions** A forensic scientist does a flame test on a substance that was found at a crime scene. What might the scientist conclude if the flame turns green?

Go Further There is another test that you can use to distinguish elements by color. With your teacher supervising, dip a wire loop in borax. Heat the loop in a flame until the borax melts. Remove the loop from the flame and let the borax cool. It will form a clear glass bead. Dip the bead in a tiny sample of solid copper sulfate and return the loop to the flame for a few seconds. Remove the loop and observe the color of the bead as it cools.

Study Guide

4.1 Studying Atoms

Key Concepts

- Dalton proposed the theory that all matter is made up of individual particles called atoms, which cannot be divided.
- Thomson's experiments provided the first evidence that atoms are made of even smaller particles.
- According to Rutherford's model, all of an atom's positive charge is concentrated in its nucleus.

Vocabulary

nucleus, *p. 105*

4.2 The Structure of an Atom

Key Concepts

- Protons, electrons. and neutrons are subatomic particles.
- Protons, electrons, and neutrons can be distinguished by mass, charge, and location in an atom.
- Atoms of different elements have different numbers of protons.
- Isotopes of an element have the same atomic number but different mass numbers because they have different numbers of neutrons.

Vocabulary

proton, *p. 108*
electron, *p. 108*
neutron, *p. 109*
atomic number, *p. 110*
mass number, *p. 110*
isotopes, *p. 112*

4.3 Modern Atomic Theory

Key Concepts

- An electron in an atom can move from one energy level to another when the atom gains or loses energy.
- Scientists use the electron cloud model to describe the possible locations of electrons around the nucleus.
- An electron cloud is a good approximation of how electrons behave in their orbitals.
- The most stable electron configuration is the one in which the electrons are in orbitals with the lowest possible energies.

Vocabulary

energy levels, *p. 114*
electron cloud, *p. 116*
orbital, *p. 117*
electron configuration, *p. 118*
ground state, *p. 118*

Thinking Visually

Table of Properties Use information from the chapter to complete the table below.

Particle	Proton	Electron	Neutron
Symbol	a.___?___	e^-	n
Relative charge	1+	b.___?___	c.___?___
Relative mass	d.___?___	$\dfrac{1}{1836}$	e.___?___

Reviewing Content

Choose the letter that best answers the question or completes the statement.

1. One of the first people to state that matter is made up of atoms was
  a. Democritus.   **b.** Aristotle.
  c. Dalton.   **d.** Rutherford.

2. Dalton's model of an atom is best described as
  a. a solar system.   **b.** a solid sphere.
  c. a plum pudding.   **d.** an electron cloud.

3. Who provided the first evidence that atoms contain subatomic particles?
  a. Dalton   **b.** Rutherford
  c. Thomson   **d.** Bohr

4. Almost all the mass of an atom is located in its
  a. protons.   **b.** electrons.
  c. electron cloud.   **d.** nucleus.

5. An electron is a particle with
  a. a negative charge, found in the nucleus.
  b. a positive charge, found in the nucleus.
  c. no charge, found outside the nucleus.
  d. a negative charge, found outside the nucleus.

6. Which particle is the least massive?
  a. proton   **b.** electron
  c. neutron   **d.** nucleus

7. All atoms of an element have the same
  a. mass number.   **b.** number of isotopes.
  c. atomic number.   **d.** number of neutrons.

8. The number of neutrons in an atom equals the
  a. mass number minus atomic number.
  b. atomic number plus number of electrons.
  c. mass number plus atomic number.
  d. atomic number minus mass number.

9. The atomic number of sulfur is 16. How many electrons are there in an atom of sulfur-34?
  a. 16   **b.** 34
  c. 18   **d.** 50

10. Atoms emit energy as light when
  a. electrons move to a higher energy level.
  b. electrons move to a lower energy level.
  c. protons move to a higher energy level.
  d. protons move to a lower energy level.

Understanding Concepts

11. Why must indirect evidence be used to study the structure of atoms?

12. What evidence convinced Dalton that elements must be made of individual particles called atoms?

13. In Thomson's experiment, why was the glowing beam repelled by a negatively charged plate?

14. What evidence supported Thomson's hypothesis that the negative particles he observed came from inside atoms?

15. Compare the mass and volume of the nucleus to the total mass and volume of an atom.

16. Compare the relative masses of protons, neutrons, and electrons in an atom.

17. What is the difference between the atomic number of an atom and its mass number?

18. If the atomic number of an atom is 11, how many electrons does the atom have? Explain.

19. If an atom has an atomic number of 6 and a mass number of 14, how many protons, electrons, and neutrons are in the atom?

20. What part of Dalton's theory was modified after the discovery of isotopes?

21. Which isotope of oxygen is represented by the drawing—oxygen-16, oxygen-17, or oxygen-18? Assume that all the protons and neutrons in the nucleus are visible in the drawing. Give a reason for your answer.

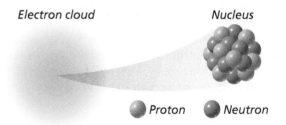

Electron cloud   *Nucleus*

● *Proton* ● *Neutron*

22. What is the main difference between Bohr's model of the atom and the atomic theory that is currently accepted?

23. What does it mean to say that an atom is in an excited state?

Critical Thinking

24. Controlling Variables Look at the drawing of the experimental setup in Figure 5A. Explain how the setup is a control for the setup in Figure 5B.

25. Predicting How would the results of Thomson's experiment change if the beam were a stream of neutrons instead of a stream of electrons?

26. Interpreting Diagrams The atomic number of carbon is 6. The atomic number of nitrogen is 7. The atomic number of oxygen is 8. Name the isotope represented by the drawing.

Electron cloud   *Nucleus*

⬤ *Proton*   ⬤ *Neutron*

27. Hypothesizing Why were the proton and electron discovered before the neutron?

28. Applying Concepts Explain why a neutral atom cannot have one proton, one neutron, and two electrons.

29. Classifying The nucleus of an atom contains six neutrons and six protons. The nucleus of a second atom contains six neutrons and five protons. Are they atoms of different elements or isotopes of the same element? Explain your answer.

Math Skills

30. Calculating The atomic number for iron is 26. How many neutrons are in the nucleus of an iron atom with a mass number of 57? How many electrons does the iron atom have?

31. Applying Concepts If a potassium atom has an atomic number of 19 and a mass number of 39, how many protons, electrons, and neutrons are in the atom?

32. Applying Concepts A helium-4 atom has twice as many protons as a hydrogen atom. How many protons and how many neutrons are in the nucleus of a helium-4 atom?

Concepts in Action

33. Comparing and Contrasting The compound in blood that carries oxygen to cells throughout the body contains iron. Iron has an atomic number of 26. Iron-59 is used to diagnose disorders in the blood. How is iron-59 different from all other isotopes of iron? How is it the same?

34. Using Analogies Scientists working in the field of nanotechnology use either a top-down or bottom-up approach to construct tiny objects. Give an example of a visible structure that was made using the bottom-up approach and one that was made using the top-down approach.

35. Inferring If you see a green color when fireworks explode, can you be certain that the fireworks contained a barium compound? Give a reason for your answer.

36. Relating Cause and Effect Brightly colored neon lights consist of tubes filled with a gas. When an electric current passes through the tubes, different colors are emitted. Why might you conclude that the tubes in a multicolored display contain more than one element?

37. Writing in Science Better technology leads to an increase in scientific knowledge. An increase in knowledge allows for the invention of new technology. Write a paragraph discussing these statements. Use a scanning tunneling microscope as your example.

Performance-Based Assessment

Preparing a Survey Write ten questions you could ask to find out what people know about the modern model of an atom. Figure out the best order for the questions to test someone's knowledge fairly. Be prepared to explain your choices.

Go Online
PHSchool.com

For: Self-grading assessment
Visit: PHSchool.com
Web Code: cca-1040

Standardized Test Prep

Choose the letter that best answers the question or completes the statement.

1. J. J. Thomson demonstrated that electrons
(A) have a negative electric charge.
(B) have a positive electric charge.
(C) are repelled by a positively charged object.
(D) are attracted to a negatively charged object.
(E) do not have an electric charge.

2. According to Dalton's atomic theory, an atom is
(A) made of smaller particles.
(B) a particle with a positive charge.
(C) the smallest particle of an element.
(D) in constant motion.
(E) a particle with a negative charge.

3. Electrons in the first energy level of an atom
(A) have no energy.
(B) have the lowest possible energy.
(C) have the highest possible energy.
(D) are in an excited state.
(E) are in an unstable state.

4. Most alpha particles pass through a thin layer of gold without deflection because gold atoms
(A) are filled with positively charged matter.
(B) have no overall charge.
(C) have a negatively charged nucleus.
(D) do not have a nucleus.
(E) have a dense nucleus surrounded by space.

Use the data table to answer Question 5.

Comparison of Oxygen Isotopes

Property	Oxygen-16	Oxygen-18
Protons	8	8
Neutrons	8	10
Electrons	8	8
Percentage in nature	99.757	0.205

5. What is the mass number of oxygen-18?
(A) 8
(B) 10
(C) 16
(D) 18
(E) 0.205

6. An electron configuration describes
(A) regions of space around the nucleus of an atom.
(B) possible energies that an electron can have.
(C) the arrangement of electrons in an atom.
(D) the emission of light from an excited atom.
(E) the number of possible orbitals in an atom.

The Periodic Table

What are periodic trends and why are they important?

The periodic table lists important information about the elements. This information is communicated in the text entries within the table and also in the arrangement of the table's rows and columns. After you have learned how to read the periodic table, create a Web page that explains periodic trends. Include both a graphic description and a written description of each trend. Your finished Web page should serve as a useful reference for someone wanting to find the information quickly.

How do science concepts apply to your world? Here are some questions you'll be able to answer after you read this chapter.

- How can a card game be a model for organizing elements? *(Section 5.1)*

- What do a piano keyboard and a periodic table of the elements have in common? *(Section 5.2)*

- Which element makes it possible for plants to capture the energy of sunlight and use it to make sugar? *(Section 5.3)*

- Why are aluminum cans such an important part of recycling programs? *(Section 5.3)*

- Can an element be both helpful and harmful to the human body? *(page 146)*

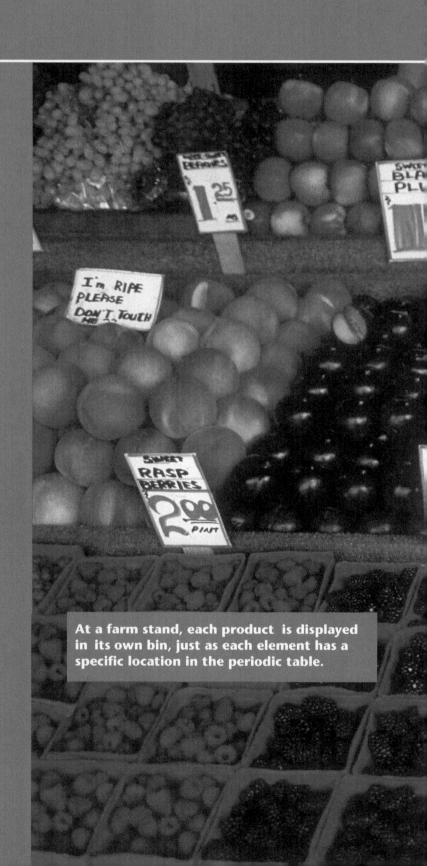

At a farm stand, each product is displayed in its own bin, just as each element has a specific location in the periodic table.

Chapter Preview

5.1 Organizing the Elements

5.2 The Modern Periodic Table

5.3 Representative Groups

Discovery
CHANNEL
SCHOOL

Video Field Trip

You Are What You Eat

Inquiry > Activity

How Much Data Do You Need to Identify a Pattern?

Procedure

1. Your teacher will give you a stapled stack of paper. Look at the squares on the top sheet of paper. Try to figure out what familiar phrase you would see if all the squares were filled in. Record your prediction on the sheet.

2. Remove the top sheet and look at the second sheet. Again, try to figure out what letters belong in the squares. Record your prediction.

3. Continue this process until you have looked at all the sheets in the stack.

Think About It

1. **Observing** How did the information on the sheets change as you moved from the top to the bottom of the stack?

2. **Drawing Conclusions** How did the number of letters provided affect your ability to predict the phrase?

3. **Using Analogies** Describe another situation in which having more data makes it easier to recognize a pattern.

5.1 Organizing the Elements

Key Concepts

- How did Mendeleev organize the elements in his periodic table?
- What evidence helped verify the usefulness of Mendeleev's table?

Vocabulary

- periodic table

Reading Strategy

Identifying Main Ideas Copy the table. As you read, write the main idea for each topic.

Topic	Main Idea
Mendeleev's proposal	a. _____?_____
Mendeleev's prediction	b. _____?_____
Evidence supporting Mendeleev's table	c. _____?_____

In a video store, the latest movies are usually placed on the shelves in alphabetical order. Older movies are grouped into categories such as Action or Comedy. The manager has to choose a set of categories and then place each movie in the most appropriate location.

Scientists faced a similar challenge when they looked for a logical way to organize the elements. They had to decide what categories to use and where to place each element. An organized table of the elements is one of the most useful tools in chemistry. The placement of elements on the table reveals the link between the atomic structure of elements and their properties.

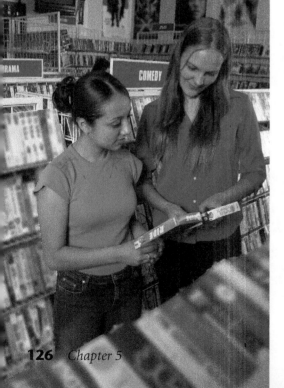

Figure 1 Older movies in video stores are placed into categories such as Drama or Comedy.

The Search for Order

Until 1750, scientists had identified only 17 elements. These were mainly metals, such as copper and iron. The rate of discovery increased rapidly as chemists began to investigate materials in a systematic way. As the number of known elements grew, so did the need to organize them into groups based on their properties.

In 1789, French chemist Antoine Lavoisier (la VWAH zee ay) grouped the known elements into categories he called metals, nonmetals, gases, and earths. For the next 80 years, scientists looked for different ways to classify the elements. But none of their systems provided an organizing principle that worked for all the known elements. A Russian chemist and teacher, Dmitri Mendeleev (Duh MEE tree Men duh LAY uff), would discover such a principle.

Mendeleev's Periodic Table

In the 1860s, Mendeleev was working on a text-book to use with his chemistry students. Because he needed to describe 63 elements, Mendeleev was looking for the best way to organize the information. He found a way to approach the problem while playing his favorite card game, a version of solitaire. In this game, the player sorts a deck of cards by suit and value. To finish the game, the player must end up with four columns, as shown in Figure 2. Each column contains cards of a single suit arranged in order by value.

Mendeleev's Proposal Mendeleev's strategy for organizing the elements was modeled on the card game. Mendeleev made a "deck of cards" of the elements. On each card, he listed an element's name, mass, and properties. He paid special attention to how each element behaved in reactions with oxygen and hydrogen. When Mendeleev lined up the cards in order of increasing mass, a pattern emerged. The key was to break the elements into rows, as shown in Figure 3.

🔑 **Mendeleev arranged the elements into rows in order of increasing mass so that elements with similar properties were in the same column.** The final arrangement was similar to a winning arrangement in solitaire, except that the columns were organized by properties instead of suits. Within a column, the masses increased from top to bottom. Mendeleev's chart was a periodic table. A **periodic table** is an arrangement of elements in columns, based on a set of properties that repeat from row to row.

Figure 2 A deck of cards can be divided into four suits—diamonds, spades, hearts, and clubs. In one version of solitaire, a player must produce an arrangement in which each suit is ordered from ace to king. This arrangement is a model for Mendeleev's periodic table.

Figure 3 This is a copy of a table that Mendeleev published in 1872. He placed the elements in groups based on the compounds they formed with oxygen or hydrogen. **Using Tables** *How many elements did Mendeleev place in Group II?*

Group I	Group II	Group III	Group IV	Group V	Group VI	Group VII	Group VIII
H = 1							
Li = 7	Be = 9.4	B = 11	C = 12	N = 14	O = 16	F = 19	
Na = 23	Mg = 24	Al = 27.3	Si = 28	P = 31	S = 32	Cl = 35.5	Fe = 56, Co = 59,
K = 39	Ca = 40	— = 44	Ti = 48	V = 51	Cr = 52	Mn = 55	Ni = 59, Cu = 63.
(Cu = 63)	Zn = 65	— = 68	— = 72	As = 75	Se = 78	Br = 80	Ru = 104, Rh = 104,
Rb = 85	Sr = 87	Yt = 88	Zr = 90	Nb = 94	Mo = 96	— = 100	Pd = 106, Ag = 108.
(Ag = 108)	Cd = 112	In = 113	Sn = 118	Sb = 122	Te = 125	I = 127	
Cs = 133	Ba = 137	Di = 138	Ce = 140	—	—	—	— — —
(—)	—	—	—	—	—	—	Os = 195, Ir = 197,
—	—	Er = 178	La = 180	Ta = 182	W = 184	—	Pt = 198, Au = 199.
(Au = 199)	Hg = 200	Tl = 204	Pb = 207	Bi = 208			
—	—	—	Th = 231	—	U = 240		

≡Quick Lab

Making a Model of a Periodic Table

Materials
plastic bag containing color chips

Procedure

1. Remove the color chips from the bag and place them on a flat surface, color side up.

2. Identify a property that you can use to divide the chips into groups. Then, identify a second property that you can use to order the chips from top to bottom within a group.

3. Use the properties you chose to arrange the chips into a table with rows and columns. Your teacher deliberately left out a chip from each bag. Decide where to leave a gap in your table for the missing chip.

Analyze and Conclude

1. **Classifying** What property did you use to divide the color chips into groups? What property did you use to arrange the chips within a group from top to bottom?

2. **Making Generalizations** What pattern repeats across each row of your table?

3. **Predicting** Based on its location on your table, describe the missing chip.

4. **Comparing and Contrasting** Compare the process you used to construct your table to the process Mendeleev used to make his table. Describe similarities and differences.

Mendeleev's Prediction Mendeleev could not make a complete table of the elements because many elements had not yet been discovered. He had to leave spaces in his table for those elements. For example, Mendeleev placed bromine (Br) in Group VII because bromine and chlorine (Cl) have similar properties. This placement left four spaces in row 4 between zinc (Zn) and bromine. Mendeleev had only two elements, arsenic and selenium, to fill those spaces, based on their masses. He placed arsenic and selenium in the columns where they fit best and left gaps in the columns labeled Groups III and IV.

Mendeleev was not the first to arrange elements in a periodic table. He was not even the first to leave spaces in a periodic table for missing elements. But he was able to offer the best explanation for how the properties of an element were related to its location in his table.

An excellent test for the correctness of a scientific model, such as Mendeleev's table, is whether the model can be used to make accurate predictions. Mendeleev was confident that the gaps in his table would be filled by new elements. He used the properties of elements located near the blank spaces in his table to predict properties for undiscovered elements. Some scientists didn't accept these predictions. Others used the predictions to help in their search for undiscovered elements.

NSTA SCILINKS

For: Links to periodic table
Visit: www.SciLinks.org
Web Code: ccn-1051

Reading Checkpoint *Why did Mendeleev place bromine in Group VII of his periodic table?*

Evidence Supporting Mendeleev's Table

Mendeleev named missing elements after elements in the same group. He gave the name eka-aluminum to the element that belonged one space below aluminum on the table. (*Eka* is a Sanskrit word meaning "one.") Mendeleev predicted that eka-aluminum would be a soft metal with a low melting point and a density of 5.9 g/cm³.

In 1875, a French chemist discovered a new element. He named the element gallium (Ga) in honor of France. (The Latin name for France is *Gallia*.) Gallium is a soft metal with a melting point of 29.7°C and a density of 5.91 g/cm³. Figure 4 shows a sample of gallium and a traffic signal that uses gallium compounds.

The properties of gallium are remarkably similar to the predicted properties of eka-aluminum. Scientists concluded that gallium and eka-aluminum are the same element. **The close match between Mendeleev's predictions and the actual properties of new elements showed how useful his periodic table could be.** The discovery of scandium (Sc) in 1879 and the discovery of germanium (Ge) in 1886 provided more evidence. With the periodic table, chemists could do more than predict the properties of new elements. They could explain the chemical behavior of different groups of elements.

Figure 4 Gallium was discovered in 1875. Heat from a person's hand can melt gallium. In some traffic signals, there are tiny light emitting diodes (LEDs) that contain a compound of gallium. **Comparing and Contrasting** *How does the melting point of gallium (29.7°C) compare to room temperature (about 25°C)?*

Section 5.1 Assessment

Reviewing Concepts

1. Describe how Mendeleev organized the elements into rows and columns in his periodic table.

2. How did the discovery of new elements such as gallium demonstrate the usefulness of Mendeleev's table?

3. Scientists before Mendeleev had proposed ways to organize the elements. Why were Mendeleev's efforts more successful?

4. What characteristic of solitaire did Mendeleev use as a model for his periodic table?

5. Why did Mendeleev leave spaces in his table?

6. In general, how can a scientist test the correctness of a scientific model?

Critical Thinking

7. **Inferring** Explain why it would not have been possible for a scientist in 1750 to develop a table like Mendeleev's.

8. **Predicting** How was Mendeleev able to predict the properties of elements that had not yet been discovered?

Writing in Science

Writing to Persuade Write a paragraph about Mendeleev's periodic table. Use the paragraph to convince a reader that the periodic table is extremely useful to scientists. (*Hint:* Use specific facts to support your argument.)

5.2 The Modern Periodic Table

Key Concepts

- How is the modern periodic table organized?
- What does the atomic mass of an element depend on?
- What categories are used to classify elements on the periodic table?
- How do properties vary across a period in the periodic table?

Vocabulary

- period
- group
- periodic law
- atomic mass unit (amu)
- metals
- transition metals
- nonmetals
- metalloids

Reading Strategy

Previewing Copy the table below. Before you read, write two questions about the periodic table on pages 132 and 133. As you read, write answers to your questions.

Questions About the Periodic Table	
Question	Answer
a._____?_____	b._____?_____
c._____?_____	d._____?_____

Figure 5 shows a synthesizer keyboard with labels for the notes that correspond to the white keys. If you strike the key labeled middle C and then play the white keys in order from left to right, you will hear the familiar do-re-mi-fa-sol-la-ti scale. The next white note is a C that is an octave above middle C. An octave is the interval between any two notes with the same name. (The prefix *octa-* means "eight.") Because the scale repeats at regular eight-note intervals, the scale is an example of a periodic pattern.

The sounds of musical notes that are separated by an octave are related, but they are not identical. In a similar way, elements in the same column of the periodic table are related because their properties repeat at regular intervals. But elements in different rows are not identical. You can use the modern periodic table of elements to classify elements and to compare their properties.

Figure 5 On this synthesizer keyboard, there is a repeating pattern of notes. The eight-note interval between any two notes with the same name is an octave. **Observing** *How many octaves are visible on the keyboard?*

B C D E F G A B Middle C D E F G A B C D E

1	H																																He
2	Li	Be																									B	C	N	O	F	Ne
3	Na	Mg																									Al	Si	P	S	Cl	Ar
4	K	Ca															Sc	Ti	V	Cr	Mn	Fe	Co	Ni	Cu	Zn	Ga	Ge	As	Se	Br	Kr
5	Rb	Sr															Y	Zr	Nb	Mo	Tc	Ru	Rh	Pd	Ag	Cd	In	Sn	Sb	Te	I	Xe
6	Cs	Ba	La	Ce	Pr	Nd	Pm	Sm	Eu	Gd	Tb	Dy	Ho	Er	Tm	Yb	Lu	Hf	Ta	W	Re	Os	Ir	Pt	Au	Hg	Tl	Pb	Bi	Po	At	Rn
7	Fr	Ra	Ac	Th	Pa	U	Np	Pu	Am	Cm	Bk	Cf	Es	Fm	Md	No	Lr	Rf	Db	Sg	Bh	Hs	Mt	Ds	Rg	Cn	Uut	Uuq	Uup	Uuh		Uuo

The Periodic Law

Mendeleev developed his periodic table before the discovery of protons. He did not know that all atoms of an element have the same number of protons. He did not know that atoms of two different elements could not have the same number of protons. **In the modern periodic table, elements are arranged by increasing atomic number (number of protons).** Figure 6 shows one way the known elements can be arranged in order by increasing atomic number.

Periods Each row in the table of elements in Figure 6 is a **period.** Period 1 has 2 elements. Periods 2 and 3 have 8 elements. Periods 4 and 5 have 18 elements. Period 6 has 32 elements. The number of elements per period varies because the number of available orbitals increases from energy level to energy level.

To understand the structure of the table, think about what happens as the atomic number increases. The first energy level has only one orbital. The one electron in a hydrogen atom and the two electrons in a helium atom can fit in this orbital. But one of the three electrons in a lithium atom must be in the second energy level. That is why lithium is the first element in Period 2. Sodium, the first element in Period 3, has one electron in its third energy level. Potassium, the first element in Period 4, has one electron in its fourth energy level. This pattern applies to all the elements in the first column on the table.

Groups Each column on the periodic table is called a **group.** The elements within a group have similar properties. **Properties of elements repeat in a predictable way when atomic numbers are used to arrange elements into groups.** The elements in a group have similar electron configurations. An element's electron configuration determines its chemical properties. Therefore, members of a group in the periodic table have similar chemical properties. This pattern of repeating properties is the **periodic law.**

Look at Figure 7 on pages 132 and 133. There are 18 groups in this periodic table. Some elements from Periods 6 and 7 have been placed below Period 7 so that the table is more compact.

Figure 6 This diagram shows one way to display a periodic table of the elements. There are 7 rows, or periods, in the table. There are 32 columns, or groups, in the table.
Comparing and Contrasting
Compare the numbers of elements in Periods 1, 3, and 5.

For: Links on periodic law
Visit: www.SciLinks.org
Web Code: ccn-1052

Periodic Table of the Elements

Figure 7 In a modern periodic table of the elements, elements are arranged in order of increasing atomic number.

		Solid
C	Li	B
Br	Hg	Liquid
H		Gas
	Tc	Not found in nature

Nonmetals   Metals   Metalloids

1
1A

1
H
Hydrogen
1.0079

2
2A

3	4
Li	**Be**
Lithium	Beryllium
6.941	9.0122

11	12
Na	**Mg**
Sodium	Magnesium
22.990	24.305

3	**4**	**5**	**6**	**7**	**8**	**9**
3B	**4B**	**5B**	**6B**	**7B**	**8B**	

19	20	21	22	23	24	25	26	27
K	**Ca**	**Sc**	**Ti**	**V**	**Cr**	**Mn**	**Fe**	**Co**
Potassium	Calcium	Scandium	Titanium	Vanadium	Chromium	Manganese	Iron	Cobalt
39.098	40.08	44.956	47.90	50.941	51.996	54.938	55.847	58.933

37	38	39	40	41	42	43	44	45
Rb	**Sr**	**Y**	**Zr**	**Nb**	**Mo**	**Tc**	**Ru**	**Rh**
Rubidium	Strontium	Yttrium	Zirconium	Niobium	Molybdenum	Technetium	Ruthenium	Rhodium
85.468	87.62	88.906	91.22	92.906	95.94	(98)	101.07	102.91

55	56	71	72	73	74	75	76	77
Cs	**Ba**	**Lu**	**Hf**	**Ta**	**W**	**Re**	**Os**	**Ir**
Cesium	Barium	Lutetium	Hafnium	Tantalum	Tungsten	Rhenium	Osmium	Iridium
132.91	137.33	174.97	178.49	180.95	183.85	186.21	190.2	192.22

87	88	103	104	105	106	107	108	109
Fr	**Ra**	**Lr**	**Rf**	**Db**	**Sg**	**Bh**	**Hs**	**Mt**
Francium	Radium	Lawrencium	Rutherfordium	Dubnium	Seaborgium	Bohrium	Hassium	Meitnerium
(223)	(226)	(262)	(261)	(262)	(263)	(264)	(265)	(268)

57	58	59	60	61	62
La	**Ce**	**Pr**	**Nd**	**Pm**	**Sm**
Lanthanum	Cerium	Praseodymium	Neodymium	Promethium	Samarium
138.91	140.12	140.91	144.24	(145)	150.4

Lanthanide Series

89	90	91	92	93	94
Ac	**Th**	**Pa**	**U**	**Np**	**Pu**
Actinium	Thorium	Protactinium	Uranium	Neptunium	Plutonium
(227)	232.04	231.04	238.03	(237)	(244)

Actinide Series

Atomic number

6
C
Carbon
12.011

Element symbol
Element name
Atomic mass

							18 8A
		13 3A	14 4A	15 5A	16 6A	17 7A	2 **He** Helium 4.0026
		5 **B** Boron 10.81	6 **C** Carbon 12.011	7 **N** Nitrogen 14.007	8 **O** Oxygen 15.999	9 **F** Fluorine 18.998	10 **Ne** Neon 20.179
		13 **Al** Aluminum 26.982	14 **Si** Silicon 28.086	15 **P** Phosphorus 30.974	16 **S** Sulfur 32.06	17 **Cl** Chlorine 35.453	18 **Ar** Argon 39.948

10	11 1B	12 2B						
28 **Ni** Nickel 58.71	29 **Cu** Copper 63.546	30 **Zn** Zinc 65.38	31 **Ga** Gallium 69.72	32 **Ge** Germanium 72.59	33 **As** Arsenic 74.922	34 **Se** Selenium 78.96	35 **Br** Bromine 79.904	36 **Kr** Krypton 83.80
46 **Pd** Palladium 106.4	47 **Ag** Silver 107.87	48 **Cd** Cadmium 112.41	49 **In** Indium 114.82	50 **Sn** Tin 118.69	51 **Sb** Antimony 121.75	52 **Te** Tellurium 127.60	53 **I** Iodine 126.90	54 **Xe** Xenon 131.30
78 **Pt** Platinum 195.09	79 **Au** Gold 196.97	80 **Hg** Mercury 200.59	81 **Tl** Thallium 204.37	82 **Pb** Lead 207.2	83 **Bi** Bismuth 208.98	84 **Po** Polonium (209)	85 **At** Astatine (210)	86 **Rn** Radon (222)
110 **Ds** Darmstadtium (269)	111 **Rg** Roentgenium (272)	112 **Cn** Copernicium (277)	*113 **Uut** Ununtrium (284)	*114 **Uuq** Ununquadium (289)	*115 **Uup** Ununpentium (288)	*116 **Uuh** Ununhexium (293)		*118 **Uuo** Ununoctium (299)

*Name not officially assigned

63 **Eu** Europium 151.96	64 **Gd** Gadolinium 157.25	65 **Tb** Terbium 158.93	66 **Dy** Dysprosium 162.50	67 **Ho** Holmium 164.93	68 **Er** Erbium 167.26	69 **Tm** Thulium 168.93	70 **Yb** Ytterbium 173.04
95 **Am** Americium (243)	96 **Cm** Curium (247)	97 **Bk** Berkelium (247)	98 **Cf** Californium (251)	99 **Es** Einsteinium (252)	100 **Fm** Fermium (257)	101 **Md** Mendelevium (258)	102 **No** Nobelium (259)

Atomic number	17
Element symbol	Cl
Element name	Chlorine
Atomic mass	35.453

Figure 8 This box provides four pieces of information about the element chlorine: its symbol, its name, its atomic number, and its atomic mass.

Atomic Mass

There are four pieces of information for each element in Figure 7: the name of the element, its symbol, its atomic number and its atomic mass. **Atomic mass is a value that depends on the distribution of an element's isotopes in nature and the masses of those isotopes.** You will use atomic masses when you study chemical reactions in Chapter 7.

Atomic Mass Units The mass of an atom in grams is extremely small and not very useful because the samples of matter that scientists work with contain trillions of atoms. In order to have a convenient way to compare the masses of atoms, scientists chose one isotope to serve as a standard. Recall that each isotope of an element has a different number of neutrons in the nuclei of its atoms. So the atoms of two isotopes have different masses.

Scientists assigned 12 atomic mass units to the carbon-12 atom, which has 6 protons and 6 neutrons. An **atomic mass unit** (amu) is defined as one twelfth the mass of a carbon-12 atom.

Isotopes of Chlorine In nature, most elements exist as a mixture of two or more isotopes. Figure 8 shows that the element chlorine has the symbol Cl, atomic number 17, and an atomic mass of 35.453 atomic mass units. (The unit for atomic mass is not listed in the periodic table, but it is understood to be the amu.) Where does the number 35.453 come from? There are two natural isotopes of chlorine, chlorine-35 and chlorine-37. An atom of chlorine-35 has 17 protons and 18 neutrons. An atom of chlorine-37 has 17 protons and 20 neutrons. So the mass of an atom of chlorine-37 is greater than the mass of an atom of chlorine-35.

Weighted Averages Your teacher may use a weighted average to determine your grade. In a weighted average, some values are more important than other values. For example, test scores may count more heavily toward your final grade than grades on quizzes or grades on homework assignments.

Figure 9 lists the atomic masses for two naturally occurring chlorine isotopes. If you add the atomic masses of the isotopes and divide by 2, you get 35.967, not 35.453. The value of the atomic mass for chlorine in the periodic table is a weighted average. The isotope that occurs in nature about 75% of the time (chlorine-35) contributes three times as much to the average as the isotope that occurs in nature about 25% of the time (chlorine-37).

Distribution of Chlorine Isotopes in Nature		
Isotope	Percentage	Atomic Mass
Chlorine-35	75.78%	34.969
Chlorine-37	24.22%	36.966

Figure 9 This table shows the distribution and atomic masses for the two natural isotopes of chlorine. **Using Tables** *Which isotope occurs more often in nature?*

 Reading Checkpoint *What is an atomic mass unit?*

Classes of Elements

The periodic table in Figure 7 presents three different ways to classify elements. First, elements are classified as solids, liquids, or gases, based on their states at room temperature. The symbols for solids are black. The symbols for liquids are purple. The symbols for gases are red.

Second, elements are divided into those that occur naturally and those that do not. All but two elements with atomic numbers 1 through 92 occur on Earth. Elements with atomic numbers of 93 and higher do not occur naturally. The symbols for these elements are white. In Chapter 10, you will find out how elements that do not occur in nature are produced.

The third classification system puts elements into categories based on their general properties. ⬤ **Elements are classified as metals, nonmetals, and metalloids.** In the periodic table, metals are located on the left, nonmetals are on the right, and metalloids are in between.

Metals The majority of the elements on the periodic table are classified as metals. In Figure 7, they are represented by blue boxes. **Metals** are elements that are good conductors of electric current and heat. Except for mercury, metals are solids at room temperature. Most metals are malleable. Many metals are ductile; that is, they can be drawn into thin wires.

Some metals are extremely reactive and some do not react easily. One way to demonstrate this difference is to compare the behavior of gold and the behavior of magnesium when these metals are exposed to the oxygen in air. Gold remains shiny because it does not react with the oxygen. Magnesium reacts with the oxygen and quickly dulls. Figure 10A shows one magnesium coil that is dull and one that is shiny. Figure 10B shows one use for a metal with a shiny surface.

Quick Lab

Defining a Metal

Procedure

1. Use forceps to put a piece of magnesium into a test tube in a test tube rack. Using a graduated cylinder, add 5 mL of hydrochloric acid to the test tube.
   CAUTION *Wear plastic gloves because the acid can burn skin or clothing.* Record your observations.

2. Repeat Step 1 with sulfur, aluminum, and silicon.

Analyze and Conclude

1. **Classifying** Based on their locations in the periodic table, classify the four elements as metals, metalloids, or nonmetals.

2. **Comparing and Contrasting** Compare the behavior of the metals with the acid to the behavior of the other elements with the acid.

3. **Forming Operational Definitions** Use your observations to write a definition of a metal.

Figure 10 Magnesium and aluminum are typical metals. **A** When magnesium reacts with oxygen, a dull layer forms on its surface. The layer can be removed to reveal magnesium's shiny surface. **B** Many telescope mirrors are coated with aluminum to produce a surface that reflects light extremely well.

Figure 11 A compound of erbium (Er) and oxygen is used to tint glass pink.

The metals in groups 3 through 12 are called transition metals. **Transition metals** are elements that form a bridge between the elements on the left and right sides of the table. Transition elements, such as copper and silver, were among the first elements discovered. One property of many transition metals is their ability to form compounds with distinctive colors. The How It Works box on page 137 describes the use of transition elements in the production of colored glass.

Some transition elements have more properties in common than elements in other groups. This is especially true of elements in the lanthanide and actinide series. These elements are so similar that chemists in the 1800s had difficulty separating them when they were found mixed together in nature. A compound of erbium and oxygen was used to tint the lenses shown in Figure 11.

Nonmetals In Figure 7, nonmetals are represented by yellow boxes. As their name implies, nonmetals generally have properties opposite to those of metals. **Nonmetals** are elements that are poor conductors of heat and electric current. Because nonmetals have low boiling points, many nonmetals are gases at room temperature. In fact, all the gases in the periodic table are nonmetals. The nonmetals that are solids at room temperature tend to be brittle. If they are hit with a hammer, they shatter or crumble.

Nonmetals vary as much in their chemical properties as they do in their physical properties. Some nonmetals are extremely reactive, some hardly react at all, and some fall somewhere in between. Fluorine in Group 17 is the most reactive nonmetal. It even forms compounds with some gases in Group 18, which are the least reactive elements in the table. The toothpaste in Figure 12 contains a compound of the nonmetal fluorine and the metal sodium. This compound helps to protect your teeth against decay.

Figure 12 Toothpaste contains a compound that helps to protect teeth from tooth decay. The compound is formed from the nonmetal fluorine and the metal sodium.

Metalloids In the periodic table in Figure 7, metalloids are represented by green boxes. **Metalloids** are elements with properties that fall between those of metals and nonmetals. For example, metals are good conductors of electric current and nonmetals are poor conductors of electric current. A metalloid's ability to conduct electric current varies with temperature. Pure silicon (Si) and germanium (Ge) are good insulators at low temperatures and good conductors at high temperatures.

 Reading Checkpoint   *Which type of metals tend to form compounds with distinctive colors?*

Making Glass

For more than 4500 years, people have made glass from sand. The float-glass process shown below is used to make large sheets of glass for windows, while molds are used to make glass bottles. Interpreting Diagrams *How is air used in making glass bottles?*

Colored glass
Metallic elements are mixed with the raw ingredients to produce colored glass. Iron or chromium is added for green, copper or gold for red, and cobalt for blue.

Cullet (waste glass)

Lime (calcium oxide)

Sand (silicon dioxide)

Soda ash (sodium carbonate)

1 **Adding the raw ingredients** Sand, lime, and soda ash are poured into the furnace and heated to 1500°C (2730°F). Recycled waste glass, called cullet, is also added, to reduce the cost of raw materials.

2 **Heating in the furnace** The furnace heats the ingredients, producing liquid glass at 1100°C (2010°F). Rollers move the hot and molten glass to the next stage.

3 **Liquid glass** The glass is floated over a bath of melted tin. The glass emerges at 600°C (1110°F) as a continuous sheet with the same thickness throughout.

4 **Cooling the glass** The glass is cooled slowly in a temperature-controlled oven to keep it from cracking.

Furnace

Rollers

Melted tin *Floating the glass on liquid tin produces a glass surface that is as smooth as the surface of the liquid tin.*

Making bottles
Mass-produced glass bottles are made by adding hot glass to a mold and shaping the glass with air at high pressure.

Air pushes the glass to the bottom of the mold, where the neck of the bottle will form.

Hot glass is placed in the mold.

Mold sealed

Air tube

Oven

Air blown through the air tube forces the liquid glass to assume the shape of the bottle mold.

Glass cutter

5 **Cutting the glass** A diamond-tipped cutter is used to cut the cooled glass.

Sodium Magnesium Aluminum Silicon Phosphorus Sulfur Chlorine Argon

Figure 13 From left to right across Period 3, there are three metals (Na, Mg, and Al), one metalloid (Si), and four nonmetals (P, S, Cl, and Ar). Many light bulbs are filled with argon gas. **Observing** *Which other element in Period 3 is a gas?*

Variation Across a Period

The properties within a period change in a similar way from left to right across the table, except for Period 1. **Across a period from left to right, the elements become less metallic and more nonmetallic in their properties.** The most reactive metals are on the left side of the table. The most reactive nonmetals are on the right in Group 17. The Period 3 elements shown in Figure 13 provide an example of this trend.

There are three metals, a metalloid, and four nonmetals in Period 3. If you were unwise enough to hold a piece of sodium in your hand, it would react quickly and violently with the water on your moist skin. But magnesium will not react with water unless the water is hot. Aluminum does not react with water, but it does react with oxygen.

Silicon is the least reactive element in Period 3 (except for argon). Under ordinary conditions, phosphorus and sulfur do not react with water, but they do react with oxygen. They also react with chlorine, which is a highly reactive nonmetal. Chlorine must be handled with as much care as sodium. Argon hardly reacts at all.

Section 5.2 Assessment

Reviewing Concepts

1. What determines the order of the elements in the modern periodic table?

2. Describe the periodic law.

3. What two factors determine the atomic mass of an element?

4. Name three categories that are used to classify the elements in the periodic table.

5. What major change occurs as you move from left to right across the periodic table?

Critical Thinking

6. **Formulating Hypotheses** The atomic mass of iodine (I) is less than the atomic mass of tellurium (Te). But an iodine atom has one more proton than a tellurium atom. Explain how this situation is possible.

7. **Applying Concepts** Explain how you know that no new element with an atomic number less than 100 will be discovered.

8. **Comparing and Contrasting** Compare the reactions with water of the elements sodium and magnesium.

Writing in Science

Explanatory Paragraph The word *isotope* comes from the Greek words *isos,* meaning "equal," and *topos,* meaning "place." Write a paragraph explaining how the isotopes chlorine-35 and chlorine-37 occupy the same place in the periodic table.

5.3 Representative Groups

Reading Focus

Key Concepts

- Why do the elements in a group have similar properties?
- What are some properties of the A groups in the periodic table?

Vocabulary

- valence electron
- alkali metals
- alkaline earth metals
- halogens
- noble gases

Reading Strategy

Monitoring Your Understanding Copy the table below. As you read, record an important fact about each element listed.

Element	Important Fact
Magnesium	a._____?
Aluminum	b._____?
Chlorine	c._____?

Why is hydrogen located on the left side of the periodic table with the active metals? It is a nonmetal gas that seems to have more in common with the nonmetals in Group 17. Hydrogen's location is related to its electron configuration, not its properties.

Valence Electrons

Did you wonder why there are two numbering schemes on the periodic table in Figure 7? When the A groups are numbered from 1 through 8, they provide a useful reminder about the electron configurations of the elements in those groups. The number of an A group matches the number of valence electrons in an electron configuration for an element in that group. A **valence electron** is an electron that is in the highest occupied energy level of an atom. These electrons play a key role in chemical reactions. Properties vary across a period because the number of valence electrons increases from left to right.

Elements in a group have similar properties because they have the same number of valence electrons. These properties will not be identical because the valence electrons are in different energy levels. Valence electrons explain the location of hydrogen. Because hydrogen has a single valence electron, it is grouped with other elements, such as lithium, that have only one valence electron.

Figure 14 Because hydrogen is flammable, it can be used as a fuel in automobiles like this one. An engine that burns hydrogen has a key advantage over an engine that burns gasoline. Only water is produced when hydrogen burns.

139

Group 1A

| 3 |
| Li |
| Lithium |

| 11 |
| Na |
| Sodium |

| 19 |
| K |
| Potassium |

| 37 |
| Rb |
| Rubidium |

| 55 |
| Cs |
| Cesium |

| 87 |
| Fr |
| Francium |

Figure 15 The element sodium is an alkali metal **A** Unlike most metals, sodium is soft enough to cut with a knife. **B** When sodium reacts with water, enough energy is released to ignite the hydrogen that is produced. **Predicting** *What happens when potassium comes in contact with water?*

The Alkali Metals

The elements in Group 1A are called **alkali metals.** These metals have a single valence electron and are extremely reactive. Because they are so reactive, alkali metals are found in nature only in compounds. The most familiar of these compounds is table salt—a compound of sodium and chlorine (sodium chloride). Sodium chloride can be obtained through the evaporation of seawater or from large salt deposits on the surface of Earth or underground.

Not all the elements in a group are equally reactive. Sodium is more reactive than lithium, potassium is more reactive than sodium, and rubidium is more reactive than potassium. **The reactivity of alkali metals increases from the top of Group 1A to the bottom.**

Sodium is about as hard as cold butter and can be cut with a sharp knife, as shown in Figure 15A. Sodium melts at about 98°C and has a lower density than water. A piece of sodium may be able to float on water, but Figure 15B shows that it won't be there for long. The sodium reacts violently with water and releases enough energy to ignite the hydrogen gas that is produced. Sodium and potassium are stored under oil to keep them from reacting with the oxygen and water vapor in air. Cesium is so reactive that it reacts with water at temperatures as low as −115°C. Cesium is usually stored in a sealed glass tube containing argon gas.

Go Online
SCIENCE NEWS®

For: Articles on elements
Visit: PHSchool.com
Web Code: cce-1053

Reading Checkpoint

How many valence electrons does an alkali metal have?

The Alkaline Earth Metals

The elements in Group 2A are called **alkaline earth metals**. All alkaline earth metals have two valence electrons. Metals in Group 2A are harder than metals in Group 1A. The melting point of magnesium is 650°C, which is much higher than the melting point of sodium—98°C.

🔑 **Differences in reactivity among the alkaline earth metals are shown by the ways they react with water.** Calcium, strontium, and barium react easily with cold water. Magnesium will react with hot water, but no change appears to occur when beryllium is added to water. Magnesium and calcium have essential biological functions and they provide materials used in construction and transportation.

Magnesium Magnesium plays a key role in the process that uses sunlight to produce sugar in plants like the one in Figure 16. The compound at the center of this process is chlorophyll (KLAWR uh fil), and at the center of chlorophyll is magnesium. A mixture of magnesium and other metals can be as strong as steel, but much lighter. Reducing overall mass without sacrificing strength is an important consideration in transportation. The frames of bicycles and backpacks often contain magnesium.

Calcium Your body needs calcium to keep your bones and teeth strong. Calcium carbonate—a compound of calcium, carbon, and oxygen—is the main ingredient in chalk, limestone, coral, and the pearl in Figure 16. Your toothpaste may contain the compound calcium carbonate because this hard substance can polish your teeth. The plaster cast in Figure 16 contains calcium sulfate, which is a compound of calcium, sulfur, and oxygen.

Group 2A

4 **Be** Beryllium
12 **Mg** Magnesium
20 **Ca** Calcium
38 **Sr** Strontium
56 **Ba** Barium
88 **Ra** Radium

Figure 16 Chlorophyll molecules in spinach contain magnesium. An oyster shell and a pearl are both made from calcium carbonate. A plaster cast contains the compound calcium sulfate.

Spinach plant

Oyster shell with pearl

Plaster cast

The Boron Family

Group 3A contains the metalloid boron, the well-known metal aluminum, and three less familiar metals (gallium, indium, and thallium). All these elements have three valence electrons.

🔑 **Aluminum is the most abundant metal in Earth's crust.** It is often found combined with oxygen in a mineral called bauxite (BAWKS eyet). Aluminum is less reactive than sodium and magnesium. It is strong, lightweight, malleable, and a good conductor of electric current.

More than 10 percent of the aluminum produced is used as packaging. Some aluminum is used in window screens, window frames, and gutters. Parts of cars and airplanes are also made from aluminum. People are encouraged to recycle aluminum because the energy needed to purify recycled aluminum is only about 5 percent of the energy needed to extract aluminum from bauxite.

A compound of boron, silicon, and oxygen is used to make a type of glass that does not shatter easily when it undergoes a rapid change in temperature. Glass that contains boron is used to make laboratory glassware, such as the flasks in Figure 17. It is also used in cookware that can go directly from the oven to the refrigerator.

Figure 17 These students are using flasks made from glass that contains boron. This type of glass does not shatter as easily as glass without boron.

Group 3A

5 **B** Boron
13 **Al** Aluminum
31 **Ga** Gallium
49 **In** Indium
81 **Tl** Thallium

Group 4A

6 **C** Carbon
14 **Si** Silicon
32 **Ge** Germanium
50 **Sn** Tin
82 **Pb** Lead

Figure 18 The clay used to make this pottery contains compounds called silicates. These compounds always contain silicon and oxygen. They usually contain aluminum and often contain other elements such as iron.

The Carbon Family

Group 4A contains a nonmetal (carbon), two metalloids (silicon and germanium), and two metals (tin and lead). Each of these elements has four valence electrons. Notice that the metallic nature of the elements increases from top to bottom within the group. In keeping with this trend, germanium is a better conductor of electric current than silicon.

Life on Earth would not exist without carbon. 🔑 **Except for water, most of the compounds in your body contain carbon.** Reactions that occur in the cells of your body are controlled by carbon compounds. Carbon and its compounds are discussed in Chapter 9, Carbon Chemistry.

Silicon is the second most abundant element in Earth's crust. It is found as silicon dioxide in quartz rocks, sand, and glass. The clay used to produce the pottery in Figure 18 contains silicon compounds called silicates. Silicon carbide, a compound of silicon and carbon, is extremely hard. Saw blades tipped with silicon carbide last many times longer than ordinary steel blades.

 Reading Checkpoint *Which Group 3A element is a nonmetal?*

The Nitrogen Family

Group 5A contains two nonmetals (nitrogen and phosphorus), two metalloids (arsenic and antimony), and one metal (bismuth). Like the groups on either side of it, Group 5A includes elements with a wide range of physical properties. Nitrogen is a nonmetal gas, phosphorus is a solid nonmetal, and bismuth is a dense metal. Despite their differences, all the elements in Group 5A have five valence electrons. Nitrogen and phosphorus are the most important elements in Group 5A.

When air is cooled, the oxygen condenses before the nitrogen because nitrogen has a lower boiling point than oxygen. Much of the nitrogen obtained from air is used to produce fertilizers, like the three shown in Figure 19. ☞ **Besides nitrogen, fertilizers often contain phosphorus.** Your body uses compounds containing nitrogen and phosphorus to control reactions and release energy from food.

Phosphorus exists as an element in several forms with different properties. White phosphorus is so reactive that it bursts into flame when it is in contact with oxygen. Red phosphorus is less reactive and is used to make matches ignite.

Figure 19 The composition of a fertilizer varies with its intended use. The numbers on the bags of fertilizer are, from left to right, the relative amounts of nitrogen, phosphorus, and potassium.
Analyzing Data *Which type of fertilizer contains the most phosphorus?*

Group 5A
7 **N** Nitrogen
15 **P** Phosphorus
33 **As** Arsenic
51 **Sb** Antimony
83 **Bi** Bismuth

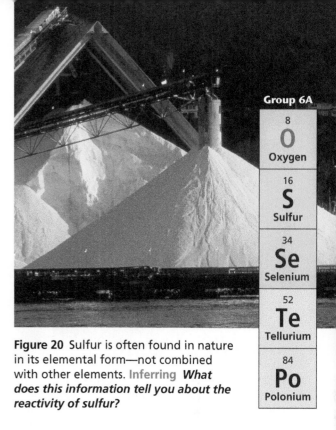

Figure 20 Sulfur is often found in nature in its elemental form—not combined with other elements. Inferring *What does this information tell you about the reactivity of sulfur?*

Group 6A
8 **O** Oxygen
16 **S** Sulfur
34 **Se** Selenium
52 **Te** Tellurium
84 **Po** Polonium

The Oxygen Family

Group 6A has three nonmetals (oxygen, sulfur, and selenium), and two metalloids (tellurium and polonium). All the elements in Group 6A have six valence electrons.

☞ **Oxygen is the most abundant element in Earth's crust.** Complex forms of life need oxygen to stay alive because oxygen is used to release the energy stored in food. Oxygen can be stored as a liquid under pressure in oxygen tanks. There must be no sparks or flames near an oxygen tank because materials that are flammable burn easily in pure oxygen.

Ozone is another form of the element oxygen. At ground level, ozone can irritate your eyes and lungs. At upper levels of the atmosphere, ozone absorbs harmful radiation emitted by the sun.

Sulfur was one of the first elements to be discovered because it is found in large natural deposits like the one in Figure 20. The main use of sulfur is in the production of sulfuric acid, a compound of sulfur, hydrogen, and oxygen. More sulfuric acid is produced in the United States than any other chemical. About 65 percent of the sulfuric acid produced is used to make fertilizers.

Group 7A

9	
F	
Fluorine	

17	
Cl	
Chlorine	

35	
Br	
Bromine	

53	
I	
Iodine	

85	
At	
Astatine	

Figure 21 At room temperature, chlorine is a gas, bromine is a liquid, and iodine is a solid. Halogens react easily with metals, such as the iron in steel wool. At a swimming pool, the chlorine content must be tested frequently. **Applying Concepts** *What process causes iodine vapor to collect in a flask of solid iodine?*

Chlorine reacting with steel wool

The Halogens

The elements in Group 7A are called **halogens.** Each halogen has seven valence electrons. Figure 21 shows the range of physical properties among the halogens. Fluorine and chlorine are gases, bromine is a liquid that evaporates quickly, and iodine is a solid that sublimes. **Despite their physical differences, the halogens have similar chemical properties.** They are highly reactive nonmetals, with fluorine being the most reactive and chlorine a close second. Halogens react easily with most metals. Figure 21 shows what happens when heated steel wool is plunged into chlorine.

Recall that a fluorine compound is used to prevent tooth decay. If you use pans with a nonstick coating to make omelets or muffins, you have seen another use of a fluorine compound. Have you ever noticed a sharp smell when adding bleach to a load of clothes? The smell comes from a small amount of chlorine gas that is released from a chlorine compound in the bleach. Chlorine is also used to kill bacteria in drinking water and swimming pools. The woman in Figure 21 is testing the level of chlorine in a swimming pool.

Your body needs iodine to keep your thyroid gland working properly. This gland controls the speed at which reactions occur in your body. Seafood is a good source of iodine. At a time when fresh fish was not available in all parts of the United States, people began to add iodine compounds to table salt. Salt that contains such compounds is called iodized salt.

The Noble Gases

The elements in Group 8A are called **noble gases.** Helium has two valence electrons. Each of the other noble gases has eight valence electrons. ⬭ **The noble gases are colorless and odorless and extremely unreactive.** In Chapter 6, you will study the relationship between the electron configurations of the noble gases and their low reactivity.

It is not easy to discover a colorless, odorless gas. It is even harder if the gas rarely reacts. Scientists discovered argon when they noticed that the density of nitrogen collected from air did not match the density of nitrogen formed during chemical changes. In time, the scientists figured out that the "impurity" in atmospheric nitrogen was an unknown element.

An element that does not react easily with other elements can be very useful. For example, during one stage in the process of making computer chips, pure silicon is heated in a furnace at 1480°C. At this temperature, silicon reacts with both oxygen and nitrogen. So the heating must take place in an argon atmosphere.

Some light bulbs are filled with argon because the glowing filament in the bulb will not react with argon as it would react with oxygen. Using argon increases the number of hours the bulb can be lit before it burns out. All the noble gases except radon are used in "neon" lights like those shown in Figure 22.

Group 8A

2 **He** Helium
10 **Ne** Neon
18 **Ar** Argon
36 **Kr** Krypton
54 **Xe** Xenon
86 **Rn** Radon

Figure 22 When electric current passes through noble gases, they emit different colors. Helium emits pink, neon emits orange-red, argon emits lavender, krypton emits white, and xenon emits blue.

Section 5.3 Assessment

Reviewing Concepts

1. ⬭ Explain why elements in a group have similar properties.

2. ⬭ What is the relationship between an alkali metal's location in Group 1A and its reactivity?

3. ⬭ What element exists in almost every compound in your body?

4. ⬭ Which Group 5A elements are found in fertilizer?

5. ⬭ Which group of elements is the least reactive?

6. Why is hydrogen located in a group with reactive metals?

7. What biological function requires magnesium?

8. Why is aluminum recycled?

9. What is the main use of sulfur?

10. Why is chlorine added to drinking water?

Critical Thinking

11. **Comparing and Contrasting** In which class of elements is there a greater range of properties, the metals or the nonmetals? Give an example to support your answer.

12. **Making Generalizations** What happens to the reactivity of nonmetals within a group from the top of the group to the bottom?

Connecting ⊂ Concepts

Using Physical Properties In Section 2.2, three ways to use physical properties are discussed. Find one example in Section 5.3 that illustrates each use. If necessary, reread pages 48 and 50.

Elemental Friends and Foes

Some elements are essential for your health, and some are extremely harmful. You need to obtain the right amounts of the twenty-five essential elements through a balanced diet, and to reduce your exposure to the harmful elements.

Eating a variety of foods helps to ensure that all the elements needed by your body are available. The required elements can be classified as major, lesser, or trace elements. An element is classified based on its percentage by mass in the body.

The six major elements are hydrogen, oxygen, carbon, nitrogen, phosphorus, and calcium. These six major elements account for almost 99 percent of your body mass. Nearly every compound in your body contains carbon and hydrogen, and many contain oxygen too. The compounds that control all the chemical changes that take place in cells contain nitrogen. Calcium is essential for healthy bones and teeth. Phosphorus is found in your DNA and in the molecules that transfer energy within cells.

The lesser elements are iron, potassium, zinc, sodium, sulfur, chlorine, and magnesium. For each lesser element, there is a recommended amount that needs to be taken in daily. These amounts vary from 15 milligrams for zinc to 400 milligrams for magnesium. Lesser elements help your body build tissues and maintain other cell processes. For example, nerves and muscles require magnesium to function properly.

The trace elements are vanadium, chromium, molybdenum, manganese, cobalt, copper, boron, tin, silicon, selenium, fluorine, and iodine. The quantities required are tiny, but trace elements perform important functions. For example, red blood cells would not mature without cobalt.

Essential Elements of the Human Body

- Major elements (approximately 98.6 percent of total)
- Lesser elements (approximately 1.4 percent of total)
- Trace elements (less than 0.01 percent of total)
- Nonessential elements

Essential elements

The 25 elements essential to the human body are generally ingested as part of compounds found in food. The roles and functions of a few of these elements are shown here.

Oxygen
This is the most abundant element in your body. The most important function of oxygen is to help release the energy stored in foods. You absorb oxygen from the air you breathe.

Carbon
Carbon is the second most common element in the human body. It is essential to life, because it is present in almost every compound in the body. If a food contains carbohydrates, proteins, or fats, it contains carbon compounds.

PASTA

Hydrogen
Hydrogen is found in foods and in water, which accounts for more than 60 percent of body mass. Chemical reactions in cells take place in water.

WATER

Iron
Iron is a very important trace element because it is part of hemoglobin. This compound transports oxygen through the blood to every cell in the body. Meat, fish, and leafy green vegetables, such as spinach, are good sources of iron.

SPINACH

Iodine
Iodine is required in small amounts for the production of thyroxine by the thyroid gland. Thyroxine controls the rate of all chemical processes in the body. Fresh fish is a good source of iodine.

RED SNAPPER

GRAPES

Vanadium
Vanadium can help control blood sugar levels. It also plays an important role in the formation of bones and teeth. Vanadium can be found in black peppercorns.

BLACK PEPPERCORNS

Potassium
Potassium is essential to muscle and nerve function, and helps keep the body's fluids in balance. It also stimulates the kidneys to remove body wastes. Potassium can be found in fruit and dairy products.

CHEESES

Harmful Elements

Some elements should be avoided completely. These foes include metals, such as lead and mercury, and the metalloid arsenic. Harmful elements may enter the body in water, air, or food. Inside the body, nonessential elements may compete with essential elements and disrupt cell functions. Large amounts of harmful elements can stress the body's normal methods for eliminating toxins. Harmful elements can build up in body tissues.

For decades lead was used in paint and in gasoline to improve engine performance. These products are now lead free. The use of mercury in thermometers has been reduced and arsenic compounds are no longer used in pesticides.

Many trace elements are only helpful if ingested in the small recommended amounts. Larger quantities of most trace elements can be harmful, as can larger-than-required amounts of lesser elements, such as sodium.

82 Pb Lead

Lead
Too much lead in the bloodstream can lead to organ damage and learning difficulties, especially in young children. For this reason, the use of lead-based paint was banned in 1978. Children may still be a risk if they live in an older house with layers of peeling paint.

80 Hg Mercury

Mercury
Mercury is used in numerous industrial processes, but it is toxic and can damage the brain and nervous system. For this reason it should be handled with great care. It is particularly important to avoid inhaling mercury vapor.

33 As Arsenic

Arsenic
Arsenic has been known as a poison for centuries, yet compounds of arsenic were used to treat some diseases before the discovery of penicillin. Arsenic compounds are no longer used to protect crops from insect pests or to preserve wood. Drinking water can absorb arsenic as it flows over rocks. But the amount of arsenic in drinking water is limited by law to less than 50 micrograms in each liter of water.

Arsenic pesticide

BEEF

TABLE SALT

Too much of a good thing

Many of the elements found in your body are needed in only very small amounts. Too much can often be harmful. The Food and Drug Administration provides guidelines on the safe daily quantities to take through food or supplements.

Zinc This trace element can be found in almost every cell of your body. Among other things, it helps to support a healthy immune system. Beef is a good source of zinc, but no more than 40 milligrams of zinc should be taken daily. Too much zinc can cause anemia by reducing iron uptake.

Sodium It is hard to avoid sodium in your diet because table salt contains a sodium compound (sodium chloride). Everybody needs some sodium each day to maintain water balance and nerve function. But too much sodium (more than 3 grams daily) can cause high blood pressure.

Selenium This trace element helps to maintain a healthy immune system. Brazil nuts are a good source of selenium, as are fruits and vegetables. While selenium supplements may be useful for some people, no more than 400 micrograms should be taken daily. Too much selenium can cause nerve damage.

BRAZIL NUTS

Going Further

- Choose a trace element other than vanadium, selenium, or iodine. Find out which foods are good sources of the element. Write a paragraph explaining how your diet meets or could be adjusted to meet your need for this element.

- Take a Discovery Channel Video Field Trip by watching "You Are What You Eat."

Predicting the Density of an Element

Density is a useful property for identifying and classifying elements. In this lab, you will determine the densities of three elements in Group 4A—silicon, tin, and lead. Then you will use your data to predict the density of another element in Group 4A—germanium.

Problem Can the densities of elements within a group be used to help predict the density of another element in the group?

Materials

- unlined white paper
- scissors
- metric ruler
- balance
- forceps
- silicon
- tin
- lead shot
- 50-mL graduated cylinder
- graph paper
- periodic table

 For the probeware version of this lab, see the Probeware Lab Manual, Lab 2.

Skills Measuring, Observing, Using Graphs, Calculating

Procedure

Part A: Measuring Mass

1. On a sheet of paper, make a copy of the data table shown.
2. Cut out three 10-cm × 10-cm pieces of paper from a sheet of unlined white paper. Label one piece of paper Silicon, the second Tin, and the third Lead. Find the mass of each piece of paper and record it in your data table.

3. Using forceps, place the silicon onto the paper labeled Silicon, as shown. Find the mass of the silicon and the paper. Record this mass in your data table. Then, subtract the mass of the paper from the mass of the silicon and paper. Record the mass of silicon in your data table. Set the paper containing the silicon aside for now.

4. Repeat Step 3 to find the masses of tin and lead.

Part B: Measuring Volume

5. Place 25 mL of water in the graduated cylinder. Measure the volume of the water to the nearest 0.1 mL. Record the volume (in cm^3) in your data table. (*Hint:* 1 mL = 1 cm^3)

6. Tilt the graduated cylinder and carefully pour the silicon from the paper into the graduated cylinder, as shown on page 151. Make sure that the silicon is completely covered by the water. Measure and record the volume of the water and silicon in your data table. Then, subtract the volume of water from the volume of the water and silicon. Record the result in your data table.

7. Repeat Steps 5 and 6 to find the volumes of tin and lead.

Data Table							
Element	Mass of Paper (g)	Mass of Paper and Element (g)	Mass of Element (g)	Volume of Water (cm^3)	Volume of Water and Element (cm^3)	Volume of Element (cm^3)	Density of Element (g/cm^3)
Silicon							
Tin							
Lead							

Part C: Calculating Density

8. To calculate the density of silicon, divide its mass by its volume.

$$\text{Density} = \frac{\text{Mass}}{\text{Volume}}$$

Record the density of silicon in your data table.

9. Repeat Step 8 to find the densities of tin and lead.

10. Make a line graph that shows the relationship between the densities of silicon, tin, and lead and the periods in which they are located in the periodic table. Place the number of the period (from 1 to 7) on the horizontal axis and the density (in g/cm^3) on the vertical axis. Draw a straight line that comes as close as possible to all three points.

11. Germanium is in Period 4. To estimate the density of germanium, draw a dotted vertical line from the 4 on the horizontal axis to the solid line. Then, draw a dotted horizontal line from the solid line to the vertical axis. Read and record the density of germanium.

12. Wash your hands with warm water and soap before you leave the laboratory.

Analyze and Conclude

1. **Classifying** List lead, silicon, and tin in order of increasing density.

2. **Comparing and Contrasting** How does your estimate of the density of germanium compare with the actual density of germanium, which is 5.3 g/cm^3?

3. **Calculating** Use the formula for percent error (PE) to calculate a percent error for your estimate of the density of germanium.

$$PE = \frac{\text{Estimated value} - \text{Accepted value}}{\text{Accepted value}} \times 100$$

4. **Drawing Conclusions** How does the density of the elements change from silicon to lead in Group 4A?

Go Further Use reference books or sites on the Internet to research properties of Group 4A elements. Construct a graph that shows how another property, such as melting point or boiling point, varies among the Group 4A elements you explored. Determine whether knowing the values for three of the elements would allow you to accurately predict a value for the fourth element.

5.1 Organizing the Elements

Key Concepts

- Mendeleev arranged the elements into rows in order of increasing mass so that elements with similar properties were in the same column.
- The close match between Mendeleev's predictions and the actual properties of new elements showed how useful his periodic table could be.

Vocabulary

periodic table, *p. 127*

5.2 The Modern Periodic Table

Key Concepts

- In the modern periodic table, elements are arranged by increasing atomic number (number of protons). Each row on the table is a period. Each column is a group.
- Properties of elements repeat in a predictable way when atomic numbers are used to arrange elements into groups.
- Atomic mass is a value that depends on the distribution of an element's isotopes in nature and the masses of those isotopes.
- Elements are classified as metals, nonmetals, and metalloids. Metals are elements that are good conductors of electric current and heat. Nonmetals are poor conductors of electric current and heat. Metalloids are elements with properties that fall between those of metals and nonmetals.
- Across a period from left to right, the elements become less metallic and more nonmetallic in their properties.

Vocabulary

period, *p. 131*

group, *p. 131*

periodic law, *p. 131*

atomic mass unit (amu), *p. 134*

metals, *p. 135*

transition metals, *p. 136*

nonmetals, *p. 136*

metalloids, *p. 136*

5.3 Representative Groups

Key Concepts

- Elements in a group have similar properties because they have the same number of valence electrons.
- The alkali earth metals in Group 1A are extremely reactive. The reactivity of these metals increases from the top of the group to the bottom.
- Differences in reactivity among the alkaline earth metals in Group 2A are shown by the ways they react with water.
- Group 3A contains the most abundant metal in Earth's crust—aluminum. The energy needed to recycle aluminum is 5 percent of the energy needed to extract aluminum from bauxite.
- Group 4A contains the nonmetal carbon. Most compounds in your body contain carbon. Carbon compounds control reactions that occur in cells.
- Fertilizers usually contain the Group 5A elements nitrogen and phosphorus.
- Oxygen, in Group 6A, is the most abundant element in Earth's crust.
- Despite their physical differences, the halogens in Group 7A are all highly reactive nonmetals.
- The noble gases, in Group 8A, are colorless and odorless and extremely unreactive.

Vocabulary

valence electron, *p. 139*

alkali metals, *p. 140*

alkaline earth metals, *p. 141*

halogens, *p. 144*

noble gases, *p. 145*

Thinking Visually

Web Diagram Use information from the chapter to complete the web diagram below. The web relates states of matter at room temperature to categories of elements.

Reviewing Content

Choose the letter that best answers the question or completes the statement.

1. Mendeleev arranged the elements in his periodic table in order of
   a. atomic number.   **b.** number of electrons.
   c. mass.   **d.** number of neutrons.

2. Mendeleev's decision to leave gaps in his periodic table was supported by the discovery of
   a. electrons.   **b.** protons.
   c. argon.   **d.** gallium.

3. In a modern periodic table, elements are arranged in order of
   a. atomic number.   **b.** number of isotopes.
   c. atomic mass.   **d.** number of neutrons.

4. How many periods does the periodic table have?
   a. 18   **b.** 7
   c. 9   **d.** 8

5. An atomic mass unit is
   a. one twelfth the mass of a carbon-12 atom.
   b. the mass of a carbon-12 atom.
   c. the mass of a neutron.
   d. the mass of a proton.

6. An element that is shiny and conducts electric current is likely to be a
   a. gas.   **b.** metal.
   c. metalloid.   **d.** nonmetal.

7. Copper is an example of
   a. an alkali metal.   **b.** an alkaline earth metal.
   c. a nonmetal.   **d.** a transition metal.

8. Elements that have the same number of valence electrons are
   a. in the same period.
   b. in the same group.
   c. called noble gases.
   d. called transition metals.

9. The most reactive metals are the
   a. transition metals.   **b.** alkaline earth metals.
   c. alkali metals.   **d.** metalloids.

10. Which elements are all gases at room temperature?
   a. Group 1A   **b.** Period 3
   c. Group 7A   **d.** Group 8A

Understanding Concepts

11. What information did Mendeleev have about the elements he organized into a periodic table?

12. How did Mendeleev know where to leave the spaces in his table?

13. Why is the table of the elements shown in Figure 7 called a periodic table?

14. Why does the number of elements vary from period to period?

15. Explain how the atomic mass of an element is affected by the distribution of its isotopes in nature.

16. List three ways that the elements in the periodic table can be classified.

17. In general, what happens to the reactivity of elements in groups labeled A as atomic numbers increase across a period?

18. Why don't the elements within an A group in the periodic table have identical properties?

19. Why was it difficult to discover the noble gases?

Use this portion of the periodic table to answer Questions 20–23.

14	15	16	17
Si	**P**	**S**	**Cl**
Silicon	Phosphorus	Sulfur	Chlorine
28.086	30.974	32.06	35.453
32	33	34	35
Ge	**As**	**Se**	**Br**
Germanium	Arsenic	Selenium	Bromine
72.59	74.922	78.96	79.904

20. How many of the elements shown are metals? How many are nonmetals? How many are metalloids?

21. Which element is a liquid at room temperature and which is a gas at room temperature?

22. Which of the two halogens shown is more reactive? Give a reason for your answer.

23. Does selenium have more in common with sulfur or bromine? Explain your answer.

Critical Thinking

24. Classifying If you know that an element is a solid at room temperature, do you have enough data to classify the element as a metal, metalloid, or nonmetal? If you know that the element is a gas at room temperature, do you have enough data? Explain your answers.

25. Applying Concepts An element on the periodic table has two naturally occurring isotopes. One isotope has an atomic mass of about 10 amu. The other isotope has an atomic mass of about 11 amu. What is the name of this element?

26. Predicting How many valence electrons would an element with atomic number 113 have?

27. Applying Concepts Why are samples of the alkali metal cesium usually stored in argon gas?

28. Applying Concepts Why are halogens found in nature only in compounds?

29. Applying Concepts Which element on the periodic table has chemical properties that are most similar to those of carbon?

30. Designing Experiments If you were trying to make a compound of the noble gas xenon, would you use nitrogen or fluorine? Explain your choice.

Use the table to answer Questions 31–33.

Properties of Elements X, Y, and Z			
Element	Melting Point	Boiling Point	Valence Electrons
X	97.80°C	883°C	1
Y	−259.34°C	−252.87°C	1
Z	−101.5°C	−34.04°C	7

31. Analyzing Data In general, where would you find Elements X, Y, and Z on the periodic table?

32. Classifying Describe the state of each element at room temperature based on its melting and boiling points.

33. Drawing Conclusions Use your answers to Questions 31 and 32 to identify element Y. Explain your reasoning.

Concepts in Action

34. Predicting What might happen to a heated beaker made from glass that does not contain boron if the beaker were placed in a pan of ice water?

35. Inferring Based on the content of most fertilizers, name two elements other than carbon that are found in compounds in plants.

36. Making Generalizations Explain how the amount of a trace element an organism is exposed to affects the element's ability to help or harm an organism. Use the example of selenium. (*Hint:* Refer to the discussion on page 149.)

37. Problem Solving Sometimes old books fall apart when they are stored in air. Use what you know about the reactivity of elements to propose a way that old books could be kept from falling apart.

38. Using Analogies Explain how a calendar is similar to a periodic table and how it is different.

39. Relating Cause and Effect When corn plants have yellow leaves, it is a sign that the plants lack an essential element. Which element must be added to the soil to produce leaves with a healthy green color?

40. Writing in Science You write for a newsletter that has a feature called Element of the Month. It is your turn to write the feature. Pick an element that you think is worthy of attention. Write a brief essay and suggest a photo to be used with your feature.

Performance-Based Assessment

Design Your Own Periodic Table Make a version of the periodic table that presents the information provided in Figure 7 in a different, but useful, way.

For: Self-grading assessment
Visit: PHSchool.com
Web Code: cca-1050

Standardized Test Prep

Test-Taking Tip

Narrowing the Choices
If after reading all the answer choices you are not sure which one is correct, eliminate those answers that you know are wrong. In the question below, first eliminate the answers that require a whole number. Then focus on the remaining choices.

| 6 |
| C |
| Carbon |
| 12.011 |

The number 12.011 is the

(A) atomic number for carbon.
(B) mass number for carbon.
(C) atomic mass of carbon-12.
(D) average atomic mass of carbon.
(E) percentage of carbon-12 in nature.

(Answer: D)

Choose the letter that best answers the question or completes the statement.

1. Which elements are as reactive as alkali metals?
   (A) alkaline earth metals
   (B) halogens
   (C) noble gases
   (D) transition metals
   (E) metalloids

2. How many valence electrons do atoms of oxygen and sulfur have?
   (A) 2
   (B) 4
   (C) 6
   (D) 8
   (E) 10

3. Moving across a period from left to right,
   (A) elements become less metallic.
   (B) elements become more metallic.
   (C) elements become more reactive.
   (D) elements become less reactive.
   (E) elements have fewer valence electrons.

4. Which statement *best* describes nonmetals?
   (A) Nonmetals are good conductors of heat and electric current.
   (B) Nonmetals are brittle solids.
   (C) Many general properties of nonmetals are opposite to those of metals.
   (D) Nonmetals are located on the left side of the periodic table.
   (E) All nonmetals are extremely reactive.

Use this portion of the periodic table to answer Questions 5–7.

13	14	15
Al	**Si**	**P**
Aluminum	Silicon	Phosphorus
26.982	28.086	30.974
31	32	33
Ga	**Ge**	**As**
Gallium	Germanium	Arsenic
69.72	72.59	74.922

5. Which list of elements contains only metalloids?
   (A) aluminum and gallium
   (B) silicon and germanium
   (C) phosphorus and arsenic
   (D) aluminum, silicon, and phosphorus
   (E) gallium, germanium, and arsenic

6. Which elements did Mendeleev leave spaces for in his first periodic table?
   (A) aluminum and phosphorus
   (B) aluminum and germanium
   (C) silicon and arsenic
   (D) gallium and germanium
   (E) gallium and aluminum

7. Which of the elements are among the most abundant in Earth's crust?
   (A) silicon and phosphorus
   (B) aluminum and phosphorus
   (C) phosphorus and arsenic
   (D) gallium and arsenic
   (E) aluminum and silicon

6 Chemical Bonds

The calcium carbonate in shells and the silicon dioxide in sand are examples of compounds with different types of bonds.

21st Century Learning
Self Direction

How can compounds be shown with electron dot diagrams?

Elements that do not have complete sets of valence electrons tend to react. In certain cases, the reaction involves the transfer of electrons between atoms. You can describe this process by using electron dot diagrams. Use the animation tools in presentation software to illustrate the formation of two different ionic compounds. Each animation should show how the transfer of one or more electrons between atoms results in the formation of the compound.

How do science concepts apply to your world? Here are some questions you'll be able to answer after you read this chapter.

- **Why is titanium metal welded in an argon atmosphere?** *(Section 6.1)*

- **What causes a crystal of rock salt to shatter when it is struck?** *(Section 6.1)*

- **Why is water a liquid while carbon dioxide is a gas at room temperature?** *(Section 6.2)*

- **What advantage does jewelry made from a gold silver alloy have over jewelry made from pure gold?** *(Section 6.4)*

- **How does mixing other elements with silicon make silicon a better conductor of electric current?** *(page 182)*

Chapter Preview

DISCOVERY
CHANNEL
SCHOOL

Video Field Trip

Good Conduct

Inquiry > Activity

What Can the Shape of a Material Tell You About the Material?

Procedure

1. Use a wood splint or small lab spatula to place a small sample of table salt on a sheet of black construction paper.

2. Use a hand lens to examine the sample. On a separate sheet of paper, sketch the shapes of some pieces in the sample.

3. Repeat Steps 1 and 2 with each of the compounds your teacher provides.

Think About It

1. **Observing** Compare the shapes of the pieces in the different compounds.

2. **Predicting** Could any differences you observed be used to identify a compound? Explain your answer.

3. **Formulating Hypotheses** What could be happening at the atomic level in compounds to produce the different shapes you observed?

6.1 Ionic Bonding

Reading Focus

Key Concepts

- When is an atom unlikely to react?
- What is one way in which elements can achieve stable electron configurations?
- How does the structure of an ionic compound affect its properties?

Vocabulary

- electron dot diagram
- ion
- anion
- cation
- chemical bond
- ionic bond
- chemical formula
- crystals

Reading Strategy

Sequencing Copy the concept map. As you read, complete the concept map to show what happens to atoms during ionic bonding.

Figure 1 The handle and body of this titanium mug were welded together in an argon atmosphere. If titanium is allowed to react with oxygen in air, the compound that forms makes the weld more brittle and more likely to break.

The handle of the titanium mug in Figure 1 was joined to the body by welding. The pieces were heated until their surfaces fused together. The welding of titanium does not take place in air. At the temperature at which welding occurs, titanium becomes hot enough to react with oxygen in the air, forming an oxide. The oxide makes the weld more brittle and likely to break. Because titanium does not react with a noble gas such as argon, the welding of titanium usually takes place in an argon atmosphere.

Argon's name is a reminder of its inactivity. It comes from the Greek word *argos*, which means "idle" or "inert." Why is argon very inactive yet oxygen is highly reactive? Chemical properties, such as reactivity, depend on an element's electron configuration.

Stable Electron Configurations

The highest occupied energy level of a noble gas atom is filled. **When the highest occupied energy level of an atom is filled with electrons, the atom is stable and not likely to react.** The noble gases have stable electron configurations with eight valence electrons (or two in the case of helium).

The chemical properties of an element depend on the number of valence electrons. Therefore, it is useful to have a model of atoms that focuses only on valence electrons. The models in Figure 2 are electron dot diagrams. An **electron dot diagram** is a model of an atom in which each dot represents a valence electron. The symbol in the center represents the nucleus and all the other electrons in the atom.

Electron Dot Diagrams for Some Group A Elements

Group							
1A	2A	3A	4A	5A	6A	7A	8A
H·							He:
Li·	·Be·	·B·	·C·	·N·	:O·	:F·	:Ne:
Na·	·Mg·	·Al·	·Si·	·P·	:S·	:Cl·	:Ar:
K·	·Ca·	·Ga·	·Ge·	·As·	:Se·	:Br·	:Kr:

Figure 2 In an electron dot diagram, each dot represents a valence electron. *Observing How many valence electrons do sodium and chlorine have?*

Ionic Bonds

Elements that do not have complete sets of valence electrons tend to react. By reacting, they achieve electron configurations similar to those of noble gases. ◯ **Some elements achieve stable electron configurations through the transfer of electrons between atoms.**

Transfer of Electrons Look at the electron dot diagram for chlorine in Figure 2. A chlorine atom has one electron fewer than an argon atom. If the chlorine atom were to gain a valence electron, it would have the same stable electron arrangement as argon. Look at the electron dot diagram for sodium. A sodium atom has one more electron than a neon atom. If a sodium atom were to lose this electron, its highest occupied energy level would have eight electrons. It would then have the same stable electron arrangement as neon.

What happens at the atomic level when sodium reacts with chlorine? An electron is transferred from each sodium atom to a chlorine atom. Each atom ends up with a more stable electron arrangement than it had before the transfer.

$$\text{Na·} + \text{·Cl:} \longrightarrow \text{Na}^+ \ \text{:Cl:}^-$$

Formation of Ions When an atom gains or loses an electron, the number of protons is no longer equal to the number of electrons. The charge on the atom is not balanced and the atom is not neutral. An atom that has a net positive or negative electric charge is called an **ion.** The charge on an ion is represented by a plus or a minus sign. Notice the plus sign next to the symbol for sodium and the minus sign next to the symbol for chlorine.

Go Online
NSTA SciLINKS

For: Links on ionic bonds
Visit: www.SciLinks.org
Web Code: ccn-1061

What Determines the Size of an Atom or Ion?

Scientists use atomic radii to compare the sizes of atoms of different elements. Remember from mathematics that the radius of a sphere is the distance from the center of the sphere to its outer edge. The radius is half the diameter of the sphere. Because atomic radii are extremely small, these distances are expressed in units called picometers (pm). As a comparison, there are one billion (10^9) picometers in a millimeter.

The table shows the atomic radius and ionic radius for six metals and six nonmetals. You will use the data to relate the size of an element's atoms to the element's location on the periodic table. You also will use the data to compare the sizes of atoms and their ions.

1. **Using Tables** Within a period, what happens to the atomic radius as the atomic number of the elements increases?

2. **Using Tables** Within Groups 1A, 2A, 6A, and 7A, what happens to the atomic radius of elements as the atomic number increases?

Atomic and Ionic Radii

1A	2A	6A	7A
Li 152 / 1+ 60	Be 112 / 2+ 31	O 66 / 2− 140	F 64 / 1− 136
Na 186 / 1+ 95	Mg 160 / 2+ 65	S 103 / 2− 184	Cl 99 / 1− 181
K 227 / 1+ 133	Ca 197 / 2+ 99	Se 117 / 2− 198	Br 114 / 1− 195

Atomic radius

Ionic radius

3. **Inferring** How does adding an occupied energy level affect the atomic radius? (*Hint:* Lithium is a Period 2 element and sodium is a Period 3 element.)

4. **Comparing and Contrasting** Compare the atomic and ionic radii for potassium (K), and for bromine (Br).

5. **Making Generalizations** What happens to the radius of an atom when the atom loses electrons? When the atom gains electrons?

6. **Relating Cause and Effect** Explain the difference in size between a metal atom and its cation.

The ion that forms when a chlorine atom gains an electron has 17 protons and 18 electrons. This ion has a charge of 1− because it has one extra electron. The symbol for the ion is written Cl^{1-}, or Cl^- for short. An ion with a negative charge is an **anion** (AN eye un). Anions like the Cl^- ion are named by using part of the element name plus the suffix *–ide*. Thus, Cl^- is called a *chloride* ion.

A sodium ion has 11 protons and 10 electrons. Because it has one extra proton, the sodium ion has a charge of 1+. The symbol for the ion is written Na^{1+}, or Na^+ for short. An ion with a positive charge is a **cation** (KAT eye un). Naming a cation is easy. You just use the element name, as in the *sodium* ion.

Formation of Ionic Bonds Remember that a particle with a negative charge will attract a particle with a positive charge. When an anion and a cation are close together, a chemical bond forms between them. A **chemical bond** is the force that holds atoms or ions together as a unit. An **ionic bond** is the force that holds cations and anions together. An ionic bond forms when electrons are transferred from one atom to another.

Ionization Energy An electron can move to a higher energy level when an atom absorbs energy. Cations form when electrons gain enough energy to escape from atoms. The energy allows electrons to overcome the attraction of the protons in the nucleus. The amount of energy used to remove an electron is called ionization energy. It varies from element to element. The lower the ionization energy, the easier it is to remove an electron from an atom.

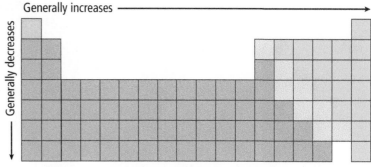

Generally increases ⟶

Generally decreases

Trends in Ionization Energy

Figure 3 shows two trends for ionization energy. Ionization energies tend to increase from left to right across a period. It takes more energy to remove an electron from a nonmetal than from a metal in the same period. Ionization energies tend to decrease from the top of a group to the bottom. In Group 1A, potassium has a lower ionization energy than sodium. So it is easier to remove an electron from potassium than from sodium, and potassium is more reactive than sodium.

Figure 3 Ionization energies generally increase from left to right across a period.
Interpreting Diagrams *What is the trend for ionization energy within a group?*

Reading Checkpoint *What is ionization energy?*

Ionic Compounds

Compounds that contain ionic bonds are ionic compounds, which can be represented by chemical formulas. A **chemical formula** is a notation that shows what elements a compound contains and the ratio of the atoms or ions of these elements in the compound. The chemical formula for sodium chloride is NaCl. From the formula, you can tell that there is one sodium ion for each chloride ion in sodium chloride.

Based on the diagram in Figure 4, what would the formula for magnesium chloride be? A magnesium atom cannot reach a stable electron configuration by reacting with just one chlorine atom. It must transfer electrons to two chlorine atoms. After the transfer, the charge on the magnesium ion is 2+ and its symbol is Mg^{2+}. The formula for the compound is $MgCl_2$. The 2 written to the right and slightly below the symbol for chlorine is a subscript. Subscripts are used to show the relative numbers of atoms of the elements present. If there is only one atom of an element in the formula, no subscript is needed.

Figure 4 Magnesium chloride forms when magnesium atoms transfer electrons to chlorine atoms. Magnesium chloride is used to control dust that is stirred up by traffic on unpaved roads.

$$Mg + \underset{\cdot\cdot}{\overset{\cdot\cdot}{Cl}} \cdot \cdot \longrightarrow Mg^{2+} \quad \underset{\cdot\cdot}{\overset{\cdot\cdot}{Cl}} \colon^{-} \quad \underset{\cdot\cdot}{\overset{\cdot\cdot}{Cl}} \colon^{-}$$

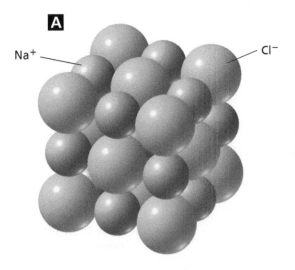

A

Na⁺

Cl⁻

Figure 5 The structure and shape of a crystal are related. **A** In a sodium chloride crystal, each ion is surrounded by six oppositely charged ions. **B** Sodium chloride crystals are shaped like cubes.

B

Crystal Lattices A chemical formula for an ionic compound tells you the ratio of the ions in the compound. But it does not tell you how the ions are arranged in the compound. If you looked at a sample of sodium chloride with a hand lens or microscope, you would be able to see that the pieces of salt are shaped like cubes. This shape is a clue to how the sodium and chloride ions are arranged in the compound.

Figure 5A shows that the ions in sodium chloride are arranged in an orderly, three-dimensional structure. Each chloride ion is surrounded by six sodium ions and each sodium ion is surrounded by six chloride ions. Each ion is attracted to all the neighboring ions with an opposite charge. This set of attractions keeps the ions in fixed positions in a rigid framework, or lattice. The repeating pattern of ions in the lattice is like the repeating pattern of designs on the wallpaper in Figure 6.

Solids whose particles are arranged in a lattice structure are called **crystals.** Compare the cubic shape of the sodium chloride crystals in Figure 5B to the arrangement of ions in Figure 5A. The shape of an ionic crystal depends on the arrangement of ions in its lattice. In turn, the arrangement of the ions depends on the ratio of ions and their relative sizes. Crystals are classified into groups based on the shape of their crystals. Crystals of ruby have a six-sided, hexagonal shape. The How It Works box on page 163 describes one way to make rubies.

Reading Checkpoint *What shape are sodium chloride crystals?*

Figure 6 This wallpaper displays a repeating pattern of flower and fruit designs. **Using Analogies** *How is this arrangement of designs similar to the arrangement of ions in a crystal?*

Synthetic Rubies

Rubies are mainly aluminum oxide, which is white. The substitution of a small percentage of chromium ions for aluminum ions gives rubies their distinctive red color. Because natural rubies are rare, rubies are often manufactured. **Interpreting Diagrams** *What substances are in the mixture used to make rubies?*

SYNTHETIC RUBY BOULE

HEXAGONAL CRYSTAL STRUCTURE

NATURAL RUBY

Synthetic ruby
A synthetic ruby boule has a hexagonal crystal structure identical to the natural ruby gemstone. Its shape is determined by the arrangement of ions in the crystal.

Making synthetic rubies
One way of making synthetic rubies is called the pulled-growth method. It was invented by Polish scientist Jan Czochralski (1885–1953).

Aluminum and chromium oxides

Seed crystal

Heater

Crucible

Rotating rod

Melt

Ruby forming

Furnace vessel

Ruby boule

1 **Seed crystal** Aluminum oxide and chromium(VI) oxide are melted. A tiny piece of ruby, called a seed crystal, is attached to a rod and placed above the molten mixture (melt).

2 **Lowering into the melt** The rod is lowered until the seed crystal touches the melt. The rod is slowly lifted, and ions in the melt begin to attach themselves to the seed crystal to form a ruby.

3 **Forming a boule** As the rod is lifted higher, an oblong-shaped crystal called a boule grows from the end. Once cooled, the boule can be cut into different shapes.

Hammer strikes crystal.

Ionic crystal shatters when struck.

Figure 7 When an ionic crystal is struck, ions are moved from their fixed positions. Ions with the same charge repel one another and the crystal shatters.

Properties of Ionic Compounds The properties of sodium chloride are typical of an ionic compound. It has a high melting point (801°C). In its solid state, sodium chloride is a poor conductor of electric current. But when melted, it is a good conductor of electric current. Sodium chloride crystals shatter when struck with a hammer. ◯ **The properties of an ionic compound can be explained by the strong attractions among ions within a crystal lattice.**

Recall that the arrangement of particles in a substance is the result of two opposing factors. The first factor is the attractions among particles in the substance. The second factor is the kinetic energy of the particles. The stronger the attractions among the particles, the more kinetic energy the particles must have before they can separate.

For an electric current to flow, charged particles must be able to move from one location to another. The ions in a solid crystal lattice have fixed positions. However, when the solid melts, the lattice breaks apart and the ions are free to flow. Melted, or molten, sodium chloride is an excellent conductor of electric current.

Rock salt contains large crystals of sodium chloride. If you tapped a crystal of rock salt sharply with a hammer, it would shatter into many smaller crystals. Figure 7 shows what happens to the positions of the ions when the crystal is struck. Negative ions are pushed into positions near negative ions, and positive ions are pushed into positions near positive ions. Ions with the same charge repel one another and cause the crystal to shatter.

Section 6.1 Assessment

Reviewing Concepts

1. ◯ When is an atom least likely to react?
2. ◯ Describe one way an element can achieve a stable electron configuration.
3. ◯ What characteristic of ionic bonds can be used to explain the properties of ionic compounds?
4. Use ionization energy to explain why metals lose electrons more easily than nonmetals.
5. Why is a rock salt crystal likely to shatter when struck?

Critical Thinking

6. **Making Generalizations** What will the ratio of ions be in any compound formed from a Group 1A metal and a Group 7A nonmetal? Explain your answer.

7. **Drawing Conclusions** Why do ionic compounds include at least one metal?
8. **Predicting** Based on their chemical formulas, which of these compounds is not likely to be an ionic compound: KBr, SO_2, or $FeCl_3$? Explain your answer.

Connecting ⊂ Concepts

Reactivity of Metals Use what you know about how ionic bonds form to explain the difference in reactivity between potassium and calcium. If necessary, reread the description of Group 1A and Group 2A properties in Section 5.3.

6.2 Covalent Bonding

Reading Focus

Key Concepts

- How are atoms held together in a covalent bond?
- What happens when atoms don't share electrons equally?
- What factors determine whether a molecule is polar?
- How do attractions between polar molecules compare to attractions between nonpolar molecules?

Vocabulary

- ◆ covalent bond
- ◆ molecule
- ◆ polar covalent bond

Reading Strategy

Relating Text and Visuals Copy the table. As you read, look closely at Figure 9. Complete the table by describing each type of model shown.

Model	Description
Electron dot	a. ___?___
Structural formula	b. ___?___
Space-filling	c. ___?___
Electron cloud	d. ___?___

Plants absorb water through their roots from soil or from a solution containing nutrients, as in Figure 8. Carbon dioxide from the air enters the plants through small openings in their leaves. The plants use the energy from sunlight to convert water and carbon dioxide into a sugar. Energy is stored in the chemical bonds of the sugar.

The elements in sugar are carbon, oxygen, and hydrogen. All three are nonmetals, which have relatively high ionization energies. A transfer of electrons does not tend to occur between nonmetal atoms. So, how are two nonmetals able to form bonds?

Covalent Bonds

You and a friend are participating in a treasure hunt. The rules state that the first person to find all eight items on a list will win a 21-speed bicycle. After about an hour, you have found six of the items on the list and your friend has found the other two. You and your friend have incomplete sets of items. But if you are willing to share your items with your friend, together you will have a complete set of items and qualify for the prize. Of course, you will have to be willing to share the bicycle, too. When nonmetals join together, they display a similar sharing strategy.

Figure 8 When plants are grown in water instead of soil, you can see their roots. Plants absorb water through their roots and carbon dioxide through small openings in their leaves.

Chemical Bonds **165**

Molecular Models	
Electron dot diagram	**Structural formula**
H:H	H—H
Space-filling model	**Electron cloud model**
	H H

Figure 9 As a space shuttle lifts off, it leaves a water vapor trail. A reaction of hydrogen and oxygen produces the water.
Using Models **How is the bond between hydrogen atoms represented in each model of a hydrogen molecule?**

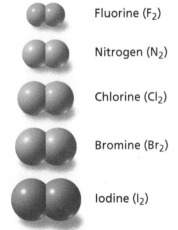

Fluorine (F$_2$)

Nitrogen (N$_2$)

Chlorine (Cl$_2$)

Bromine (Br$_2$)

Iodine (I$_2$)

Figure 10 These space-filling models represent diatomic molecules of five elements.
Using Models **How many atoms are in a diatomic molecule?**

Sharing Electrons A hydrogen atom has one electron. If it had two electrons, it would have the same electron configuration as a helium atom. Two hydrogen atoms can achieve a stable electron configuration by sharing their electrons and forming a covalent bond. A **covalent bond** is a chemical bond in which two atoms share a pair of valence electrons. When two atoms share one pair of electrons, the bond is called a single bond.

Figure 9 shows four different ways to represent a covalent bond. In the electron dot model, the bond is shown by a pair of dots in the space between the symbols for the hydrogen atoms. In the structural formula, the pair of dots is replaced by a line. The electron cloud model and the space-filling model show that orbitals of atoms overlap when a covalent bond forms.

Molecules of Elements Two hydrogen atoms bonded together form a unit called a molecule. A **molecule** is a neutral group of atoms that are joined together by one or more covalent bonds. The hydrogen molecule is neutral because it contains two protons (one from each atom) and two electrons (one from each atom). What keeps the hydrogen atoms together in the molecule? **The attractions between the shared electrons and the protons in each nucleus hold the atoms together in a covalent bond.**

A chemical formula can be used to describe the molecules of an element as well as a compound. The element hydrogen has the chemical formula H_2. The subscript 2 indicates that there are two atoms in a molecule of hydrogen.

Many nonmetal elements exist as diatomic molecules. *Diatomic* means "two atoms." Four of the models in Figure 10 are of halogens. A halogen atom has seven valence electrons. If two halogen atoms share a valence electron from each atom, both atoms have eight valence electrons.

Quick Lab

Analyzing Inks

Materials

test paper, metric ruler, felt-tip markers, stapler, beaker, alcohol-water mixture, Petri dish

Procedure

1. Place the test paper on a clean surface. Use the ruler to draw the pencil line shown in the drawing. Use your markers to place color dots at the locations shown in the drawing.

2. With the ink marks on the outside, staple the two ends of the paper together to form a tube.

3. Pour the alcohol-water mixture into the beaker to a depth of 0.5 cm. Stand the paper in the beaker so that the dots are at the bottom. The paper should not touch the sides of the beaker. Invert the Petri dish over the beaker.

4. When the mixture reaches the top of the paper, remove the paper from the beaker. Unstaple the paper and lay it flat. Make a drawing of the results with each colored area labeled.

Analyze and Conclude

1. **Observing** Which markers contained inks that were mixtures of colored substances?

2. **Formulating Hypotheses** How did some molecules in the ink move up the paper?

3. **Predicting** Assume that molecules in the test paper are more polar than molecules in the alcohol-water mixture. Would you expect the most polar molecules in ink to stick tightly to the paper or to move with the liquid? Explain.

4. **Designing Experiments** How could the procedure from this lab be used to identify a black ink whose composition is unknown?

Multiple Covalent Bonds Nitrogen has five valence electrons. If two nitrogen atoms shared a pair of electrons, each one would have only six valence electrons. If they shared two pairs of electrons, each atom would have only seven valence electrons. When the atoms in a nitrogen molecule (N_2) share three pairs of electrons, each atom has eight valence electrons. Each pair of shared electrons is represented by a long dash in the structural formula $N \equiv N$. When two atoms share three pairs of electrons, the bond is called a triple bond. When two atoms share two pairs of electrons, the bond is called a double bond.

 Reading Checkpoint *What does the subscript 2 in the formula for a hydrogen molecule indicate?*

Unequal Sharing of Electrons

In general, elements on the right of the periodic table have a greater attraction for electrons than elements on the left have (except for noble gases). In general, elements at the top of a group have a greater attraction for electrons than elements at the bottom of a group have. Fluorine is on the far right and is at the top of its group. It has the strongest attraction for electrons and is the most reactive nonmetal.

For: Links on covalent bonding
Visit: www.SciLinks.org
Web Code: ccn-1062

Figure 11 Shared electrons in a hydrogen chloride molecule spend less time near the hydrogen atom than near the chlorine atom. *Inferring* **Which element has a greater attraction for electrons—hydrogen or chlorine?**

HCl

Polar Covalent Bonds

In a molecule of an element, the atoms that form covalent bonds have the same ability to attract an electron. Shared electrons are attracted equally to the nuclei of both atoms. In a molecule of a compound, electrons may not be shared equally.

Figure 11 shows models of the molecule that forms when hydrogen reacts with chlorine. A chlorine atom has a greater attraction for electrons than a hydrogen atom does. In a hydrogen chloride molecule, the shared electrons spend more time near the chlorine atom than near the hydrogen atom. A covalent bond in which electrons are not shared equally is called a **polar covalent bond.** (One meaning of the term *polar* is "opposite in character, nature, or direction.")

When atoms form a polar covalent bond, the atom with the greater attraction for electrons has a partial negative charge. The other atom has a partial positive charge. The symbols δ– and δ+ are used to show which atom has which charge. (δ is the lowercase version of the Greek letter delta.)

Polar and Nonpolar Molecules

Can you assume that a molecule that contains a polar covalent bond is polar? If a molecule has only two atoms, it will be polar. But, when molecules have more than two atoms, the answer is not as obvious. The type of atoms in a molecule and its shape are factors that determine whether a molecule is polar or nonpolar.

Compare the models of carbon dioxide and water in Figure 12. In carbon dioxide, there are double bonds between each oxygen atom and the central carbon atom. Because oxygen has a greater attraction for electrons than carbon does, each double bond is polar. However, the molecule is linear: all three atoms are lined up in a row. The carbon-oxygen double bonds are directly opposite each other. There is an equal pull on the electrons from opposite directions. The pulls cancel out and the molecule as a whole is nonpolar.

There are two single bonds in a water molecule. The bonds are polar because oxygen has a greater attraction for electrons than hydrogen does. Because the water molecule has a bent shape rather than a linear shape, the polar bonds do not cancel out. The two hydrogen atoms are located on the same side of the molecule, opposite the oxygen atom. The oxygen side of the molecule has a partial negative charge. The hydrogen side of the molecule has a partial positive charge.

CO_2

H_2O

Figure 12 In a carbon dioxide (CO_2) molecule, the polar bonds between the carbon atom and the oxygen atoms cancel out because the molecule is linear. In a water (H_2O) molecule, the polar bonds between the oxygen atom and the hydrogen atoms do not cancel out because the molecule is bent.

Attraction Between Molecules

In a molecular compound, there are forces of attraction between molecules. These attractions are not as strong as ionic or covalent bonds, but they are strong enough to hold molecules together in a liquid or solid. **Attractions between polar molecules are stronger than attractions between nonpolar molecules.**

Water molecules are similar in mass to methane (CH_4) molecules. Yet, methane boils at −161.5°C and water boils at 100°C because methane molecules are nonpolar and water molecules are polar. Each dashed line in Figure 13 represents an attraction between a partially positive hydrogen atom in one water molecule and a partially negative oxygen atom in another. Molecules on the surface of a water sample are attracted to molecules that lie below the surface and are pulled toward the center of the sample. These attractions increase the energy required for water molecules to evaporate. They raise the temperature at which vapor pressure equals atmospheric pressure—the boiling point.

Attractions among nonpolar molecules are weaker than attractions among polar molecules, but they do exist. After all, carbon dioxide can exist as solid dry ice. Attractions among nonpolar molecules explain why nitrogen can be stored as a liquid at low temperatures and high pressures. Because electrons are constantly in motion, there are times when one part of a nitrogen molecule has a small positive charge and one part has a small negative charge. At those times, one nitrogen molecule can be weakly attracted to another nitrogen molecule.

Figure 13 Each dashed line in the drawing represents an attraction between a hydrogen atom and an oxygen atom.
Interpreting Diagrams **In a water molecule, which atom has a partial negative charge? Which has a partial positive charge?**

Section 6.2 Assessment

Reviewing Concepts

1. What attractions hold atoms together in a covalent bond?

2. What happens to the charge on atoms when they form a polar covalent bond?

3. Name the two factors that determine whether a molecule is polar.

4. Compare the strength of attractions between polar molecules to the strength of attractions between nonpolar molecules.

5. What is a molecule?

Critical Thinking

6. **Applying Concepts** Which of these elements does not bond to form molecules: oxygen, chlorine, neon, or sulfur?

7. **Inferring** Why is the boiling point of water higher than the boiling point of chlorine?

8. **Using Diagrams** Based on their electron dot diagrams, what is the formula for the covalently bonded compound of nitrogen and hydrogen?

Connecting Concepts

Viscosity Review the description of the physical property viscosity in Section 2.2. Then write a paragraph explaining how attractions between molecules might affect the viscosity of a liquid.

6.3 Naming Compounds and Writing Formulas

Key Concepts

- What information do the name and formula of an ionic compound provide?

- What information do the name and formula of a molecular compound provide?

Vocabulary

- polyatomic ion

Reading Strategy

Predicting Copy the table. Before you read, predict the meaning of the term *polyatomic ion*. After you read, if your prediction was incorrect, revise your definition.

Vocabulary Term	Before You Read	After You Read
Polyatomic ion	a. ___?___	b. ___?___

Thomas Drummond was a Scottish surveyor and inventor. Around 1826, he discovered that a white solid called lime emits a bright light when heated to a high temperature. This discovery was extremely useful in the era before electric lighting. Limelight was used to produce a light that could be focused on a single spot on a stage. It also was used to produce lighthouse beams that could be seen from a great distance.

People have used mixtures of lime and water for centuries to white-wash houses and fences. The flowerpots in Figure 14 were coated with a lime wash to which paint pigments were added. Other names for lime are quicklime and unslaked lime. Having two or more names for a compound can be confusing. Also, names like lime or quicklime don't tell you much about the composition of a compound.

Chemists use a system for naming compounds that is based on rules established by the International Union of Pure and Applied Chemistry (IUPAC). In this system, the chemical name for lime is calcium oxide and its chemical formula is CaO. This formula tells you that there is a one-to-one ratio of calcium ions to oxide ions in calcium oxide. The formula of a compound serves as a reminder of the composition of the compound.

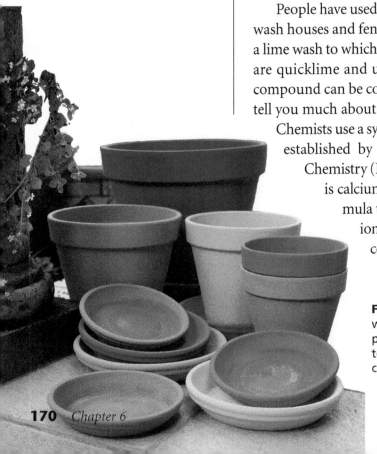

Figure 14 These flowerpots were coated with a solution of lime and water. Paint pigments were mixed with the lime wash to produce the different colors. The chemical name for lime is calcium oxide.

Figure 15 The brass vase on the left is coated with an oxide of copper that is red. Most of the surface of the plate on the right is coated with an oxide of copper that is black.
Classifying *How can you be sure that the oxides of copper are different compounds?*

Describing Ionic Compounds

Both of the objects in Figure 15 are coated with compounds of copper and oxygen. Based on the two colors of the coatings, copper and oxygen must form at least two compounds. One name cannot describe all the compounds of copper and oxygen. There must be at least two names to distinguish red copper oxide from black copper oxide. ☞ **The name of an ionic compound must distinguish the compound from other ionic compounds containing the same elements. The formula of an ionic compound describes the ratio of the ions in the compound.**

Binary Ionic Compounds A compound made from only two elements is a binary compound. (The Latin prefix *bi-* means "two," as in bicycle or bisect.) Naming binary ionic compounds, such as sodium chloride and cadmium iodide, is easy. The names have a predictable pattern: the name of the cation followed by the name of the anion. Remember that the name for the cation is the name of the metal without any change: sodium atom and sodium ion. The name for the anion uses part of the name of the nonmetal with the suffix *–ide:* iodine atom and iodide ion. Figure 16 shows the names and charges for eight common anions.

Figure 16 The table lists the element names, ion names, symbols, and charges for eight anions. The name of an anion is formed by adding the suffix –ide to the stem of the name of the nonmetal.

Common Anions			
Element Name	**Ion Name**	**Ion Symbol**	**Ion Charge**
Fluorine	Fluoride	F^-	1–
Chlorine	Chloride	Cl^-	1–
Bromine	Bromide	Br^-	1–
Iodine	Iodide	I^-	1–
Oxygen	Oxide	O^{2-}	2–
Sulfur	Sulfide	S^{2-}	2–
Nitrogen	Nitride	N^{3-}	3–
Phosphorus	Phosphide	P^{3-}	3–

Some Metal Cations			
Ion Name	Ion Symbol	Ion Name	Ion Symbol
Copper(I)	Cu^+	Chromium(II)	Cr^{2+}
Copper(II)	Cu^{2+}	Chromium(III)	Cr^{3+}
Iron(II)	Fe^{2+}	Titanium(II)	Ti^{2+}
Iron(III)	Fe^{3+}	Titanium(III)	Ti^{3+}
Lead(II)	Pb^{2+}	Titanium(IV)	Ti^{4+}
Lead(IV)	Pb^{4+}	Mercury(II)	Hg^{2+}

Figure 17 Many paint pigments contain compounds of transition metals. These metals often form more than one type of ion. The ion names must contain a Roman numeral. **Using Tables** *How is the Roman numeral in the name related to the charge on the ion?*

Ammonium ion
(NH_4^+)

Figure 18 The atoms in an ammonium ion are joined by covalent bonds. The ion loses a valence electron as it forms. This loss leaves only 10 electrons to balance the charge on 11 protons.

Metals With Multiple Ions The alkali metals, alkaline earth metals, and aluminum form ions with positive charges equal to the group number. For example, the symbol for a potassium ion is K^+, the symbol for a calcium ion is Ca^{2+}, and the symbol for an aluminum ion is Al^{3+}.

Many transition metals form more than one type of ion. Notice the two copper ions listed in Figure 17, a copper(I) ion with a 1+ charge and a copper(II) ion with a 2+ charge. When a metal forms more than one ion, the name of the ion contains a Roman numeral to indicate the charge on the ion. These ion names can distinguish red copper(I) oxide from black copper(II) oxide. The formula for "copper one oxide" is Cu_2O because it takes two Cu^{1+} ions to balance the charge on an O^{2-} ion. The formula for "copper two oxide" is CuO because it takes only one Cu^{2+} ion to balance the charge on an O^{2-} ion.

Polyatomic Ions The electron dot diagram in Figure 18 describes a group of atoms that includes one nitrogen and four hydrogen atoms. It is called an ammonium ion. The atoms are joined by covalent bonds. Why does the group have a positive charge? The nitrogen atom has seven protons, and each hydrogen atom has one proton—eleven in total. But the group has only ten electrons to balance the charge on the protons—eight valence electrons and nitrogen's two inner electrons.

A covalently bonded group of atoms that has a positive or negative charge and acts as a unit is a **polyatomic ion.** The prefix *poly-* means "many." Most simple polyatomic ions are anions. Figure 19 lists the names and formulas for some polyatomic ions. Sometimes there are parentheses in a formula that includes polyatomic ions. For example, the formula for iron(III) hydroxide is $Fe(OH)_3$. The subscript 3 indicates that there are three hydroxide ions for each iron(III) ion.

Reading Checkpoint   *When are Roman numerals used in compound names?*

Modeling Molecules

Materials

blue plastic-foam ball, black plastic-foam ball, 7 white gumdrops, toothpicks

Procedure

1. To make a model of an ammonia molecule (NH_3), insert a toothpick in each of 3 gumdrops. The gumdrops represent hydrogen atoms and the toothpicks represent bonds.

2. An ammonia molecule is like a pyramid with the nitrogen at the top and the hydrogen atoms at the corners of the base. Insert the toothpicks in the blue foam ball (nitrogen) so that each gumdrop is the same distance from the ball.

3. The hydrogen atoms in a methane molecule (CH_4) are equally spaced around the carbon. Use the black ball to make a model of methane.

Analyze and Conclude

1. **Comparing and Contrasting** Compare the shapes of the methane and ammonia molecules.

2. **Using Models** Why is carbon in the center of the methane molecule?

Writing Formulas for Ionic Compounds If you know the name of an ionic compound, you can write its formula. Place the symbol of the cation first, followed by the symbol of the anion. Use subscripts to show the ratio of the ions in the compound. Because all compounds are neutral, the total charges on the cations and anions must add up to zero.

Suppose an atom that gains two electrons, such as sulfur, reacts with an atom that loses one electron, such as sodium. There must be two sodium ions (Na^+) for each sulfide ion (S^{2-}). The formula for sodium sulfide is Na_2S. The 2− charge on one sulfide ion is balanced by the 1+ charges on two sodium ions.

Some Polyatomic Ions			
Name	**Formula**	**Name**	**Formula**
Ammonium	NH_4^+	Acetate	$C_2H_3O_2^-$
Hydroxide	OH^-	Peroxide	O_2^{2-}
Nitrate	NO_3^-	Permanganate	MnO_4^-
Sulfate	SO_4^{2-}	Hydrogen sulfate	HSO_4^-
Carbonate	CO_3^{2-}	Hydrogen carbonate	HCO_3^-
Phosphate	PO_4^{3-}	Hydrogen phosphate	HPO_4^{2-}
Chromate	CrO_4^{2-}	Dichromate	$Cr_2O_7^{2-}$
Silicate	SiO_3^{2-}	Hypochlorite	OCl^-

Figure 19 This table lists the names and formulas of some polyatomic ions. Except for the ammonium ion, all the ions listed are anions. **Using Tables** *Which element is found in all the anions whose names end in -ate?*

Math > Skills

Writing Formulas for Ionic Compounds
What is the formula for the ionic compound calcium chloride?

1 **Read and Understand**
What information are you given?

> The name of the compound is calcium chloride.

2 **Plan and Solve**
List the symbols and charges for the cation and anion.

> Ca with a charge of 2+ and Cl with a charge of 1−

Determine the ratio of ions in the compound.

> It takes two 1− charges to balance the 2+ charge. There will be two chloride ions for each calcium ion.

Write the formula for calcium chloride.

> $CaCl_2$

3 **Look Back and Check**
Is your answer reasonable?

> Each calcium atom loses two electrons and each chlorine atom gains one electron. So there should be a 1-to-2 ratio of calcium ions to chloride ions.

Math > Practice

1. Write the formula for the compound calcium oxide.

2. Write the formula for the compound copper(I) sulfide.

3. Write the formula for the compound sodium sulfate.

4. What is the name of the compound whose formula is NaOH?

Describing Molecular Compounds

Like ionic compounds, molecular compounds have names that identify specific compounds, and formulas that match those names. With molecular compounds, the focus is on the composition of molecules. ⚷ **The name and formula of a molecular compound describe the type and number of atoms in a molecule of the compound.**

Naming Molecular Compounds The general rule is that the most metallic element appears first in the name. These elements are farther to the left in the periodic table. If both elements are in the same group, the more metallic element is closer to the bottom of the group. The name of the second element is changed to end in the suffix -*ide*, as in carbon dioxide.

Go Online
NSTA SCiLINKS

For: Links on chemical formulas
Visit: www.SciLinks.org
Web Code: ccn-1063

Two compounds that contain nitrogen and oxygen have the formulas N_2O_4 and NO_2. The names of these two compounds reflect the actual number of atoms of nitrogen and oxygen in a molecule of each compound. You can use the Greek prefixes in Figure 20 to describe the number of nitrogen and oxygen atoms in each molecule.

In an N_2O_4 molecule, there are two nitrogen atoms and four oxygen atoms. The Greek prefixes for two and four are *di-* and *tetra-*. The name for the compound with the formula N_2O_4 is dinitrogen tetraoxide. In an NO_2 molecule, there are one nitrogen atom and two oxygen atoms. The Greek prefixes for one and two are *mono-* and *di-*. So a name for the compound with the formula NO_2 is mononitrogen dioxide. However, the prefix *mono-* often is not used for the first element in the name. A more common name for the compound with the formula NO_2 is nitrogen dioxide.

Writing Molecular Formulas Writing the formula for a molecular compound is easy. Write the symbols for the elements in the order the elements appear in the name. The prefixes indicate the number of atoms of each element in the molecule. The prefixes appear as subscripts in the formulas. If there is no prefix for an element in the name, there is only one atom of that element in the molecule.

What is the formula for diphosphorus tetrafluoride? Because the compound is molecular, look for elements on the right side of the periodic table. Phosphorus has the symbol P. Fluorine has the symbol F. *Di-* indicates two phosphorus atoms and *tetra-* indicates four fluorine atoms. The formula for the compound is P_2F_4.

Prefixes For Naming Compounds

Number of Atoms	Prefix
1	mono-
2	di-
3	tri-
4	tetra-
5	penta-
6	hexa-
7	hepta-
8	octa-
9	nona-
10	deca-

Figure 20 These Greek prefixes are used to name molecular compounds. The prefix *octa-* means "eight," as in the eight tentacles of an octopus.

Section 6.3 Assessment

Reviewing Concepts

1. ☞ What does the formula of an ionic compound describe?

2. ☞ What do the name and formula of a molecular compound describe?

3. What suffix is used to indicate an anion?

4. Why are Roman numerals used in the names of compounds that contain transition metals?

5. What is a polyatomic ion?

Critical Thinking

6. **Applying Concepts** How is it possible for two different ionic compounds to contain the same elements?

7. **Calculating** How many potassium ions are needed to bond with a phosphate ion?

Math **Practice**

8. What are the names of these ionic compounds: LiCl, BaO, Na_3N, and $PbSO_4$?

9. Name the molecular compounds with these formulas: P_2O_5 and CO.

10. What is the formula for the ionic compound formed from potassium and sulfur?

6.4 The Structure of Metals

Reading Focus

Key Concepts

- What are the forces that give a metal its structure as a solid?

- How do metallic bonds produce some of the typical properties of metals?

- How are the properties of alloys controlled?

Vocabulary

- metallic bond
- alloy

Reading Strategy

Relating Cause and Effect Copy the concept map. As you read, complete the map to relate the structure of metals to their properties.

Figure 21 This photograph of the tungsten filament from a light bulb was taken with a scanning electron microscope. Color was added to the photo. The filament is magnified more than 100 times. The diameter of the wire is about 15 μm, or 0.0015 cm.

Light bulbs are easy to ignore unless a bulb burns out and you are searching for a replacement in the dark. But in the decades just before the year 1900, light bulbs were an exciting new technology. One challenge for researchers was to find the best material for the filaments in light bulbs. The substance had to be ductile enough to be drawn into a narrow wire. It could not melt at the temperatures produced when an electric current passes through a narrow wire. It had to have a low vapor pressure so that particles on the surface were not easily removed by sublimation.

The substance the researchers found was tungsten (W), a metal whose name means "heavy stone" in Swedish. Figure 21 shows a magnified view of the narrow coils in a tungsten filament. Tungsten has the highest melting point of any metal—3410°C—and it has the lowest vapor pressure. The properties of a metal are related to bonds within the metal.

Metallic Bonds

Metal atoms achieve stable electron configurations by losing electrons. But what happens if there are no nonmetal atoms available to accept the electrons? There is a way for metal atoms to lose and gain electrons at the same time. In a metal, valence electrons are free to move among the atoms. In effect, the metal atoms become cations surrounded by a pool of shared electrons. A **metallic bond** is the attraction between a metal cation and the shared electrons that surround it.

Hammer strikes metal.

Metal changes shape
but does not break.

🔑 **The cations in a metal form a lattice that is held in place by strong metallic bonds between the cations and the surrounding valence electrons.** Although the electrons are moving among the atoms, the total number of electrons does not change. So, overall, the metal is neutral.

The metallic bonds in some metals are stronger than in other metals. The more valence electrons an atom can contribute to the shared pool, the stronger the metallic bonds will be. The bonds in an alkali metal are relatively weak because alkali metals contribute only a single valence electron. The result is that alkali metals, such as sodium, are soft enough to cut with a knife and have relatively low melting points. Sodium melts at 97.8°C. Transition metals, such as tungsten, have more valence electrons to contribute and, therefore, are harder and have higher melting points. Recall that tungsten melts at 3410°C.

Figure 22 In a metal, cations are surrounded by shared valence electrons. If a metal is struck, the ions move to new positions, but the ions are still surrounded by electrons. **Classifying** *What property of metals is displayed when a hammer strikes a metal?*

Explaining Properties of Metals

The structure within a metal affects the properties of metals. 🔑 **The mobility of electrons within a metal lattice explains some of the properties of metals.** The ability to conduct an electric current and malleability are two important properties of metals.

Recall that a flow of charged particles is an electric current. A metal has a built-in supply of charged particles that can flow from one location to another—the pool of shared electrons. An electric current can be carried through a metal by the free flow of the shared electrons.

The lattice in a metal is flexible compared to the rigid lattice in an ionic compound. Figure 22 is a model of what happens when someone strikes a metal with a hammer. The metal ions shift their positions and the shape of the metal changes. But the metal does not shatter because ions are still held together by the metallic bonds between the ions and the electrons. Metallic bonds also explain why metals, such as tungsten and copper, can be drawn into thin wires without breaking.

Reading Checkpoint

What two important properties of metals can be explained by their structure?

Alloys

A friend shows you a beautiful ring that she says is made from pure gold. Your friend is lucky to have such a valuable object. The purity of gold is expressed in units called karats. Gold that is 100 percent pure is labeled 24-karat gold. Gold jewelry that has a 12-karat label is only 50 percent gold. Jewelry that has an 18-karat label is 75 percent gold.

The surface of an object made from pure gold can easily be worn away by contact with other objects or dented because gold is a soft metal. When silver, copper, nickel, or zinc is mixed with gold, the gold is harder and more resistant to wear. These gold mixtures are alloys. An **alloy** is a mixture of two or more elements, at least one of which is a metal. Alloys have the characteristic properties of metals.

DK SCIENCE and History

Milestones in Metallurgy

The science of metallurgy includes ways to extract metals from ores, refine metals, and use metals. Described here are some advances in metallurgy since 1850.

Hot gas flame *The flame from a burning gas melts the surfaces where two metal parts will join.*

BESSEMER CONVERTER

Vanadium steel *This alloy becomes popular in car manufacturing because it is lightweight and strong.*

Gas torch

GAS WELDING

1856 Henry Bessemer develops an efficient process for producing steel by blowing air through molten iron.

1886 Charles Hall and Paul Héroult independently develop a method for using electricity to obtain aluminum from aluminum oxide.

1908 Henry Ford uses vanadium steel (an alloy of iron with carbon and vanadium) extensively in his Model T Fords.

1914 The start of World War I leads to the wide-scale use of welding techniques, such as gas welding with acetylene, for ship building.

1850	1880	1910

Copper Alloys The first important alloy was bronze, whose name is associated with an important era in history—the Bronze Age. Metalworkers in Thailand may have been the first to make bronze. But people in other locations probably thought they were the first to make bronze. News didn't travel quickly in that era.

Metalworkers might have noticed that the metal they extracted by heating deposits of copper was not always the same. The difference in properties could be traced to the presence of tin. In its simplest form, bronze contains only copper and tin, which are relatively soft metals. Mixed together in bronze, the metals are much harder and stronger than either metal alone. **Scientists can design alloys with specific properties by varying the types and amounts of elements in an alloy.**

Writing in Science

Cause-Effect Paragraph
Write a paragraph about Henry Ford's decision to use vanadium steel for automobile parts. Where did Ford first see parts made from vanadium steel? What properties of this type of steel impressed Ford? Did Ford need to overcome any problems before going ahead with his plan?

Steel-framed structure *The Empire State Building is supported by a framework of steel columns and beams that weigh 60,000 tons.*

EMPIRE STATE BUILDING

1931 The 102-story Empire State Building in New York City is completed. Skyscrapers would be impossible without steel-framed construction.

Metal parts, *such as the gears in this gold watch, are made by applying heat and pressure to powdered metal in a mold.*

METAL PARTS FROM POWDER

1942 Making small, complex parts from metal powders is less wasteful than machining. World War II spurs advances in iron powder metallurgy.

Superalloys containing rhenium are used in jet engines.

1991 New alloys containing rhenium are introduced. These superalloys are capable of retaining their strength at very high temperatures.

| 1940 | 1970 | 2000 |

Chemical Bonds **179**

Figure 23 This ancient statue of horses from Venice, Italy, and this modern French horn are both made from copper alloys. The statue is made from bronze, an alloy of copper and tin. The French horn is made from brass, an alloy of copper and zinc.

Go Online
SCIENCE NEWS®

For: Articles on metals
Visit: PHSchool.com
Web Code: cce-1064

Bronze is hard and durable enough to be used for propellers on ships and for statues, such as the statue of horses in Figure 23. A bronze bell has a clear, loud tone that lasts for several seconds.

A brass bell has a duller tone that dies away quickly. Brass is another alloy of copper that has been known for centuries. In its simplest form, brass contains only copper and zinc. Although both bronze and brass are alloys of copper, they have distinctly different properties. Brass is softer than bronze and is easier to shape into forms such as the French horn in Figure 23. Brass is shinier than bronze but is likely to weather more quickly.

Steel Alloys The 1900s could be called the Age of Steel because of the skyscrapers, automobiles, and ships that were built from steel during the 1900s. Steel is an alloy of iron that contains small quantities of carbon, ranging from less than 0.2 percent to about 3 percent by mass. The smaller carbon atoms fit in the spaces between the larger iron atoms in the lattice. The carbon atoms form bonds with neighboring iron atoms. These bonds make the lattice harder and stronger than a lattice that contains only iron.

The properties of any particular type of steel depend on which elements other than iron and carbon are used and how much of those elements are included. Stainless steels contain more than 10 percent chromium by mass, but almost no carbon. Stainless steels are durable because chromium forms an oxide that protects the steel from rusting. But stainless steel is more brittle than steels that contain more carbon. The steel cables in the bridge in Figure 24 have to be strong enough to resist forces that might stretch the cables or cause them to break. The steel used contains sulfur, manganese, phosphorus, silicon, and 0.81 percent carbon.

Figure 24 The Golden Gate Bridge is a landmark in San Francisco, California. Its cables, towers, and deck contain steel. The steel in the cables needs to resist forces that pull on the cables. The steel in the towers needs to resist the compression forces caused by the weight of the cables, the deck, and the vehicles that travel across the bridge.
Drawing Conclusions *Would the steel used for the cables and the steel used for the towers have the same composition? Give a reason for your answer.*

Other Alloys Airplane parts are made of many different alloys that are suited to particular purposes. The body of a plane is large and needs to be made from a lightweight material. Pure aluminum is lighter than most metals, but it bends and dents too easily. If a small amount of copper or manganese is added to aluminum, the result is a stronger material that is still lighter than steel.

For certain aircraft parts, even lighter materials are needed. Alloys of aluminum and magnesium are used for these parts. Magnesium is much less dense than most metals used to build structures. However, pure magnesium is soft enough to cut with a knife, and it burns in air. An aluminum-magnesium alloy keeps the advantages of magnesium without the disadvantages.

Section 6.4 Assessment

Reviewing Concepts

1. What holds metal ions together in a metal lattice?

2. What characteristic of a metallic bond explains some of the properties of metals?

3. How can scientists design alloys with specific properties?

4. Explain why the metallic bonds in some metals are stronger than the bonds in other metals.

5. Why are metals good conductors of electric current?

6. How does adding carbon to steel make the steel harder and stronger?

Critical Thinking

7. **Predicting** Which element has a higher melting point, potassium in Group 1A or calcium in Group 1B? Give a reason for your answer.

8. **Applying Concepts** Can two different elements form a metallic bond together?

Writing in Science

Compare-Contrast Paragraph Write a paragraph comparing the properties of ionic compounds and alloys. Relate their properties to the structure of their lattices.

Chipping In

Tasks done by computers that filled an entire room in the 1950s are now done by devices the size of a credit card. This miniaturization in the electronics industry is due to semiconductors.

Semiconductors are solid substances, such as silicon, that have poor electrical conductivity at ordinary temperatures. Silicon has four valence electrons. In pure silicon, each atom forms single bonds with four other atoms. This arrangement leaves no electrons free to move through the silicon. The conductivity of silicon is greatly improved by adding small amounts of other elements to silicon, a process called doping.

Doping
An element with five valence electrons, such as phosphorus, can be added to silicon. After a phosphorus atom bonds with four atoms, there is an extra electron that is free to move. Silicon doped with phosphorus is called *n*-type silicon because electrons have a negative charge. An element with three valence electrons, such as boron, can be added to silicon. Adding boron leaves holes to which electrons can move from neighboring atoms. Because the lack of an electron has the effect of a positive charge, silicon with boron is called *p*-type silicon.

Silicon wafer

Pure Silicon

Silicon with boron

Silicon with phosphorus

Silicon crystal

Wafers and chips
Silicon crystals are cut into wafer-thin slices. Each wafer can be made into hundreds of silicon chips.

Vacuum tube
Glass vacuum tubes used in early computers were fragile and took up space.

Integrated circuit on a silicon chip

Computer chip
In 1974, the first computer microchip contained 6000 transistors. Today, more than 40 million transistors can be placed on a single computer chip.

Diode
In a diode, a layer of *p*-type silicon is joined to a layer of *n*-type silicon. When the leads on a diode are correctly connected in a circuit, electrons flow toward the junction between the two types of silicon. Electrons from the *n*-type silicon fill holes in the *p*-type silicon. In devices that use batteries, a diode can keep electrons from flowing if the batteries are not inserted correctly. Some diodes emit light when the circuit is complete.

Transistor
In a transistor, there are three layers of doped silicon. There is a layer of *p*-type silicon sandwiched between two layers of *n*-type silicon or a layer of *n*-type silicon between two layers of p-type silicon. Transistors are used to amplify current. A small current applied to the central layer of a transistor can produce a larger current.

Going Further

- Research and write about the development of transistors. Why were researchers looking for a replacement for vacuum tubes? How did replacing vacuum tubes with transistors affect the size of radios and computers?

- Take a Discovery Channel Video Field Trip by watching "Good Conduct."

DISCOVERY CHANNEL SCHOOL™
Video Field Trip

Improving the Dyeing of Nonpolar Fabrics

Most natural fibers, such as cotton and wool, consist of large molecules that have regions with a partial positive or partial negative charge. These polar molecules have a strong attraction for dyes that contain either polar molecules or ions.

The molecules in some manufactured fibers, such as nylon, are nonpolar molecules. These synthetic fibers are difficult to dye. Molecules of other synthetic fibers, such as polyester and rayon, have only a few polar regions. As you might suspect, polyester and rayon have intermediate attractions for dyes. In this lab, you will investigate a process for improving a fiber's ability to absorb and retain dye.

Problem How can you increase the dye-holding capacity of nonpolar fibers?

Materials
- tongs
- 2 fabric test strips
- hot dye bath containing methyl orange
- clock or watch
- paper towels
- scissors
- soap
- hot iron(II) sulfate solution

Skills Observing, Drawing Conclusions

Procedure

Part A: Dyeing Without Treatment

1. On a sheet of paper, copy the data table shown.

2. Use the tongs to immerse a fabric test strip in the methyl orange dye bath. **CAUTION** *The dye bath is hot. Do not touch the glass. The dye will stain skin and clothing.*

3. After 7 minutes, remove the strip from the dye bath. Allow as much of the dye solution as possible to drip back into the bath as shown on page 185. Rinse off the excess dye with water in the sink.

4. Place the strip on a paper towel to dry. Be careful to avoid splashes when transferring the strip between the dye bath and paper towel. Record your observations in your data table.

5. After the fabric strip is dry, test it for colorfastness, or the ability to hold dye. Cut the strip in half lengthwise and wash one half of the strip in the sink with soap and water.

Data Table		
Dye Treatment	Dyeing of Fibers	Colorfastness of Fibers
Methyl orange		
Iron sulfate and methyl orange		

6. Allow the washed half-strip to dry and then compare the washed half to the unwashed half. Record your observations in your data table. Staple the half-strips to a sheet of paper and label each half-strip to indicate how you treated it.

Part B: Dyeing With Treatment

7. Use the tongs to place the second fabric strip in the iron(II) sulfate solution for 25 minutes. Then use tongs to lift the strip and allow it to drain into the iron(II) sulfate solution. Wring the strip as dry as possible over the solution. **CAUTION** *The strip will be hot. Allow it to cool before touching it. Wear plastic gloves.*

8. Repeat Steps 2, 3, and 4 using the strip that you treated with iron(II) sulfate.

9. To test the strip for colorfastness, repeat Steps 5 and 6.

10. Clean up your work area and wash your hands thoroughly with warm water and soap before leaving the laboratory.

Analyze and Conclude

1. **Comparing and Contrasting** How did the color of the untreated strip compare with the color of the treated strip?

2. **Comparing and Contrasting** How did the colorfastness of the untreated strip compare to the colorfastness of the treated strip?

3. **Applying Concepts** Silk blouses and shirts can be purchased in many intense colors. Why do you think silk is able to hold a variety of intense dyes?

4. **Drawing Conclusions** How does iron(II) sulfate affect the ability of a fabric to absorb dyes? (*Hint:* What kind of compound is iron(II) sulfate?)

5. **Predicting** A care label might say *Wash in cold water only.* What might happen to the color of a piece of clothing with this label if you washed the clothing in hot water?

6.1 Ionic Bonding

Key Concepts

- When the highest occupied energy level of an atom is filled with electrons, the atom is stable and not likely to react.
- Some elements achieve stable electron configurations through the transfer of electrons between atoms. An ionic bond forms when electrons are transferred from one atom to another.
- The properties of an ionic compound can be explained by the strong attractions among ions within a crystal lattice.

Vocabulary

electron dot diagram, *p. 158*

ion, *p. 159*

anion, *p. 160*

cation, *p. 160*

chemical bond, *p. 160*

ionic bond, *p. 160*

chemical formula, *p. 161*

crystals, *p. 162*

6.2 Covalent Bonding

Key Concepts

- The attractions between the shared electrons and the protons in each nucleus hold the atoms together in a covalent bond.
- When atoms form a polar covalent bond, the atom with the greater attraction for electrons has a partial negative charge. The other atom has a partial positive charge.
- The type of atoms in a molecule and its shape are factors that determine whether a molecule is polar or nonpolar.
- Attractions between polar molecules are stronger than attractions between nonpolar molecules.

Vocabulary

covalent bond, *p. 166*

molecule, *p. 166*

polar covalent bond, *p. 168*

6.3 Naming Compounds and Writing Formulas

Key Concepts

- The name of an ionic compound must distinguish the compound from other ionic compounds containing the same elements. The formula of an ionic compound describes the ratio of the ions in the compound.
- The name and formula of a molecular compound describe the type and number of atoms in a molecule of the compound.

Vocabulary

polyatomic ion, *p. 172*

6.4 The Structure of Metals

Key Concepts

- The cations in a metal form a lattice that is held in place by strong metallic bonds between the cations and the surrounding valence electrons.
- The mobility of electrons within a metal lattice explains some of the properties of metals.
- Scientists can design alloys with specific properties by varying the types and amounts of elements in an alloy.

Vocabulary

metallic bond, *p. 176*

alloy, *p. 178*

Thinking Visually

Concept Map Use information from the chapter to complete the concept map below.

Assessment

Reviewing Content

Choose the letter that best answers the question or completes the statement.

1. When an atom loses an electron, it forms a(n)
   a. anion.   **b.** cation.
   c. polyatomic ion. **d.** neutral ion.

2. The charge on a chloride ion in $AlCl_3$ is
   a. 1+.   **b.** 3+.
   c. 1−.   **d.** 3−.

3. Which pair has the same electron configuration?
   a. Cl^- and Ar   **b.** Cl^- and Ar^-
   c. Cl and Ar   **d.** Cl^+ and Ar

4. A chemical bond that forms when atoms share electrons is always a(n)
   a. polar bond.   **b.** ionic bond.
   c. metallic bond.   **d.** covalent bond.

5. When two fluorine atoms share a pair of electrons, the bond that forms is a(n)
   a. polar covalent bond.
   b. ionic bond.
   c. nonpolar covalent bond.
   d. double bond.

6. The chemical formula for magnesium bromide is
   a. MgBr.   **b.** $MgBr_2$.
   c. $Mg(II)Br_2$.   **d.** Mg_2Br.

7. The compound with the formula $SiCl_4$ is
   a. silicon chloride.   **b.** silicon chlorine.
   c. silicon(I) chloride. **d.** silicon tetrachloride.

8. The attraction among water molecules is stronger than the attraction among
   a. sodium and chloride ions.
   b. carbon dioxide molecules.
   c. the atoms in a polyatomic ion.
   d. atoms in a diatomic molecule.

9. Which type of solid is likely to be the best conductor of electric current?
   a. ionic compound   **b.** covalent compound
   c. metal element   **d.** nonmetal element

10. An alloy contains
   a. at least one metallic element.
   b. at least one nonmetallic element.
   c. only metallic elements.
   d. only nonmetallic elements.

Understanding Concepts

11. What is a stable electron configuration?

12. What does each dot in an electron dot diagram represent?

13. What process changes atoms into ions?

14. What keeps the ions in their fixed positions within a crystal lattice?

15. What are subscripts used for in chemical formulas?

16. Explain why a melted ionic compound is a good conductor of electric current, but a solid ionic compound is a poor conductor of electric current.

17. What distinguishes single, double, and triple covalent bonds?

18. Explain why the covalent bonds in molecules of elements are always nonpolar.

19. Explain why, in a covalent bond between oxygen and hydrogen, the hydrogen atom has a partial positive charge and the oxygen atom has a partial negative charge.

20. What is the name of the binary compound formed from potassium and iodine?

21. Write the formulas for the compounds called copper(I) chloride and copper(II) chloride.

22. Name the compounds represented by the space-filling models labeled A, B, and C.

■ *Sulfur* ■ *Oxygen* ■ *Carbon* ■ *Nitrogen*

23. In general, what determines the strength of metallic bonds?

24. What properties of copper and tin change when these metals are mixed together to form bronze?

25. What advantage of magnesium is retained in magnesium alloys? What disadvantage is reduced?

Critical Thinking

26. Classifying What does a fluoride ion have in common with a neon atom and a sodium ion?

27. Comparing and Contrasting How are molecules and polyatomic ions similar?

28. Classifying Classify the bonds in each of these compounds as ionic, polar covalent, or nonpolar covalent: SO_3, CaO, and I_2.

29. Applying Concepts Write the names for the compounds with these chemical formulas: SCl_2, Ag_2SO_4, LiF, CS_2, and $Ca(OH)_2$.

Use these diagrams to answer Questions 30–34.

30. Using Models Which of the three elements are metals and which are nonmetals?

31. Applying Concepts Element Q forms compounds with element X and with element Z. Write the formulas for these two compounds.

32. Calculating What would the formula be for a compound containing chromium(III) ions and ions of element Z?

33. Applying Concepts Draw an electron dot structure for a compound of fluorine and Z.

34. Predicting If an atom of X reacts with an atom of X, what kind of bond forms?

Math Skills

35. Calculating What is the total number of shared electrons in a carbon dioxide molecule?

36. Making Generalizations What is the ratio of anions to cations in a compound formed by a Group 2A metal and a Group 7A nonmetal?

37. Applying Concepts Write the formulas for barium fluoride, sodium oxide, iron(II) sulfate, and ammonium sulfate.

Concepts In Action

38. Using Models A solution of hydrogen peroxide (H_2O_2) and water is sometimes used to disinfect a cut. Which of the following formulas is the correct structural formula for hydrogen peroxide?

39. Relating Cause and Effect In a carbonated beverage, the main ingredients are water and carbon dioxide. Carbon dioxide gas is released when the bottle is opened. Why is water a liquid but carbon dioxide a gas at room temperature?

40. Classifying The shells shown on page 156 contain the compound calcium carbonate ($CaCO_3$). Explain how this compound can contain both ionic and covalent bonds.

41. Relating Cause and Effect How does adding some phosphorus to silicon make silicon a better conductor of electric current?

42. Writing in Science Compare what happens to the valence electron in a hydrogen atom when the atom bonds with another hydrogen atom and when the atom bonds with an oxygen atom.

Performance-Based Assessment

Designing an Advertisement You own a store that sells bronze bells. Design a quarter-page ad for your store to be published in your local directory of businesses. Write copy for your ad. Describe a photograph to use in the ad. Also supply a sketch showing how you want the copy and the photograph to be laid out on the page.

For: Self-grading assessment
Visit: PHSchool.com
Web Code: cca-1060

Standardized Test Prep

Choose the letter that best answers the question or completes the statement.

1. How many electrons does a Group 7A atom need to gain in order to achieve a stable electron configuration?
(A) 0
(B) 1
(C) 2
(D) 7
(E) 8

2. What type of bond forms when electrons are transferred from one atom to another?
(A) nonpolar covalent bond
(B) ionic bond
(C) polar covalent bond
(D) polyatomic bond
(E) metallic bond

3. Metallic bonds form between
(A) cations and protons.
(B) anions and protons.
(C) cations and anions.
(D) cations and electrons.
(E) anions and electrons.

Use the table to answer Questions 4 and 5.

Some Ions and Their Symbols			
Ion Name	Ion Symbol	Ion Name	Ion Symbol
Copper(I)	Cu^+	Nitrate	NO_3^-
Copper(II)	Cu^{2+}	Sulfate	SO_4^{2-}
Iron(II)	Fe^{2+}	Carbonate	CO_3^{2-}
Iron(III)	Fe^{3+}	Phosphate	PO_4^{3-}

4. What is the formula for copper(II) nitrate?
(A) $CuNO_3$
(B) $Cu_2(NO_3)_2$
(C) $Cu(NO_3)_2$
(D) Cu_2NO_3
(E) $CuNO_2$

5. In the compound iron(II) carbonate, the ratio of iron(II) ions to carbonate ions will be
(A) one to one.
(B) two to one.
(C) three to one.
(D) one to two.
(E) one to three.

6. All steels contain
(A) copper and zinc.
(B) copper and tin.
(C) iron and chromium.
(D) chromium and carbon.
(E) iron and carbon.

7. What is the reason that water has a higher boiling point than expected?
(A) Attractions among nonpolar water molecules are strong.
(B) Water molecules have a linear shape.
(C) Water molecules are not very massive.
(D) There are strong attractions among polar water molecules.
(E) There are no attractions among water molecules.

How do scientists classify reactions?

Scientists classify chemical reactions based on the type of reactant or the number of reactants and products. Work in a group to develop a slide-show presentation that summarizes general types of reactions. First, determine how the slide show will be organized. Then work as a group or split up into smaller groups to cover the different reaction types. Present the final slide show in class or publish it on your class Web site.

How do science concepts apply to your world? Here are some questions you'll be able to answer after you read this chapter.

- What happens to a piece of charcoal as it burns? *(Section 7.1)*

- How do air bags inflate? *(Section 7.2)*

- Why does a propane stove need a spark in order for the propane to ignite? *(Section 7.3)*

- How do firefighters put out wildfires? *(page 210)*

- How does a refrigerator keep food fresh? *(Section 7.4)*

- What changes take place inside a closed container of water? *(Section 7.5)*

Chapter Preview

7.1 **Describing Reactions**

7.2 **Types of Reactions**

7.3 **Energy Changes in Reactions**

7.4 **Reaction Rates**

7.5 **Equilibrium**

Video Field Trip

Taming the Flames

Autumn leaves change color as a result of a series of chemical reactions.

Inquiry Activity

How Is Mass Conserved in a Chemical Change?

Procedure

1. Pour 100 mL of water into a resealable plastic bag. Flatten the bag to remove all of the air and then seal the bag. Measure and record the mass of the bag and the water.

2. Measure and record the mass of a square piece of paper with sides of 10 cm. Place an antacid tablet on the paper. Measure and record the mass of the tablet and the paper together. To find the mass of just the tablet, subtract the mass of the paper from the combined masses of the tablet and the paper.

3. Record the combined masses of the bag, the water, and the antacid tablet.

4. Slightly open one side of the bag and drop the tablet into the water. Quickly reseal the bag. After the bubbling has stopped, measure and record the mass of the bag and its contents.

Think About It

1. **Applying Concepts** How do you know whether a chemical change took place?

2. **Inferring** What happened to the mass of the plastic bag and its contents after the bubbling stopped? What might this information tell you about a chemical change?

7.1 Describing Reactions

Reading Focus

Key Concepts

- What is the law of conservation of mass?
- Why must chemical equations be balanced?
- Why do chemists use the mole?
- How can you calculate the mass of a reactant or product in a chemical reaction?

Vocabulary

- reactants
- products
- chemical equation
- coefficients
- mole
- molar mass

Reading Strategy

Monitoring Your Understanding Preview the Key Concepts, topic headings, vocabulary, and figures in this section. List two things you expect to learn. After reading, state what you learned about each item you listed.

What I Expect to Learn	What I Learned
a. _____?_____	b. _____?_____
c. _____?_____	d. _____?_____

What type of change is happening in Figure 1? When charcoal burns, it changes into other substances while producing heat and light. Burning is a chemical change. When a substance undergoes a chemical change, a chemical reaction is said to take place. In order to understand chemical reactions, you first must be able to describe them.

Chemical Equations

A useful way of describing a change is to state what is present before and after the change. For example, suppose you wanted to show how your appearance changed as you grew older. You could compare a photo of yourself when you were younger with a photo that was taken recently.

A useful description of a chemical reaction tells you the substances present before and after the reaction. In a chemical reaction, the substances that undergo change are called **reactants.** The new substances formed as a result of that change are called **products.** In Figure 1, the reactants are the carbon in the charcoal and the oxygen in the air. The product of the reaction is carbon dioxide gas.

Using Equations to Represent Reactions During a chemical reaction, the reactants change into products. You can summarize this process with a word equation.

$$\text{Reactants} \longrightarrow \text{Products}$$

Figure 1 Burning is an example of a chemical reaction. When charcoal burns, the carbon in the charcoal reacts with oxygen in the air to produce carbon dioxide and heat.

To describe the burning of charcoal, you can substitute the reactants and products of the reaction into the word equation as follows.

$$\text{Carbon} + \text{Oxygen} \longrightarrow \text{Carbon dioxide}$$

You can then simplify the word equation by writing the reactants and products as chemical formulas.

$$C + O_2 \longrightarrow CO_2$$

Now you have a chemical equation. A **chemical equation** is a representation of a chemical reaction in which the reactants and products are expressed as formulas. You can read the equation above as, "Carbon and oxygen react and form carbon dioxide," or, "The reaction of carbon and oxygen yields carbon dioxide."

 Reading Checkpoint *What is a chemical equation?*

Conservation of Mass As a piece of charcoal burns, it gets smaller and smaller until it is finally reduced to a tiny pile of ash. Although the charcoal seems to disappear as it burns, it is actually being converted into carbon dioxide gas. If you measured the mass of the carbon dioxide produced, it would equal the mass of the charcoal and oxygen that reacted.

During chemical reactions, the mass of the products is always equal to the mass of the reactants. This principle, established by French chemist Antoine Lavoisier (1743–1794), is known as the law of conservation of mass. 🔑 **The law of conservation of mass states that mass is neither created nor destroyed in a chemical reaction.** Recall that mass is a measure of the amount of matter. So, this law is also known as the law of conservation of matter. By demonstrating that mass is conserved in various reactions, Lavoisier laid the foundation for modern chemistry.

Figure 2 illustrates how a chemical equation can be restated in terms of atoms and molecules. The equation reads, "One atom of carbon reacts with one molecule of oxygen and forms one molecule of carbon dioxide." Suppose you have six carbon atoms. If each carbon atom reacts with one oxygen molecule to form one carbon dioxide molecule, then six carbon atoms react with six oxygen molecules to form six carbon dioxide molecules. Notice that the number of atoms on the left side of the equation equals the number of atoms on the right. The equation shows that mass is conserved.

For: Links on conservation of mass
Visit: www.SciLinks.org
Web Code: ccn-1071

Figure 2 Whether you burn one carbon atom or six carbon atoms, the equation used to describe the reaction is the same.
Using Models *How do both models of the reaction below show that mass is conserved?*

Burning of Carbon

| C | | O₂ | | CO₂ |
| Carbon | + | Oxygen | → | Carbon dioxide |

Figure 3 Water is a compound made up of the elements hydrogen and oxygen.

Go Online
active art

For: Activity on balancing equations
Visit: PHSchool.com
Web Code: ccp-1071

Figure 4 In the unbalanced equation, the hydrogen atoms are balanced but the oxygen atoms are not. After changing the coefficients, both the hydrogen and oxygen atoms are balanced. Applying Concepts *Why must chemical equations be balanced?*

Balancing Equations

Water is formed by the reaction of hydrogen and oxygen. You can describe the reaction by writing a chemical equation.

$$H_2 + O_2 \longrightarrow H_2O$$

If you examine this equation carefully, you will notice that the number of atoms on the left side does not equal the number of atoms on the right. The equation is not balanced. **In order to show that mass is conserved during a reaction, a chemical equation must be balanced.**

You can balance a chemical equation by changing the **coefficients,** the numbers that appear before the formulas. In the unbalanced equation above, the coefficients are understood to be 1. When you change a coefficient, you change the amount of that reactant or product represented in the chemical equation. As you balance equations, you should never change the subscripts in a formula. Changing the formula changes the identity of that reactant or product.

The first step in balancing an equation is to count the number of atoms of each element on each side of the equation, as shown in Figure 4. The left side of the unbalanced equation has two hydrogen atoms and two oxygen atoms. The right side has two hydrogen atoms and one oxygen atom. The oxygen atoms need to be balanced.

The next step is to change one or more coefficients until the equation is balanced. You can balance the oxygen atoms by changing the coefficient of H_2O to 2.

$$H_2 + O_2 \longrightarrow 2H_2O$$

The oxygen atoms are now balanced. However, the hydrogen atoms have become "unbalanced," with two on the left, and four on the right. To balance the hydrogen atoms, change the coefficient of H_2 to 2.

$$2H_2 + O_2 \longrightarrow 2H_2O$$

The equation is now balanced. Each side of the balanced equation has four hydrogen atoms and two oxygen atoms, as shown in Figure 4. According to the balanced equation, two molecules of hydrogen react with one molecule of oxygen to yield two molecules of water.

Unbalanced Chemical Equation	
H_2 + O_2 $\longrightarrow$ H_2O	
Reactants	Product
2 hydrogen atoms	2 hydrogen atoms
2 oxygen atoms	1 oxygen atom

Balanced Chemical Equation	
$2H_2$ + O_2 $\longrightarrow$ $2H_2O$	
Reactants	Product
4 hydrogen atoms	4 hydrogen atoms
2 oxygen atoms	2 oxygen atoms

Balancing Chemical Equations

Write a balanced equation for the reaction between copper and oxygen to produce copper(II) oxide, CuO.

1 Read and Understand

What information are you given?

Reactants: Cu, O_2 Product: CuO

2 Plan and Solve

Write a chemical equation with the reactants on the left side and the product on the right.

$$Cu + O_2 \longrightarrow CuO$$

This equation is not balanced. Change the coefficient of CuO in order to balance the number of oxygen atoms.

$$Cu + O_2 \longrightarrow 2CuO$$

Change the coefficient of Cu in order to balance the number of copper atoms.

$$2Cu + O_2 \longrightarrow 2CuO$$

3 Look Back and Check

Is your answer reasonable?

The number of atoms on the left equals the number of atoms on the right.

1. Hydrogen chloride, or HCl, is an important industrial chemical. Write a balanced equation for the production of hydrogen chloride from hydrogen and chlorine.

2. Balance the following chemical equations.
   a. $H_2O_2 \longrightarrow H_2O + O_2$
   b. $Mg + HCl \longrightarrow$
      $H_2 + MgCl_2$

3. Ethylene, C_2H_4, burns in the presence of oxygen to produce carbon dioxide and water vapor. Write a balanced equation for this reaction.

Counting With Moles

How many shoes do you own? Because shoes come in twos, you would most likely count them by the pair rather than individually. The counting units you use depend on what you are counting. For example, you might count eggs by the dozen or paper by the ream.

Chemists also need practical units for counting things. Although you can describe a reaction in terms of atoms and molecules, these units are too small to be practical. ● **Because chemical reactions often involve large numbers of small particles, chemists use a counting unit called the mole to measure amounts of a substance.**

A **mole** (mol) is an amount of a substance that contains approximately 6.02×10^{23} particles of that substance. This number is known as Avogadro's number. In chemistry, a mole of a substance generally contains 6.02×10^{23} atoms, molecules, or ions of that substance. For instance, a mole of iron is 6.02×10^{23} atoms of iron.

Figure 5 Shoes are often counted by the pair, eggs by the dozen, and paper by the ream (500 sheets). To count particles of a substance, chemists use the mole (6.02×10^{23} particles).

Figure 6 The molar mass of carbon is 12.0 grams. The molar mass of sulfur is 32.1 grams. *Inferring If each of the carbon and sulfur samples contains one mole of atoms, why do the samples have different masses?*

Molar Mass A dozen eggs has a different mass than a dozen oranges. Similarly, a mole of carbon has a different mass than a mole of sulfur, as shown in Figure 6. The mass of one mole of a substance is called a **molar mass.** For an element, the molar mass is the same as its atomic mass expressed in grams. For example, the atomic mass of carbon is 12.0 amu, so the molar mass of carbon is 12.0 grams.

For a compound, you can calculate the molar mass by adding up the atomic masses of its component atoms, and then expressing this sum in grams. A carbon dioxide molecule is composed of one carbon atom (12.0 amu) and two oxygen atoms (2×16.0 amu $= 32.0$ amu). So carbon dioxide has a molar mass of 44.0 grams.

Mole-Mass Conversions Once you know the molar mass of a substance, you can convert moles of that substance into mass, or a mass of that substance into moles. For either calculation, you need to express the molar mass as a conversion factor. For example, the molar mass of CO_2 is 44.0 grams, which means that one mole of CO_2 has a mass of 44.0 grams. This relationship yields the following conversion factors.

$$\frac{44.0 \text{ g } CO_2}{1 \text{ mol } CO_2} \qquad \frac{1 \text{ mol } CO_2}{44.0 \text{ g } CO_2}$$

Suppose you have 55.0 grams of CO_2. To calculate how many moles of CO_2 you have, multiply the mass by the conversion factor on the right.

$$55.0 \text{ g } CO_2 \times \frac{1 \text{ mol } CO_2}{44.0 \text{ g } CO_2} = 1.25 \text{ mol } CO_2$$

You can check your answer by using the conversion factor on the left.

$$1.25 \text{ mol } CO_2 \times \frac{44.0 \text{ g } CO_2}{1 \text{ mol } CO_2} = 55.0 \text{ g } CO_2$$

≡Quick〉Lab

Modeling a Mole

Materials

bolt, 2 nuts, 2 washers, balance

Procedure

1. Measure and record the mass of one bolt, one nut, and one washer. Each piece of hardware will represent an atom of a different element.

2. Assemble the bolt, nuts, and washers together so that they form a model of a molecule known as BN_2W_2.

3. Predict the mass of BN_2W_2.

4. Test your prediction by finding the mass of your model.

Analyze and Conclude

1. **Analyzing Data** Did your prediction match the actual mass of your model? Explain.

2. **Calculating** How many models of your molecule can you make with 20 washers and as many nuts and bolts as you need?

3. **Calculating** How many models of your molecule can you make with 100 grams of nuts and as many bolts and washers as you need?

Chemical Calculations

Think about baking a cake like the one in Figure 7. The directions on a box of cake mix might tell you to add two eggs and one cup of water to the cake mix. Suppose you wanted to make three cakes. Although the directions don't tell you specifically how many eggs and how much water are required for three cakes, you could figure out the amounts. To make three cakes, you would need three times as much of each ingredient—six eggs, three cups of water, and three packages of cake mix.

Chemical equations can be read as recipes for making new substances. Figure 8 shows the balanced equation for the formation of water. You can read this equation as, "Two molecules of hydrogen react with one molecule of oxygen and form two molecules of water." In terms of moles, the equation reads, "Two moles of hydrogen react with one mole of oxygen and form two moles of water." To convert from moles to mass, you need to use the molar masses as conversion factors. Figure 8 shows how the same equation can also be read as, "4.0 grams of H_2 reacts with 32.0 grams of O_2 and forms 36.0 grams of H_2O."

How many grams of oxygen would you need to make 144 grams of water? ⌐ **In chemical reactions, the mass of a reactant or product can be calculated by using a balanced chemical equation and molar masses of the reactants and products.** The chemical equation tells you how to relate amounts of reactants to amounts of products. Molar masses let you convert those amounts into masses.

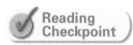 **Reading Checkpoint** *How do you convert from moles to mass?*

Converting Mass to Moles To calculate how much oxygen is required to make 144 grams of water, you need to begin with a balanced chemical equation for the reaction.

$$2H_2 + O_2 \longrightarrow 2H_2O$$

The first step in your calculations is to determine how many moles of water you are trying to make. By using the molar mass of water, you can convert the given mass of water into moles.

$$144 \text{ g } H_2O \times \frac{1 \text{ mol H2O}}{18.0 \text{ g H2O}} = 8.00 \text{ mol } H_2O$$

Formation of Water					
Equation	$2H_2$	+	O_2	→	$2H_2O$
Amount	2 mol		1 mol		2 mol
Molar Mass	2.0 g/mol		32.0 g/mol		18.0 g/mol
Mass (Moles × Molar Mass)	4.0 g	+	32.0 g	→	36.0 g

Figure 7 A cake recipe tells you how much of each ingredient to use for each cake you bake. **Using Analogies** *How is a cake recipe like a chemical equation?*

Figure 8 In a balanced chemical equation, the number of atoms of each element on the left equals the number of atoms of each element on the right. By using molar masses, you can show that the mass of the reactants equals the mass of the products.

Using Mole Ratios Remember the balanced chemical equation for the formation of water. You can read it as, "Two moles of hydrogen react with one mole of oxygen and form two moles of water." Because each mole of oxygen that reacts will yield two moles of water, you can write the following conversion factors, or mole ratios.

$$\frac{1 \text{ mol } O_2}{2 \text{ mol } H_2O} \qquad \frac{2 \text{ mol } H_2O}{1 \text{ mol } O_2}$$

The mole ratio on the left allows you to convert moles of water to moles of oxygen. Now you can calculate how many moles of oxygen are required to produce eight moles of water:

$$8.00 \text{ mol } H_2O \times \frac{1 \text{ mol } O_2}{2 \text{ mol } H_2O} = 4.00 \text{ mol } O_2$$

Converting Moles to Mass The last step is to convert moles of O_2 to grams of O_2 by using the molar mass of O_2 as a conversion factor.

$$4.00 \text{ mol } O_2 \times \frac{32.0 \text{ g } O_2}{1 \text{ mol } O_2} = 128 \text{ g } O_2$$

So, in order to produce 144 grams of H_2O, you must supply 128 grams of O_2. Notice that you used the concept of a mole in two ways to solve this problem. In the first and last step, you used a molar mass to convert between mass and moles. In the middle step, you used the mole ratio to convert moles of a product into moles of a reactant.

Section 7.1 Assessment

Reviewing Concepts

1. What is the law of conservation of mass?

2. Why does a chemical equation need to be balanced?

3. Why do chemists use the mole as a counting unit?

4. What information do you need to predict the mass of a reactant or product in a chemical reaction?

5. What is a mole ratio?

Critical Thinking

6. Applying Concepts The following equation describes how sodium and chlorine react to produce sodium chloride.

$$2Na + Cl_2 \longrightarrow 2NaCl$$

Is the equation balanced? Explain your answer.

7. Calculating Ammonia, NH_3, can be made by reacting nitrogen with hydrogen.

$$N_2 + 3H_2 \longrightarrow 2NH_3$$

How many moles of NH_3 can be made if 7.5 moles of H_2 react with enough N_2?

8. Calculating What mass of NH_3 can be made from 35.0 g of N_2?

9. Balance the following equation.

$$K + Br_2 \longrightarrow KBr$$

10. Write a balanced chemical equation for the formation of magnesium oxide, MgO, from magnesium and oxygen.

7.2 Types of Reactions

Reading Focus

Key Concepts

- What are the general types of chemical reactions?
- How did the discovery of subatomic particles affect the classification of reactions?

Vocabulary

- synthesis reaction
- decomposition reaction
- single-replacement reaction
- double-replacement reaction
- combustion reaction
- oxidation-reduction reaction

Reading Strategy

Previewing Skim the section and begin a concept map like the one below that identifies types of reactions with a general form. As you read, add the general form of each type of reaction.

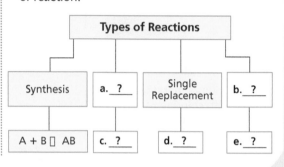

Types of Reactions

Synthesis — a. ? — Single Replacement — b. ?

$A + B \rightarrow AB$ — c. ? — d. ? — e. ?

The walls of the cave shown in Figure 9 are solid limestone. When hydrochloric acid is dropped on limestone, a chemical reaction occurs in which a gas is produced. Geologists can use this reaction to determine whether a rock sample contains the mineral calcium carbonate, $CaCO_3$. When a rock containing calcium carbonate reacts with hydrochloric acid, it fizzes. The bubbles contain carbon dioxide gas.

Many other reactions produce carbon dioxide. For example, heating limestone produces carbon dioxide. So does burning gasoline. However, just because two reactions have the same product, you cannot assume that they are the same type of reaction.

Classifying Reactions

Just as you can classify matter into different types, you can classify chemical reactions into different types. Reactions are often classified by the type of reactant or the number of reactants and products. **Some general types of chemical reactions are synthesis reactions, decomposition reactions, single-replacement reactions, double-replacement reactions, and combustion reactions.** Each type describes a different way in which reactants interact to form products.

Figure 9 The walls and other formations of Blanchard Springs Caverns in Arkansas contain the mineral calcium carbonate, $CaCO_3$.

Figure 10 Sodium metal reacts vigorously with chlorine to form sodium chloride, NaCl.
Interpreting Photos *What evidence in this photograph tells you that a chemical reaction is taking place?*

Synthesis A **synthesis reaction** is a reaction in which two or more substances react to form a single substance. The reactants may be either elements or compounds. The product synthesized is always a compound. The general equation for a synthesis reaction is

$$A + B \longrightarrow AB$$

Figure 10 shows what happens when sodium reacts with chlorine. The product of this reaction is the compound sodium chloride, which appears as a whitish cloud of solid particles. You are probably more familiar with sodium chloride as table salt. You can describe the synthesis of sodium chloride with the following equation.

$$2Na + Cl_2 \longrightarrow 2NaCl$$

Another example of a synthesis reaction is hydrogen and oxygen reacting to form water.

$$2H_2 + O_2 \longrightarrow 2H_2O$$

This reaction is used to generate electricity for satellites and spacecraft.

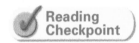 **Reading Checkpoint** *What is a synthesis reaction?*

Decomposition The opposite of synthesis is decomposition. A **decomposition reaction** is a reaction in which a compound breaks down into two or more simpler substances. The reactant in a decomposition reaction must be a compound. The products may be elements or compounds. The general equation for a decomposition reaction is

$$AB \longrightarrow A + B$$

When electricity passes through water, the water decomposes into hydrogen gas and oxygen gas. You can describe the decomposition of water by writing the following equation.

$$2H_2O \longrightarrow 2H_2 + O_2$$

Notice that this reaction is the opposite of the synthesis of water.

Another example of decomposition occurs in the making of cement. Cement factories use a giant kiln, or oven, to heat a mixture of clay and limestone. The heat causes the calcium carbonate in the limestone to decompose into lime, CaO, and carbon dioxide.

$$CaCO_3 \longrightarrow CaO + CO_2$$

The carbon dioxide escapes the kiln through a smokestack. The clay-and-lime mixture is cooled and ground into cement powder.

The How It Works box on page 201 describes a decomposition reaction that is used to make automobiles safer.

Go Online
SCILINKS

For: Links on chemical reactions
Visit: www.SciLinks.org
Web Code: ccn-1076

Automobile Safety: Air Bags

Air bags are inflatable cushions built into a car's steering wheel or dashboard. In a crash, the bags inflate, protecting both the driver and the passenger. The whole process takes 0.04 second. **Interpreting Diagrams** *What is the source of the gas that fills an air bag?*

Testing air bags
Air bags have been shown to reduce the risk of serious injury in a head-on collision by 30 percent. New cars have air bags on both the driver and passenger sides.

1 Collision A collision triggers the car's crash sensors, which send an electrical signal to the igniter in the steering wheel.

Crash sensor

Ignition unit

Igniter

Sodium azide pellets

Air bag folded into steering wheel

Steering wheel

Nitrogen gas leaks through holes

Nitrogen gas

2 Air bag inflates The igniter sets off a combustion reaction that heats up the sodium azide (NaN_3) contained in the ignition unit. When it is heated, the sodium azide decomposes into metallic sodium (Na) and nitrogen gas (N_2). The nitrogen gas inflates the air bag. The decomposition reaction is $2NaN_3 \rightarrow 2Na + 3N_2$.

Nontoxic residue of secondary reactions

Deflated air bag

Igniter

Sodium azide pellets decomposing

Electrical signal from crash sensor

3 Air bag deflates The nitrogen escapes through tiny holes in the bag, causing immediate deflation of the air bag. Because sodium is dangerous (due to its high reactivity), the ignition unit also contains other chemicals that react with sodium to form a nontoxic material.

Figure 11 A single-replacement reaction occurs when copper wire is submerged in a solution of silver nitrate. As the copper replaces the silver in the silver nitrate solution, the solution turns blue, and silver crystals form on the wire.

Figure 12 Potassium reacts with water in a single-replacement reaction that produces hydrogen gas and potassium hydroxide.

Single Replacement A **single-replacement reaction** is a reaction in which one element takes the place of another element in a compound. Single-replacement reactions have the general form

$$A + BC \longrightarrow B + AC$$

Suppose you dip a coil of copper wire into a solution of silver nitrate and water, as shown in Figure 11. A vivid chemical reaction takes place as the solution turns blue and the submerged part of the wire becomes coated with a silvery metal. In this reaction, the copper replaces the silver in silver nitrate to form copper(II) nitrate. The equation for this reaction is

$$Cu + 2AgNO_3 \longrightarrow 2Ag + Cu(NO_3)_2$$

Notice that one of the products is silver, which you can see adhering to the wire in Figure 12. The other product, copper(II) nitrate, gives the solution its blue color.

Recall that alkali metals are very reactive elements. Figure 12 shows potassium reacting with water. This is another example of a single-replacement reaction, as the element potassium replaces hydrogen in water to form potassium hydroxide, KOH.

$$2K + 2H_2O \longrightarrow H_2 + 2KOH$$

The heat produced by this chemical reaction causes the hydrogen gas to ignite explosively.

 Reading Checkpoint *What is a single-replacement reaction?*

Double Replacement A **double-replacement reaction** is one in which two different compounds exchange positive ions and form two new compounds. The general form of a double replacement reaction is

$$AB + CD \longrightarrow AD + CB$$

Notice that two replacements take place in this reaction. Not only is A replacing C, but C is also replacing A.

Solutions of lead(II) nitrate, $Pb(NO_3)_2$, and potassium iodide, KI, are both colorless. However, when these solutions are mixed, as shown in Figure 13, a yellow precipitate forms as a result of a double-replacement reaction. The equation for this reaction is

$$Pb(NO_3)_2 + 2KI \longrightarrow PbI_2 + 2KNO_3$$

The lead ions in $Pb(NO_3)_2$, trade places with the potassium ions in KI. The products are lead(II) iodide, PbI_2, which precipitates out of solution, and potassium nitrate, KNO_3, which remains in solution.

When geologists test the calcium carbonate content in a rock, they make use of the following double-replacement reaction.

$$CaCO_3 + 2HCl \longrightarrow CaCl_2 + H_2CO_3$$

One of the products of this reaction is calcium chloride, $CaCl_2$. The other product is carbonic acid, H_2CO_3, which decomposes into carbon dioxide gas and water.

$$H_2CO_3 \longrightarrow CO_2 + H_2O$$

Figure 13 When potassium iodide solution is poured into a solution of lead(II) nitrate, a double-replacement reaction takes place. Lead(II) iodide forms as a yellow precipitate. **Comparing and Contrasting** *How does a double-replacement reaction differ from a single-replacement reaction?*

Quick Lab

Identifying a Type of Reaction

Materials
piece of zinc, copper(II) sulfate ($CuSO_4$) solution, 250-mL beaker, tongs, paper towel

Procedure

1. Place the zinc in the beaker and add enough $CuSO_4$ solution to cover the zinc as shown. **CAUTION** *Be careful when using chemicals. Copper sulfate is toxic.*

2. After 5 minutes, carefully remove the zinc from the solution using the tongs and place the zinc on the paper towel to dry. Observe any changes that have occurred to the zinc and the solution of $CuSO_4$. **CAUTION** *Follow your teacher's instructions for disposal of used chemicals. Wash your hands with soap or detergent before leaving the laboratory.*

Analyze and Conclude

1. **Observing** What clues indicate that a chemical reaction has taken place?

2. **Applying Concepts** What were the reactants in this reaction? What were the products? Write a balanced chemical equation for the reaction.

3. **Classifying** Is this a single-replacement or double-replacement reaction? Explain.

Combustion

A **combustion reaction** is one in which a substance reacts rapidly with oxygen, often producing heat and light. The burning of natural gas, shown in Figure 14, is an example of combustion. The main component of natural gas is methane, CH_4. When methane burns in an unlimited supply of oxygen, the following reaction occurs.

$$CH_4 + 2O_2 \longrightarrow CO_2 + 2H_2O$$

The products of the reaction are carbon dioxide and water. The combustion of methane also generates both heat and light.

By now you know the chemical equation for the combustion of hydrogen.

$$2H_2 + O_2 \longrightarrow 2H_2O$$

Notice that you could also classify this reaction as the synthesis of water. The classifications for chemical reactions sometimes overlap.

Reactions as Electron Transfers

So far, you have learned that chemical reactions can be identified by the type of reactant or by the number of reactants and products. For example, in a combustion reaction one of the reactants must be oxygen. In a synthesis reaction, two or more reactants combine to form a single product.

As scientists learned more about the structure of the atom, they found different ways to describe how reactions take place. **The discovery of subatomic particles enabled scientists to classify certain chemical reactions as transfers of electrons between atoms.** A reaction in which electrons are transferred from one reactant to another is called an **oxidation-reduction reaction,** or redox reaction.

Oxidation For a long time, people have known that metals react with oxygen. Calcium, for instance, reacts with oxygen and forms calcium oxide (CaO), shown in Figure 15. Iron reacts with oxygen and forms rust, or iron(III) oxide (Fe_2O_3). These types of synthesis reactions, in which a metal combines with oxygen, traditionally have been classified as oxidations.

When calcium reacts with oxygen, the following reaction takes place.

$$2Ca + O_2 \longrightarrow 2CaO$$

Notice that while the atoms of both reactants (Ca and O_2) are neutral, the product of the reaction is a compound composed of ions (Ca^{2+} and O^{2-}). When calcium reacts with oxygen, each neutral calcium atom loses two electrons and becomes a calcium ion with a charge of 2+.

$$Ca \longrightarrow Ca^{2+} + 2e^-$$

Figure 14 A Bunsen burner generates heat and light by the combustion of natural gas.
Interpreting Photos *What reactants or products are visible in the reaction shown above?*

Figure 15 Calcium oxide, or lime, is produced when calcium burns in the presence of oxygen. In this reaction, the calcium is oxidized and the oxygen is reduced.

Any process in which an element loses electrons during a chemical reaction is called oxidation. A reactant is oxidized if it loses electrons. Note that the modern definition of oxidation is much broader than the original meaning. Oxygen doesn't always have to be present in order for an element to lose electrons. For example, when sodium reacts with chlorine, each neutral sodium atom loses one electron and becomes a sodium ion, Na^+.

Reduction As calcium atoms lose electrons during the synthesis of calcium oxide, the oxygen atoms gain electrons. As each neutral oxygen atom gains two electrons, it becomes an ion with a charge of $2-$.

$$O + 2e^- \longrightarrow O^{2-}$$

The process in which an element gains electrons during a chemical reaction is called reduction. A reactant is said to be reduced if it gains electrons.

Oxidation and reduction always occur together. When one element loses electrons, another element must gain electrons. Note that oxidation-reduction reactions do not always involve complete transfers of electrons. For example, in the synthesis of water, hydrogen is oxidized as it partially loses electrons. Oxygen is reduced as it partially gains electrons.

For: Links on oxidation and reduction

Visit: www.SciLinks.org

Web Code: ccn-1072

Section 7.2 Assessment

Reviewing Concepts

1. What are five general types of reactions?
2. How did the discovery of subatomic particles affect the classification of reactions?
3. The synthesis of water is described by the equation $2H_2 + O_2 \longrightarrow 2H_2O$. How is the decomposition of water related to this reaction? Explain, using a chemical equation.
4. Explain the difference between a single-replacement reaction and a double-replacement reaction.
5. Propane, C_3H_8, is frequently used in camping stoves. When propane undergoes combustion, what are the products formed?
6. Is the reaction represented by the following equation a redox reaction? Explain your answer.

$$2Hg + O_2 \longrightarrow 2HgO$$

Critical Thinking

7. **Predicting** What is the product of the synthesis reaction between magnesium and iodine? Explain your answer.
8. **Classifying** Identify these reactions as synthesis, decomposition, single replacement, double replacement, or combustion.
   a. $Pb(NO_3)_2 + 2HCl \longrightarrow PbCl_2 + 2HNO_3$
   b. $2C_2H_6 + 7O_2 \longrightarrow 4CO_2 + 6H_2O$
   c. $Ca + 2HCl \longrightarrow CaCl_2 + H_2$
   d. $2SO_2 + O_2 \longrightarrow 2SO_3$

Writing in Science

Explanatory Paragraph Write a paragraph explaining why the formation of water can be classified as a synthesis, combustion, or oxidation-reduction reaction.

7.3 Energy Changes in Reactions

Reading Focus

Key Concepts
- What happens to chemical bonds during a chemical reaction?
- What happens to energy during a chemical reaction?

Vocabulary
- chemical energy
- exothermic reaction
- endothermic reaction

Reading Strategy

Comparing and Contrasting Copy the Venn diagram. As you read, complete it to show the differences between exothermic and endothermic reactions.

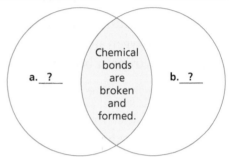

Exothermic Reaction   Endothermic Reaction

a. ?   Chemical bonds are broken and formed.   b. ?

If you've ever had a barbecue, you may have used a gas grill like the one shown in Figure 16. Many types of gas grills use propane, C_3H_8. You can think of a propane grill as the scene of a chemical reaction—specifically, a combustion reaction. The reactants are propane and oxygen, and the products are carbon dioxide and water. However, the description of this reaction is incomplete unless you consider the heat and light produced. Heat, after all, is the reason for using a propane grill.

Chemical Bonds and Energy

The heat produced by a propane grill is a form of energy. When you write the chemical equation for the combustion of propane, you can include "heat" on the right side of the equation.

$$C_3H_8 + 5O_2 \longrightarrow 3CO_2 + 4H_2O + \text{Heat}$$

This equation states that the heat released in the reaction came from the reactants. **Chemical energy** is the energy stored in the chemical bonds of a substance. A propane molecule has ten single covalent bonds (eight C—H bonds and two C—C bonds). The chemical energy of a propane molecule is the energy stored in these bonds. Likewise, oxygen, carbon dioxide, and water molecules all have energy stored in their chemical bonds.

Figure 16 Many portable barbecue grills burn propane gas.

Energy changes in chemical reactions are determined by changes that occur in chemical bonding. ◉ **Chemical reactions involve the breaking of chemical bonds in the reactants and the formation of chemical bonds in the products.** In the combustion of propane, the bonds in propane and oxygen molecules are broken, while the bonds in carbon dioxide and water molecules are formed.

Breaking Bonds As Figure 17 illustrates, each propane molecule reacts with five oxygen molecules. In order for the reaction to occur, eight C—H single bonds, two C—C single bonds, and five O==O double bonds must be broken. Breaking chemical bonds requires energy. This is why propane grills have an igniter, a device that produces a spark. The spark provides enough energy to break the bonds of reacting molecules and get the reaction started.

Forming Bonds Figure 17 also shows you that for each molecule of propane burned, three molecules of carbon dioxide and four molecules of water are formed. This means that six C==O double bonds and eight O—H single bonds are formed in the reaction. The formation of chemical bonds releases energy. The heat and light given off by a propane stove result from the formation of new chemical bonds. The bonds form as the carbon, hydrogen, and oxygen atoms in the propane and oxygen molecules are rearranged into molecules of carbon dioxide and water.

 Reading Checkpoint *Does breaking chemical bonds require energy or release energy?*

Propane Combustion

C_3H_8	+	$5O_2$	$\longrightarrow$	$3CO_2$	+	$4H_2O$	+	Heat
propane		oxygen		carbon dioxide		water		
8 C–H, 2 C–C bonds broken		5 O=O bonds broken	$\longrightarrow$	6 C=O bonds formed		8 O–H bonds formed		

Figure 17 In order for the combustion of propane to occur, all the chemical bonds in the reactants (propane and oxygen) must be broken. The formation of the chemical bonds in the products completes the reaction.
Inferring *How does the chemical energy of the reactants compare to the chemical energy of the products in this reaction?*

A **B**

Figure 18 In chemical reactions, energy is either released or absorbed. **A** In an exothermic reaction, energy is released to the surroundings. **B** In an endothermic reaction, energy is absorbed from the surroundings. **Using Graphs** *How do the energy diagrams show that energy is conserved in chemical reactions?*

Exothermic and Endothermic Reactions

Recall that physical changes can release or absorb energy. During an exothermic change, such as freezing, energy is released to the surroundings. During an endothermic change, such as melting, energy is absorbed from the surroundings. Energy also flows into and out of chemical changes. **During a chemical reaction, energy is either released or absorbed.**

Exothermic Reactions A chemical reaction that releases energy to its surroundings is called an **exothermic reaction.** In exothermic reactions, the energy released as the products form is greater than the energy required to break the bonds in the reactants.

Combustion is an example of an extremely exothermic reaction. When 1 mole of propane reacts with 5 moles of oxygen, 2220 kJ (kilojoules) of heat is released. You can use this value to replace "heat" in the combustion equation written earlier.

$$C_3H_8 + 5O_2 \longrightarrow 3CO_2 + 4H_2O + 2220 \text{ kJ}$$

Figure 18A shows how chemical energy changes during an exothermic reaction. Notice that the chemical energy of the reactants is greater than the chemical energy of the products. The difference between these amounts of energy equals the amount of heat given off by the reaction.

In any reaction, the chemical energy reaches a peak before the reactants change into products. This peak represents the amount of energy required to break the chemical bonds of the reactants. Unless reacting particles collide with enough energy to break these bonds, the reaction will not occur. For example, at room temperature, the collisions between propane and oxygen molecules are not energetic enough to result in combustion. However, if you increase the temperature by adding a spark, some of the molecules around the spark move faster and are able to collide with enough energy to react.

Endothermic Reactions A chemical reaction that absorbs energy from its surroundings is called an **endothermic reaction.** In an endothermic reaction, more energy is required to break the bonds in the reactants than is released by the formation of the products.

Figure 18B shows the energy diagram for an endothermic reaction. Notice that the energy of the products is greater than the energy of the reactants. The difference between these amounts of energy equals the amount of heat that must be absorbed from the surroundings.

When mercury(II) oxide is heated to a temperature of about 450°C, it breaks down into mercury and oxygen, as shown in Figure 19. The decomposition of mercury(II) oxide is an endothermic reaction that can be described by the following equation.

$$2HgO + 181.7 \text{ kJ} \longrightarrow 2Hg + O_2$$

Because heat is absorbed, the energy term appears on the left side of the equation. For every 2 moles of HgO that decomposes, 181.7 kJ of heat must be absorbed.

Conservation of Energy

In an exothermic reaction, the chemical energy of the reactants is converted into heat plus the chemical energy of the products. In an endothermic reaction, heat plus the chemical energy of the reactants is converted into the chemical energy of the products. In both cases, the total amount of energy before and after the reaction is the same. This principle is known as the law of conservation of energy. You will read more about how energy is conserved later.

Figure 19 The orange-red powder in the bottom of the test tube is mercury(II) oxide. At about 450°C, mercury(II) oxide decomposes into oxygen gas (which escapes from the test tube) and mercury (droplets of which can be seen collecting on the sides of the test tube).

Section 7.3 Assessment

Reviewing Concepts

1. ⬤ What happens to chemical bonds as a chemical reaction occurs?

2. ⬤ How do chemical reactions involve energy?

3. Is the combustion of propane endothermic or exothermic?

4. When propane reacts with oxygen, does the surrounding area become warmer or cooler?

5. Is energy created during an exothermic reaction? Explain.

Critical Thinking

6. **Inferring** Explain why methane does not react with oxygen at room temperature.

7. **Calculating** Methane reacts with oxygen in the following combustion reaction.

$$CH_4 + 2O_2 \longrightarrow CO_2 + 2H_2O$$

What bonds are broken when one molecule of methane reacts with two molecules of oxygen?

⟨ **Connecting** ⊂ **Concepts** ⟩

Chemical Bonds Reread the descriptions of chemical bonds in Sections 6.1 and 6.2. Then, describe the decomposition of mercury(II) oxide. Specify which bonds are ionic and which bonds are covalent.

Firefighting

Uncontrolled fires threaten lives and property and can have a devastating effect on the environment. To fight fires, it is necessary to understand how they start, and what sustains them.

Fire is the result of combustion, a rapid reaction between oxygen and fuel. During combustion, fuel and oxygen react to form carbon dioxide, water, and heat. Most fires in rural areas, called wildfires, are caused by people being careless with campfires or cigarettes. Arson and lightning are also common causes. Usually the fire starts in an area of dry grass, which will ignite at a temperature of 150–200°C. Burning grass can create enough heat to ignite bushes, and these, in turn, may be tall enough to carry the flames into trees. (Wood has a higher ignition temperature, around 260°C.) Environmental conditions, such as drought that has left vegetation dry, and strong winds, can cause a small fire to spread. Wind also carries fire forward into new areas. Burning twigs and branches that become detached from trees can be blown into new areas of vegetation.

Dousing
Planes or helicopters are used to drop water or a fire-retardant slurry on a large fire. The slurry contains ammonium sulfate, $(NH_4)_2SO_4$, which helps smother the fire.

Firefighter
Firefighters wear protective clothing, helmets, and goggles. This firefighter also carries a shovel for digging trenches to stop a fire spreading.

Backburning

One way to stop a big fire is to start a smaller fire. This technique, called backburning, burns off vegetation between the fireline and the main fire. When the two fires meet, the blaze stops spreading because the land on either side has already been burned.

Boundary of Hanford site

Extent of fire

Smoke plume

Firebreaks

In parts of the world where wildfires are common, strips of land are cleared of combustible vegetation to create firebreaks. Firefighters also dig firebreaks during fires to prevent fires from spreading.

Wildfire in Washington State

This satellite picture shows a forest fire that raged for two months in 2000 at the Department of Energy's site at Hanford. The fire was started by a vehicle fire and reached more than 500 square kilometers.

Going Further

- Write a paragraph explaining how dousing, backburning, and firebreaks affect the chemical reactions involved in wildfires.

- Take a Discovery Channel Video Field Trip by watching "Taming the Flames."

DISCOVERY CHANNEL SCHOOL
Video Field Trip

7.4 Reaction Rates

Key Concept

- What does a reaction rate tell you?
- What factors cause reaction rates to change?

Vocabulary

- reaction rate
- catalyst

Reading Strategy

Building Vocabulary
Copy the partially completed web diagram at the right. Then, as you read, complete it with key terms from this section.

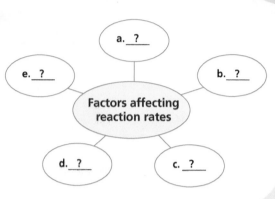

a. ___?___
b. ___?___
c. ___?___
d. ___?___
e. ___?___

Factors affecting reaction rates

Figure 20 A cyclist burns the Calories in a banana faster than a person walking would. But burning the banana outside the body would release the energy of the banana even faster.

You may have heard of athletes "burning Calories" when they exercise. A Calorie is a unit of energy used in the field of nutrition. The average banana, for instance, contains about 100 Calories. The cyclist in Figure 20 can use up, or burn, as many as 10,000 Calories during the course of a race. That adds up to a lot of bananas!

If you eat a banana, you provide your body with about 100 Calories to burn. This energy is released in a series of reactions that take place inside your body. A much faster way of releasing the energy contained in a banana is to burn it—outside the body—in a combustion reaction. In both cases, the total amount of energy released is the same. However, the time it takes for the energy to be released is different in each case.

Reactions Over Time

The progress of any chemical reaction can be measured over time. Different reactions have different durations. Some reactions, such as the explosion of TNT, happen almost instantaneously. Other reactions, such as tree leaves changing color during autumn, happen gradually.

Any change that happens over a period of time can be expressed as a rate. For example, speed is the rate that distance changes over time. A **reaction rate** is the rate at which reactants change into products over time. **Reaction rates tell you how fast a reaction is going.** That is, how fast the reactants are being consumed, how fast the products are being formed, or how fast energy is being absorbed or released.

Factors Affecting Reaction Rates

Recall that chemical reactions involve collisions between particles of reactants. The reaction rate depends on how often these particles collide. If the collisions occur more frequently, then the reaction rate increases. If the collisions occur less frequently, then the reaction rate decreases. Almost any reaction rate can be changed by varying the conditions under which the reaction takes place. ◯ **Factors that affect reaction rates include temperature, surface area, concentration, stirring, and catalysts.**

Temperature Suppose you are frying an egg in a frying pan. What happens if you increase the heat under the pan? The hotter the pan, the faster the egg will cook. Generally, an increase in temperature will increase the reaction rate, while a decrease in temperature will decrease the reaction rate. For instance, you store milk in a refrigerator to slow down the reactions that cause the milk to spoil. These reactions don't stop completely. Even milk stored in a refrigerator will eventually spoil. But the rate of spoiling decreases if the milk is kept cold.

Increasing the temperature of a substance causes its particles to move faster, on average. Particles that move faster are both more likely to collide and more likely to react. If the number of collisions that produce reactions increases, then the reaction rate increases.

 Reading Checkpoint *How does temperature affect reaction rates?*

Surface Area Grain may not strike you as a dangerous material, but it can be explosive under the right conditions. The cause of the fire in Figure 21 was a combustion reaction between grain dust (suspended in the air) and oxygen. The rate of combustion was very rapid due to the small particle size of the grain dust.

The smaller the particle size of a given mass, the larger is its surface area. Imagine using a newspaper to cover the floor of a room. If you keep all the sections folded together, you can only cover a small area. However, if you separate the newspaper into pages and lay them out like tiles, you can cover a much larger area with the same mass of paper.

An increase in surface area increases the exposure of reactants to one another. The greater this exposure, the more collisions there are that involve reacting particles. With more collisions, more particles will react. This is why increasing the surface area of a reactant tends to increase the reaction rate.

For: Links on factors affecting reaction rate
Visit: www.SciLinks.org
Web Code: ccn-1074

Figure 21 This grain elevator in Potlatch, Idaho, exploded when grain dust reacted with oxygen in the air.
Applying Concepts *How does surface area affect reaction rates?*

Observing the Action of Catalysts

Materials

5 test tubes, test-tube rack, marking pencil, dropper pipet, wood splint, platinum wire, 0.1 g manganese dioxide (MnO_2), 5 drops of copper(II) chloride ($CuCl_2$) solution, 0.1 g raw potato, graduated cylinder, 25 mL hydrogen peroxide (H_2O_2)

Procedure

1. Label the 5 test tubes from A to E with the marking pencil.

2. Put a small piece of platinum wire in test tube A. Add a tiny amount (about the tip of the wood splint) of MnO_2 to test tube B. Use the dropper pipet to put 5 drops of $CuCl_2$ in test tube C. Put a piece of potato in test tube D. Test tube E should remain empty for now. **CAUTION** MnO_2 and $CuCl_2$ are toxic.

3. Carefully add 5 mL of hydrogen peroxide to test tube A. **CAUTION** Be careful when using chemicals. Observe how fast the bubbles are produced.

4. Repeat Step 3 with test tubes B through E.

Analyze and Conclude

1. **Observing** What effect did the platinum wire, MnO_2, $CuCl_2$, and the potato have on the rate at which the bubbles were produced in the hydrogen peroxide?

2. **Comparing and Contrasting** Which catalyst(s) caused the reaction to go the fastest? The slowest?

3. **Inferring** Why did you put only hydrogen peroxide in test tube E?

Stirring You can also increase the exposure of reactants to each other by stirring them. For example, when you wash your clothes in a washing machine, particles of detergent react with particles of the stains on your clothes. This reaction would go slowly if you just left your clothes soaking in a tub of water and detergent. A washing machine speeds up the reaction by stirring the contents back and forth. Collisions between the particles of the reactants are more likely to happen. Stirring the reactants will generally increase the reaction rate.

Concentration Another way you can change the reaction rate is to change the concentration of the reactants. Concentration refers to the number of particles in a given volume. The more reacting particles that are present in a given volume, the more opportunities there are for collisions involving those particles. The reaction rate is faster.

Both of the beakers in Figure 22 contain a piece of material dipped in dye solution. Dyeing is a chemical reaction in which dye particles react with the particles of the material being dyed. The material dipped in the more concentrated dye becomes colored more quickly.

For gases, concentration changes with pressure. The greater the pressure of a gaseous reactant, the greater is its concentration, and the faster is the reaction rate.

Figure 22 The dye solution in the left beaker is more concentrated than the solution in the right. Increasing the concentration of the dye increases the rate of color change in the material.

Catalysts Sometimes you can change a reaction rate by using catalysts. A **catalyst** is a substance that affects the reaction rate without being used up in the reaction. Chemists often use catalysts to speed up a reaction or enable a reaction to occur at a lower temperature. In the making of sulfuric acid, one of the steps involved is the reaction of sulfur dioxide with oxygen to form sulfur trioxide. This reaction happens very slowly without a catalyst such as vanadium(V) oxide.

$$2SO_2 + O_2 \xrightarrow{V_2O_5} 2SO_3$$

Since the catalyst is neither a reactant nor a product, it is written over the arrow. Because the catalyst is not consumed, it can be used to speed up the same reaction over and over again.

Recall that in order for a reaction to take place, the reacting particles must collide with enough energy to break the chemical bonds of those particles. As shown in Figure 23, a catalyst lowers this energy barrier. One way that a catalyst can do this is by providing a surface on which the reacting particles can come together. Imagine that you go to a party and make several new friends. By bringing people together, the party has made it easier for you to form those friendships. Similarly, a catalyst can "invite" reacting particles together so that they are more likely to react.

Reaction Energy—Catalyzed and Uncatalyzed

Reaction without catalyst
Reaction with catalyst

Figure 23 The graph above shows how a catalyst lowers the amount of energy required for effective collisions between reacting particles.
Using Graphs *In an exothermic reaction, how does a catalyst affect the amount of energy released?*

Section 7.4 Assessment

Reviewing Concepts

1. ⬤ What does a reaction rate tell you?
2. ⬤ What five factors affect reaction rates?
3. Explain why reactions take place faster at higher temperatures.
4. When you add baking soda to vinegar, the mixture fizzes as carbon dioxide gas is produced. Suppose you added water to the vinegar before you mixed it with the baking soda. What do you think would happen to the rate of carbon dioxide production?
5. How does a catalyst make a reaction go faster?
6. Platinum is a catalyst for the decomposition of hydrogen peroxide into water and oxygen.

$$2H_2O_2 \xrightarrow{Pt} 2H_2O + O_2$$

What would you expect to see if platinum were added to hydrogen peroxide solution?

Critical Thinking

7. **Applying Concepts** Explain why, if you want to store uncooked hamburger meat for a month, you put it in a freezer rather than a refrigerator.
8. **Evaluating** The reaction between magnesium and hydrochloric acid produces hydrogen. If you increase the concentration of HCl, the reaction takes place faster. Could HCl be considered a catalyst for this reaction? Explain your answer.

Writing in Science

Compare and Contrast Paragraph Write a paragraph explaining how temperature, concentration, surface area, and catalysts affect reaction rates.

Suppose you're waiting in line for a toll booth at a bridge, like some of the cars shown in Figure 24. You notice that every time a car passes by a toll booth in the direction you are traveling, another car passes through the toll plaza in the opposite direction. The rate of cars entering equals the rate of cars exiting. As a result, the number of cars on either side of the toll plaza remains constant, although cars are continually entering and exiting the bridge.

Types of Equilibria

The traffic at a toll bridge is similar to a system in equilibrium. **Equilibrium** (plural *equilibria*) is a state in which the forward and reverse paths of a change take place at the same rate.

Recall that changes to matter are either physical or chemical. When opposing physical changes take place at the same rate, a physical equilibrium is reached. When opposing chemical changes take place at the same rate, a chemical equilibrium is reached.

Figure 24 About 190,000 vehicles pass through the toll plaza of New York City's Verrazano-Narrows Bridge every day.

Physical Equilibrium What happens when you pour some water into a jar and then close the lid? You might think that nothing happens at all. But in fact, some of the water undergoes a physical change by evaporating. As more water evaporates, some of the water vapor condenses. Eventually, the rate of evaporation equals the rate of condensation, and the system reaches equilibrium as shown in Figure 25.

When liquid water is in equilibrium with water vapor, you can describe the system by writing this equation.

$$H_2O(l) \rightleftharpoons H_2O(g)$$

Here, *l* stands for liquid and *g* stands for gas. The pair of arrows in this equation indicates that the forward change (evaporation) and the reverse change (condensation) are happening simultaneously and at the same rate. Both the forward and reverse changes are physical changes, so this equation represents a physical equilibrium. **When a physical change does not go to completion, a physical equilibrium is established between the forward and reverse changes.**

Chemical Equilibrium All the chemical equations you have seen so far have been written with single arrows, which suggest that all reactions go to completion in one direction. In reality, however, most reactions are reversible to some extent. A **reversible reaction** is a reaction in which the conversion of reactants into products and the conversion of products into reactants can happen simultaneously.

In the previous section, you read about the synthesis of sulfur trioxide from sulfur dioxide and oxygen. This is actually a reversible reaction that can be expressed as

$$2SO_2(g) + O_2(g) \rightleftharpoons 2SO_3(g)$$

If sulfur dioxide and oxygen are mixed in a closed container, the forward reaction will start to produce sulfur trioxide. However, once molecules of sulfur trioxide form, some of them will change back into the reactants by the reverse reaction. Eventually, the rate of the forward reaction (synthesis) will equal the rate of the reverse reaction (decomposition), and the system will reach equilibrium. **When a chemical reaction does not go to completion, a chemical equilibrium is established between the forward and reverse reactions.** During chemical equilibrium, the reactants change into products just as fast as the products change back into reactants.

 Reading Checkpoint *What happens during chemical equilibrium?*

Figure 25 Liquid water left in a closed container eventually reaches equilibrium with its vapor. **Interpreting Diagrams** *What do the arrows represent in the diagram above?*

H₂O molecules

For: Links on factors affecting equilibrium
Visit: www.SciLinks.org
Web Code: ccn-1075

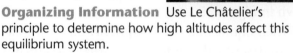

Recreating High Altitudes

An important chemical equilibrium in your blood involves the reaction of hemoglobin (Hb) with oxygen (O_2) to form oxyhemoglobin (HbO_2).

$$Hb + O_2 \rightleftharpoons HbO_2$$

This equilibrium changes with altitude. As you move from lower to higher elevations, the concentration of oxygen in the air decreases, and the equilibrium shifts in the direction that produces less oxyhemoglobin. Your body responds to the shift by producing more hemoglobin. Studies have shown that athletes can improve their performance at sea level by living or training at high altitudes. Some training facilities are designed to recreate high altitudes. Imagine that you are asked to build such a facility.

Defining the Problem In your own words, state the problem you face.

Organizing Information Use Le Châtelier's principle to determine how high altitudes affect this equilibrium system.

Creating a Solution The physical properties of the air inside the training facility include temperature, pressure, and composition. Figure out how to shift the equilibrium in the direction you want by changing one of these properties.

Presenting Your Plan Write a proposal to an athletic team that could benefit from using your training facility. Explain how your facility recreates a high-altitude environment.

Figure 26 French Chemist Henri-Louis Le Châtelier (1850–1936) published the first version of his principle of chemical equilibrium in 1884.

Factors Affecting Chemical Equilibrium

Like reaction rates, chemical equilibria can change depending on the conditions of the reaction. While a reaction rate either increases or decreases in response to a change, an equilibrium shifts. That is, the equilibrium favors either the forward or the reverse reaction. **When a change is introduced to a system in equilibrium, the equilibrium shifts in the direction that relieves the change.** This rule was first observed by Henri Le Châtelier, shown in Figure 26. Today, the rule is known as Le Châtelier's principle.

The making of ammonia is an example of a process in which chemists apply Le Châtelier's principle. Ammonia is an important industrial chemical used to make fertilizers, cleaning agents, dyes, and plastics. The following equation describes the synthesis of ammonia.

$$N_2(g) + 3H_2(g) \rightleftharpoons 2NH_3(g) + \text{Heat}$$

Suppose you have a system that contains nitrogen, hydrogen, and ammonia in equilibrium. By applying Le Châtelier's principle, you can predict how this system will be affected by changes in temperature, pressure, and concentration. In the ammonia plant shown in Figure 27, chemists must consider these same factors.

Temperature In the equation for the synthesis of ammonia, heat is written as a product. This tells you that the forward reaction is exothermic. In the reverse reaction, heat is a reactant. So the decomposition of ammonia is endothermic.

What would happen if you increased the temperature of a system that contained nitrogen, hydrogen, and ammonia? According to Le Châtelier's principle, if you added heat to the system, the equilibrium would shift in the direction that removes heat from the system. The system would favor the reverse reaction, which is endothermic. So by increasing the temperature, you would decrease the amount of ammonia.

Pressure Suppose you increased the pressure of the system. According to Le Châtelier's principle, if you increased the pressure, the equilibrium would shift in the direction that decreases the pressure of the system. In order to decrease pressure, the system would favor the reaction that produces fewer gas molecules. You can see that the left side of the equation has four gas molecules, while the right side has two. So by increasing the pressure, you would shift the equilibrium to the right, producing more ammonia.

Concentration A change in concentration of the reactants or products can also affect equilibrium. Suppose you removed ammonia from the nitrogen-hydrogen-ammonia system. Le Châtelier's principle tells you that the equilibrium would shift in the direction that produces ammonia. In order to produce ammonia, the system would favor the forward reaction.

Figure 27 Operating an ammonia plant at relatively low temperature, high pressure, and low ammonia concentration maximizes the amount of ammonia produced.

Section 7.5 Assessment

Reviewing Concepts

1. What happens when a physical change does not go to completion? What happens when a reaction does not go to completion?

2. Once a chemical reaction has reached equilibrium, how does the system respond to change?

3. What does the double-ended arrow indicate in the following chemical equation?

$$CaCO_3 \rightleftharpoons Ca^{2+} + CO_3^{2-}$$

4. For which of the following reactions are both reactants and products likely to be found when the reaction appears to be complete? Explain.

$$Mg + O_2 \longrightarrow 2MgO$$

$$HF + H_2O \rightleftharpoons H_3O^+ + F^-$$

Critical Thinking

5. **Inferring** Suppose the following reaction is allowed to come to equilibrium.

$$2NO_2(g) \rightleftharpoons N_2O_4(g)$$

How will increasing the pressure on this system affect the amount of N_2O_4 formed?

6. **Using Models** At 0°C, liquid water is in equilibrium with ice. Make a drawing of water molecules at this temperature, and describe what is happening.

Connecting Concepts

Phase Changes Write an equation for a system in which the sublimation and deposition of water have reached equilibrium. Use what you studied in Section 3.3 to explain what changes are happening.

Manipulating Chemical Equilibrium

Chemical reactions tend to go to equilibrium. It is possible to shift the equilibrium by changing the conditions under which the reaction occurs. Factors that can affect chemical equilibrium include the concentration of reactants and products, temperature, and pressure. In this lab, you will observe a chemical reaction and use your observations to predict how one factor will shift the equilibrium of the reaction. Then, you will perform an experiment to test your prediction.

Problem
How can you change the equilibrium of a chemical reaction?

Materials
- iodine-starch solution
- 150-mL beaker
- 4 dropper pipets
- spot plate
- ascorbic acid (vitamin C) solution
- chlorine bleach (sodium hypochlorite, NaOCl) solution

Skills
Formulating Hypotheses, Designing Experiments, Observing

Procedure

Part A: Observing a Reversible Reaction

1. Pour 50 mL of iodine-starch solution into the 150-mL beaker. The dark color of this solution is due to the presence of iodine molecules (I_2) within the grains of starch. **CAUTION** *Handle iodine solutions with care. Iodine is toxic.*

2. Use a dropper pipet to transfer 3 drops of iodine-starch solution from the beaker to one well on the spot plate.

3. Use another clean dropper pipet to add one drop of ascorbic acid solution to the iodine-starch solution on the spot plate. Continue to add ascorbic acid solution to the mixture on the spot plate, one drop at a time, until the mixture becomes clear. When an iodine molecule reacts with ascorbic acid, the iodine molecule is reduced and breaks down into two colorless iodide ions ($2I^-$).

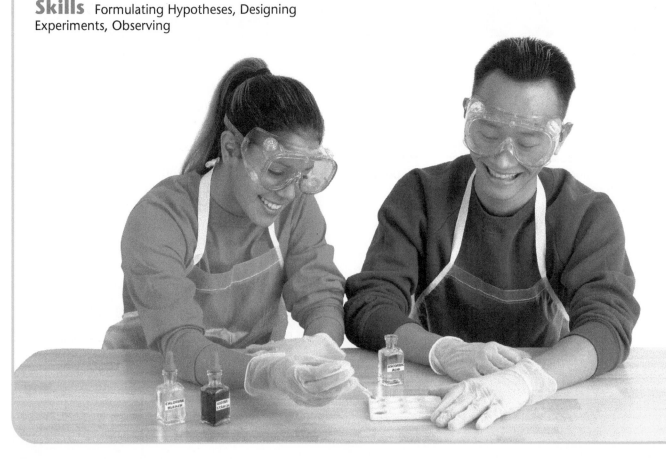

Sample Data Table			
Initial Solution	Solution Added	Quantity Added (mL)	Color of Resulting Mixture

4. Use the third clean dropper pipet to transfer one drop of colorless iodide solution to a second well on the spot plate.

5. Use the last clean dropper pipet to add bleach solution to the drop of colorless iodide solution, one drop at a time. Continue until the dark color of the iodine-starch solution reappears. **CAUTION** *Bleach can damage skin and clothing.* The chlorine bleach (NaOCl) oxidizes iodide ions (I^-), converting them to iodine molecules (I_2).

6. Write a chemical equation showing the equilibrium between iodine molecules and iodide ions. This equation does not need to be balanced. Label the two sides of your equation to indicate which substance appears dark and which appears colorless.

Part B: Design Your Experiment

7. **Predicting** Select one of the solutions used earlier that affects the equilibrium between iodine molecules and iodide ions. Record your prediction of the change you will observe in an iodine-starch solution as you add the solution that you selected.

8. **Designing Experiments** Design an experiment to test your prediction. Your experimental plan should describe in detail how you will perform your experiment.

9. Construct a data table like the sample data table shown, in which to record your observations. (*Note:* Your data table may not be exactly like the sample data table.)

10. Perform your experiment only after your teacher has approved your plan. Record your observations in your data table.
CAUTION *Wash your hands with soap or detergent before leaving the laboratory.*

Analyze and Conclude

1. **Analyzing Data** What factor did you investigate? How did it affect the equilibrium between iodine molecules and iodide ions?

2. **Predicting** How would you expect the equilibrium to change if you added more iodide ions to the mixture? Explain your answer.

3. **Calculating** When chlorine bleach (sodium hypochlorite, NaOCl) oxidizes iodide ions to iodine molecules, sodium hypochlorite is reduced to sodium chloride (NaCl) and water (H_2O). Write a balanced chemical equation for this reaction, beginning with the reactants sodium hypochlorite, iodide ions, and hydrogen ions (H^+).

4. **Drawing Conclusions** How does the addition of more product affect the chemical equilibrium of a reaction?

Go Further Design an experiment to determine whether other substances that are easily oxidized or reduced, such as iron ions, can reduce iodine to iodide, or oxidize iodide to iodine. Then, with your teacher's approval and supervision, perform your experiment.

7.1 Describing Reactions

🔑 Key Concepts

- The law of conservation of mass states that mass is neither created nor destroyed.
- In order to show that mass is conserved during a reaction, a chemical equation must be balanced.
- Because chemical reactions often involve large numbers of small particles, chemists use a unit called the mole to measure amounts of a substance.
- In chemical reactions, the mass of a reactant or product can be calculated by using a balanced chemical equation and molar masses.

Vocabulary

reactants, *p. 192;* products, *p. 192;* chemical equation, *p. 193;* coefficients, *p. 194;* mole, *p. 195;* molar mass, *p. 196*

7.2 Types of Reactions

🔑 Key Concepts

- The general types of chemical reactions are synthesis reactions, decomposition reactions, single-replacement reactions, double-replacement reactions, and combustion reactions.
- Scientists classify certain chemical reactions as transfers of electrons between atoms.

Vocabulary

synthesis reaction, *p. 200;* decomposition reaction, *p. 200;* single-replacement reaction, *p. 202;* double-replacement reaction, *p. 203;* combustion reaction, *p. 204;* oxidation-reduction reaction, *p. 204*

7.3 Energy Changes in Reactions

🔑 Key Concepts

- Chemical reactions involve the breaking of chemical bonds in the reactants and the formation of chemical bonds in the products.
- During a chemical reaction, energy is either released or absorbed.

Vocabulary

chemical energy, *p. 206;* exothermic reaction, *p. 208;* endothermic reaction, *p. 209*

7.4 Reaction Rates

🔑 Key Concepts

- Reaction rates tell you how fast a reaction is going.
- Factors that affect reaction rates include temperature, surface area, concentration, stirring, and catalysts.

Vocabulary

reaction rate, *p. 212;* catalyst, *p. 215*

7.5 Equilibrium

🔑 Key Concepts

- When a physical change does not go to completion, a physical equilibrium is established between the forward and reverse changes. When a chemical reaction does not go to completion, a chemical equilibrium is established between the forward and reverse reactions.
- When a change is introduced to a system in equilibrium, the equilibrium shifts in the direction that relieves the change.

Vocabulary

equilibrium, *p. 216;* reversible reaction, *p. 217*

Thinking Visually

Concept Map Use information from the chapter to complete the concept map below.

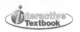
Reviewing Content

Choose the letter that best answers the question or completes the statement.

1. In the following equation, what are the reactants?
$$NaHCO_3 + HCl \longrightarrow NaCl + H_2O + CO_2$$
   a. $NaHCO_3$ and HCl **b.** $NaHCO_3$ and NaCl
   c. HCl and NaCl   **d.** NaCl, H_2O, and CO_2

2. Which of the following is a statement of the law of conservation of mass?
   a. Mass is created but not destroyed.
   b. Mass is destroyed but not created.
   c. Mass is neither created nor destroyed.
   d. Mass is both created and destroyed, depending on the chemical reaction.

3. The mass of a hydrogen atom is 1.0 amu, and the mass of a carbon atom is 12.0 amu. What is the molar mass of methane, CH_4?
   a. 13.0 amu   **b.** 13.0 g
   c. 16.0 amu   **d.** 16.0 g

4. In what type of reaction does one reactant form two or more products?
   a. synthesis   **b.** decomposition
   c. single replacement **d.** double replacement

5. What particle is transferred from one atom to another in a redox reaction?
   a. electron   **b.** neutron
   c. proton   **d.** nucleus

6. Which of the following is a single replacement?
   a. $KOH + HCl \longrightarrow KCl + H_2O$
   b. $2Na + 2H_2O \longrightarrow H_2 + 2NaOH$
   c. $2C_2H_6 + 7O_2 \longrightarrow 4CO_2 + 6H_2O$
   d. $H_2O + CO_2 \longrightarrow H_2CO_3$

7. How are reactions related to chemical bonds?
   a. Bonds in the reactants are broken, and bonds in the products are formed.
   b. Bonds in the products are broken, and bonds in the reactants are formed.
   c. Bonds in both the reactants and products are broken.
   d. Bonds are formed in both the reactants and the products.

8. What type of reaction always releases energy?
   a. endothemic   **b.** exothermic
   c. decomposition **d.** oxidation-reduction

9. In general, an increase in temperature
   a. increases reaction rate.
   b. decreases reaction rate.
   c. does not affect reaction rate.
   d. acts as a catalyst.

10. What takes place at chemical equilibrium?
   a. Reactants form more quickly than products.
   b. Products form more quickly than reactants.
   c. Reactants and products stop forming.
   d. Reactants and products form at the same rate.

Understanding Concepts

11. Write the following chemical equation in words.
$$CaCO_3 + Heat \longrightarrow CaO + CO_2$$

12. Explain how a balanced chemical equation shows that mass is conserved.

13. Explain the following diagram in your own words.

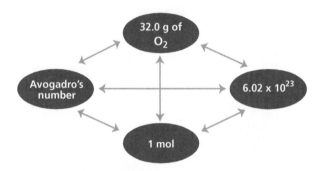

14. Compare oxidation and reduction.

15. Paper burns by combining with oxygen. Why doesn't paper burn every time it contacts oxygen?

16. Give an example of a chemical reaction that occurs slowly. Give another example of a chemical reaction that occurs quickly.

Answer Questions 17–18 based on the equation below.
$$C(s) + H_2O(g) + Heat \rightleftharpoons CO(g) + H_2(g)$$

17. How would you adjust the temperature to increase the amount of product?

18. Does the removal of hydrogen gas as it is produced shift the reaction to the left or the right?

Critical Thinking

19. Observing Explain how you know that a chemical reaction takes place when iron rusts.

20. Inferring As a candle burns, its mass decreases. However, mass is conserved in this reaction. Explain this observation.

21. Making Generalizations In a certain chemical reaction, two reactants undergo change to form two products. Why can't you determine what type of reaction occurred from this information?

22. Applying Concepts Use the reaction that occurs when magnesium burns in oxygen to show how a reaction might be included in more than one category of reaction.

23. Classifying Is breaking bonds an endothermic process or an exothermic process? Explain.

24. Inferring Explain how energy is conserved in an endothermic reaction.

Use the diagram below to answer Questions 25–26.

A

B

25. Comparing and Contrasting The volume of the cube in A equals the total volume of the cubes in B. Compare the surface areas of the cubes in A and B.

26. Using Models Use the diagram to explain how surface area affects reaction rates.

27. Predicting You are performing an experiment and want to increase the rate of reaction. You stop stirring the reactants and, instead, increase the concentration of one reactant. Can you expect the reaction to proceed at a faster rate? Explain.

Math Skills

28. Applying Concepts Balance each of the following chemical equations.
  a. $KI \longrightarrow K + I_2$
  b. $Na + H_2O \longrightarrow H_2 + NaOH$
  c. $CH_4 + O_2 \longrightarrow CO_2 + H_2O$

29. Calculating What mass of KBr is contained in 2.50 moles of the compound?

30. Calculating How many moles of Na_2CrO_4 are contained in 74.3 grams of the compound?

Concepts in Action

31. Inferring Kept at room temperature, batteries will eventually lose their charge. Why will keeping batteries in the freezer make them last longer?

32. Drawing Conclusions Octane, C_8H_{18}, is one of the compounds present in gasoline. The products of the burning of octane are water and carbon dioxide. In this reaction, which contain more energy, the bonds in the reactants or the bonds in the products? Explain.

33. Writing in Science Write a paragraph describing a chemical reaction that you have observed recently.

Performance-Based Assessment

Designing an Experiment Choose a chemical reaction that reaches equilibrium and includes at least one gas. Design an experiment that will show the effects of concentration, temperature, and pressure on the system. You will not actually perform the experiment, so you are not limited by the equipment available in your laboratory. Prepare a lab report that includes a hypothesis, all steps of the procedure, and any expected results.

For: Self-grading assessment
Visit: PHSchool.com
Web Code: cca-1070

Standardized Test Prep

Choose the letter that best answers the question or completes the statement.

1. Balance this chemical equation.

$$MgO + H_3PO_4 \longrightarrow Mg_3(PO_4)_2 + H_2O$$

(A) $3MgO + 2H_3PO_4 \longrightarrow Mg_3(PO_4)_2 + 3H_2O$
(B) $3MgO + 2H_3PO_4 \longrightarrow Mg_3(PO_4)_2 + 2H_2O$
(C) $6MgO + 2H_3PO_4 \longrightarrow Mg_3(PO_4)_2 + 3H_2O$
(D) $6MgO + 2H_3PO_4 \longrightarrow 2Mg_3(PO_4)_2 + 6H_2O$
(E) $6MgO + 4H_3PO_4 \longrightarrow 2Mg_3(PO_4)_2 + 3H_2O$

Questions 2 and 3 refer to the following reaction.

$$C_4H_{10} + O_2 \longrightarrow CO_2 + H_2O$$

2. What type of reaction is described by this equation?
(A) synthesis   (B) decomposition
(C) combustion   (D) double replacement
(E) single replacement

3. Balance the equation for the reaction between butane (C_4H_{10}) and oxygen, and then determine how many grams of CO_2 are formed when 5.00 grams of C_4H_{10} react.
(A) 1.65 grams   (B) 3.79 grams
(C) 15.1 grams   (D) 20.0 grams
(E) 26.4 grams

4. Which equation describes a synthesis?
(A) $Ba(OH)_2 + 2HCl \longrightarrow BaCl_2 + 2H_2O$
(B) $CH_4 + 2O_2 \longrightarrow CO_2 + 2H_2O$
(C) $Zn + CuSO_4 \longrightarrow Cu + ZnSO_4$
(D) $2H_2 + O_2 \longrightarrow 2H_2O$
(E) $CaCO_3 \longrightarrow CaO + CO_2$

Use the energy diagram to answer Question 5.

Reaction Energy for $A_2 + 2B \rightleftharpoons 2AB$

5. What effect would a catalyst have on the reaction $A_2 + 2B \rightleftharpoons 2AB$?
(A) It gives the products more energy.
(B) It makes the reaction endothermic.
(C) It gives the reacting particles more energy.
(D) It provides a new reaction pathway for the reactants.
(E) none of the above

6. The following equation shows the formation of ammonia (NH_3) from nitrogen (N_2) and hydrogen (H_2). This reaction is in equilibrium.

$$N_2(g) + 3H_2(g) \rightleftharpoons 2NH_3(g) + \text{Heat}$$

If the pressure of the system is decreased, the equilibrium will shift
(A) to the right because there are fewer moles of gas on the product side of the equation.
(B) to the left because there are more moles of gas on the reactant side of the equation.
(C) to the right because a drop in pressure brings the reactants together so they can react.
(D) to the left because a drop in pressure pulls the product molecules apart.
(E) in neither direction because pressure does not affect chemical equilibriums.

10 Nuclear Chemistry

How is radiocarbon dating used to date objects?

The use of radioisotopes to date rocks and artifacts has helped scientists piece together a clearer picture of Earth's past. Use the library or Internet to learn more about an archaeological site that you have heard about in the news. Find out how the age of the site was determined. Digitally record a podcast about the site and the methods used by scientists to date the site and/or its artifacts. Post the podcast on your class Web site.

How do science concepts apply to your world? Here are some questions you'll be able to answer after you read this chapter.

- **Why is radon gas dangerous?** *(Section 10.1)*

- **How can you measure the age of a rock?** *(Section 10.2)*

- **How does a smoke detector work?** *(Section 10.3)*

- **How can doctors diagnose certain types of cancer?** *(page 306)*

- **How does a nuclear reactor generate electricity?** *(Section 10.4)*

This false-color image from a bubble chamber shows the tracks of subatomic particles at high speed.

Chapter Preview

Inquiry ⟩ Activity

What Happens When an Atom Decays?

Procedure

1. Using green beads to represent protons and purple beads to represent neutrons, make a model of a nucleus of a beryllium atom that contains 4 protons and 4 neutrons.

2. Atomic nuclei such as the one you modeled can decay by losing a particle that contains 2 protons and 2 neutrons. Remove the appropriate number of beads from your model to represent this process.

Think About It

1. **Observing** How many protons and how many neutrons are left in your nuclear model?

2. **Using Models** What element does your nuclear model now represent?

10.1 Radioactivity

Key Concepts

- What happens during nuclear decay?
- What are three types of nuclear radiation?
- How does nuclear radiation affect atoms?
- What devices can detect nuclear radiation?

Vocabulary

- radioactivity
- radioisotope
- nuclear radiation
- alpha particle
- beta particle
- gamma ray
- background radiation

Reading Strategy

Previewing Copy the table below. Before you read the section, rewrite the topic headings as *how, why,* and *what* questions. As you read, write an answer to each question.

Question	Answer
What is nuclear decay?	a._____?_____
b._____?_____	Alpha, beta, gamma
c._____?_____	d._____?_____
e._____?_____	f._____?_____

Figure 1 Due to rainy weather, Henri Becquerel postponed his intended experiment with uranium salts. **A** Without any exposure to sunlight, the salts still produced a foggy image on a photographic plate. **B** For his discovery of radioactivity, Becquerel shared the 1903 Nobel Prize for Physics with Marie and Pierre Curie.

In 1896, French physicist Antoine Henri Becquerel (1852–1908) was experimenting with uranium salts. He hypothesized that the salts, which glow after being exposed to light, produced X-rays while they glowed. To test his hypothesis, Becquerel performed an experiment. First, he wrapped a photographic plate in paper. Then, he placed some uranium salts on the plate and set it outside in the sunlight, which caused the salts to glow. When Becquerel developed the plate, he got a foggy image. At the time, Becquerel thought that X-rays from the salts had penetrated the paper and fogged the plate.

Like any good scientist, Becquerel wanted to repeat his experiment, but a spell of bad weather forced him to wait. In the meantime, he left a wrapped photographic plate and uranium salts in a desk drawer. After several days, Becquerel decided to develop the plate without exposing the uranium to sunlight. To his surprise, he got the foggy image shown in Figure 1A. Later, Becquerel determined that the uranium salts had emitted rays that had *never* been observed before.

Nuclear Decay

Becquerel's experiment marked the discovery of radioactivity. **Radioactivity** is the process in which an unstable atomic nucleus emits charged particles and energy. Any atom containing an unstable nucleus is called a radioactive isotope, or **radioisotope** for short.

Radioisotopes of uranium—primarily uranium-238—were the source of radioactivity in Becquerel's experiment. (Recall that the name of an isotope includes its mass number.) Another common radioisotope is carbon-14, which can be found in fossils like the ones shown in Figure 2.

Unlike stable isotopes such as carbon-12 or oxygen-16, radioisotopes spontaneously change into other isotopes over time. When the composition of a radioisotope changes, the radioisotope is said to undergo nuclear decay. ⬤ **During nuclear decay, atoms of one element can change into atoms of a different element altogether.** For example, uranium-238 decays into thorium-234, which is also a radioisotope.

Figure 2 About 26,000 years ago, more than 100 mammoths died at a sinkhole in Hot Springs, South Dakota. Scientists figured out how old the remains were by measuring amounts of the radioisotope carbon-14 contained in the mammoth bones.

Types of Nuclear Radiation

Scientists can detect a radioactive substance by measuring the nuclear radiation it gives off. **Nuclear radiation** is charged particles and energy that are emitted from the nuclei of radioisotopes. ⬤ **Common types of nuclear radiation include alpha particles, beta particles, and gamma rays.** Figure 3 shows the properties of these three types of radiation.

Alpha Decay When a uranium-238 sample decays, it emits alpha particles. An **alpha particle** is a positively charged particle made up of two protons and two neutrons—the same as a helium nucleus. It has a 2+ charge. The common symbol for an alpha particle is $_2^4\text{He}$. The subscript is the atomic number (the number of protons). The superscript is the mass number (the sum of the numbers of protons and neutrons). Another symbol for an alpha particle is the Greek letter α.

Alpha decay, which refers to nuclear decay that releases alpha particles, is an example of a nuclear reaction. Like chemical reactions, nuclear reactions can be expressed as equations. The following nuclear equation describes the alpha decay of uranium-238.

$$_{92}^{238}\text{U} \rightarrow \, _{90}^{234}\text{Th} + \, _2^4\text{He}$$

In alpha decay, the product isotope has two fewer protons and two fewer neutrons than the reactant isotope. In the equation above, the mass number on the left (238) equals the sum of the mass numbers on the right (234 + 4). Also, the atomic number on the left (92) equals the sum of the atomic numbers on the right (90 + 2). In other words, the equation is balanced.

Alpha particles are the least penetrating type of nuclear radiation. Most alpha particles travel no more than a few centimeters in air, and can be stopped by a sheet of paper or by clothing.

Figure 3 Within a few years of Becquerel's discovery of radioactivity, Ernest Rutherford classified three types of nuclear radiation based on his own studies of uranium compounds. *Comparing and Contrasting How do alpha particles, beta particles, and gamma rays differ in terms of charge? In terms of mass?*

Characteristics of Nuclear Radiation				
Radiation Type	**Symbol**	**Charge**	**Mass (amu)**	**Common Source**
Alpha particle	α, $_2^4\text{He}$	2+	4	Radium-226
Beta particle	β, $_{-1}^0\text{e}$	1−	$\dfrac{1}{1836}$	Carbon-14
Gamma ray	γ	0	0	Cobalt-60

Beta Decay When thorium-234 decays, it releases negatively charged radiation called beta particles. A **beta particle** is an electron emitted by an unstable nucleus. In nuclear equations, a beta particle is written as $_{-1}^{0}e$ or β. Because of its single negative charge, a beta particle is assigned an atomic number of −1. In Chapter 4, you learned that an electron has very little mass when compared with a proton. For this reason, a beta particle is assigned a mass number of 0.

How can an atomic nucleus, which has a positive charge, emit a negatively charged particle? During beta decay, a neutron decomposes into a proton and an electron. The proton stays trapped in the nucleus, while the electron is released. The following equation describes the beta decay of thorium-234.

$$^{234}_{90}\text{Th} \rightarrow\ ^{234}_{91}\text{Pa} +\ ^{0}_{-1}e$$

In beta decay, the product isotope has one proton more and one neutron fewer than the reactant isotope. The mass numbers of the isotopes are equal because the emitted beta particle has essentially no mass.

Due to their smaller mass and faster speed, beta particles are more penetrating than alpha particles. As Figure 4 illustrates, beta particles pass through paper, but can be stopped by a thin sheet of metal.

 Reading Checkpoint *What is a beta particle?*

Gamma Decay Not all nuclear radiation consists of charged particles. A **gamma ray** is a penetrating ray of energy emitted by an unstable nucleus. The symbol for a gamma ray is γ. Gamma radiation has no mass and no charge. Like X-rays and visible light, gamma rays are energy waves that travel through space at the speed of light.

Figure 4 Alpha particles (shown in red) are the least penetrating type of nuclear radiation. Gamma rays (shown in green) are the most penetrating. A concrete slab can block most but not all of the gamma rays released by a radioactive source.
Interpreting Diagrams *Which type of radiation can penetrate paper but is blocked by aluminum foil?*

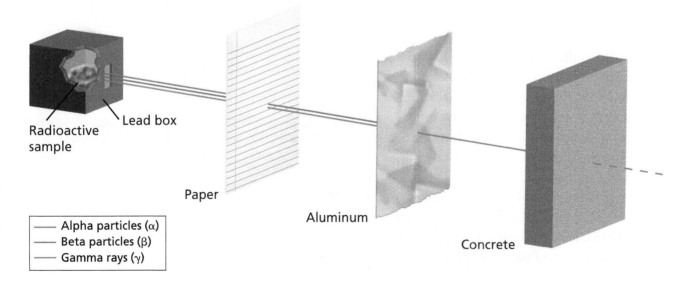

Radioactive sample

Lead box

Paper

Aluminum

Concrete

— Alpha particles (α)
— Beta particles (β)
— Gamma rays (γ)

Balancing Nuclear Equations

Write a balanced nuclear equation for the alpha decay of polonium-210.

 1 **Read and Understand**

What information are you given?

Reactant isotope = polonium-210

Radiation emitted = $_2^4\text{He}$ (alpha particle)

Use the periodic table to obtain the atomic number of polonium.

Reactant isotope = $_{84}^{210}\text{Po}$

2 **Plan and Solve**

What unknowns are you trying to calculate?

Atomic number of product isotope, Z = ?

Mass number of product isotope, A = ?

Chemical symbol of product isotope, X = ?

What equation contains the given information?

$$_{84}^{210}\text{Po} \rightarrow {}_Z^A\text{X} + {}_2^4\text{He}$$

Write and solve equations for atomic mass and atomic number.

$210 = A + 4$	$84 = Z + 2$
$210 - 4 = A$	$84 - 2 = Z$
$206 = A$	$82 = Z$

According to the periodic table, the element with an atomic number of 82 is lead, Pb. So, X is Pb. The balanced nuclear equation is shown below.

$$_{84}^{210}\text{Po} \rightarrow {}_{82}^{206}\text{Pb} + {}_2^4\text{He}$$

 3 **Look Back and Check**

Is your answer reasonable?

The mass number on the left equals the sum of the mass numbers on the right. The atomic number on the left equals the sum of the atomic numbers on the right. The equation is balanced.

 Math **Practice**

1. Write a balanced nuclear equation for the alpha decay of thorium-232.

2. Write a balanced nuclear equation for the beta decay of carbon-14.

3. Determine the product of alpha decay for americium-241.

4. Determine the product of beta decay for strontium-90.

Figure 5 The mineral autunite is an important source of uranium.

During gamma decay, the atomic number and mass number of the atom remain the same, but the energy of the nucleus decreases. Gamma decay often accompanies alpha or beta decay. For example, thorium-234 emits both beta particles and gamma rays (abbreviated as γ) as it decays.

$$^{234}_{90}\text{Th} \rightarrow \,^{234}_{91}\text{Pa} + \,^{0}_{-1}\text{e} + \gamma$$

Gamma rays are much more penetrating than either alpha particles or beta particles. It can take several centimeters of lead or several meters of concrete to stop gamma radiation.

Effects of Nuclear Radiation

You may not realize it, but you are exposed to nuclear radiation every day. Most of this is **background radiation,** or nuclear radiation that occurs naturally in the environment. Radioisotopes in air, water, rocks, plants, and animals all contribute to background radiation. Most rocks, such as the one in Figure 5, contain at least trace amounts of radioactive elements. Another source of background radiation is cosmic rays. Cosmic rays are streams of charged particles (mainly protons and alpha particles) from outer space. Collisions between cosmic rays and Earth's atmosphere shower the surface below with nuclear radiation. All this radioactivity may sound dangerous. However, background radiation levels are generally low enough to be safe.

When nuclear radiation exceeds background levels, it can damage the cells and tissues of your body. ⬤ **Nuclear radiation can ionize atoms.** When cells are exposed to nuclear radiation, the bonds holding together proteins and DNA molecules may break. As these molecules change, the cells may no longer function properly.

Figure 6 Radon gas is produced underground as the uranium in rocks and soil decays. As the radon seeps up through the ground, it can get into buildings by passing through cracks or holes in their foundations.
Inferring **How would ventilation of the basement affect radon levels in the house shown below?**

Alpha particles, beta particles, and gamma rays are all forms of ionizing radiation. Alpha particles can cause skin damage similar to a burn, but they are not a serious health hazard unless an alpha-emitting substance is inhaled or eaten. For example, radon gas is a potentially dangerous natural source of alpha particles because it can be inhaled. Radon-222 is formed through a series of nuclear decays that begins with uranium-238 in rocks deep underground. As radon-222 is produced, it seeps upward toward the surface. It sometimes collects in the basements of buildings that lack proper ventilation, as shown in Figure 6. Prolonged exposure to radon-222 can lead to lung cancer.

Insulation, modern windows, and modern building materials keep radon from escaping.

Radon gas dissolved in water is released through agitation.

Radon naturally diffuses up through the ground.

Radon enters through pinholes and cracks in the foundation.

Radon is produced by the nuclear decay of uranium found in rocks and soil.

When exposure to nuclear radiation is external, the amount of tissue damage depends on the penetrating power of the radiation. For example, beta particles can damage tissues in the body more than alpha particles, but less than gamma rays. Gamma rays can penetrate deeply into the human body, potentially exposing all organs to ionization damage.

Detecting Nuclear Radiation

Although you can't see, hear, or feel the radioactivity around you, scientific instruments can measure nuclear radiation. **Devices that are used to detect nuclear radiation include Geiger counters and film badges.** A Geiger counter, shown in Figure 7, uses a gas-filled tube to measure ionizing radiation. When nuclear radiation enters the tube, it ionizes the atoms of the gas. The ions produce an electric current, which can be measured. The greater the amount of nuclear radiation, the greater the electric current produced in the tube is.

Recall that in Becquerel's experiment, nuclear radiation left an image on a photographic plate. Today, many people who work with or near radioactive materials wear film badges to monitor their exposure to nuclear radiation. A film badge contains a piece of photographic film wrapped in paper. The film is developed and replaced with a new piece periodically. The exposure on the film indicates the amount of radiation exposure for the person wearing the badge.

Figure 7 Wearing protective clothing, a firefighter uses a Geiger counter to test the ground for radioactivity. Firefighters sometimes help clean up accidents involving radioactive materials.

Section 10.1 Assessment

Reviewing Concepts

1. How does an element change during nuclear decay?

2. What are three types of nuclear radiation?

3. How are atoms affected by nuclear radiation?

4. What devices can be used to detect nuclear radiation?

5. How do types of nuclear radiation differ in electric charge?

6. Describe the penetrating power of each common type of radiation.

7. What is background radiation? List some of its sources.

Critical Thinking

8. **Predicting** What is the effect of beta decay on the composition of a nucleus?

9. **Inferring** Why do you think airplane pilots wear film badges?

Math Practice

10. Write a balanced nuclear equation for the alpha decay of radium-226.

11. Write a nuclear equation that describes the beta decay of hydrogen-3.

10.2 Rates of Nuclear Decay

Reading Focus

Key Concepts

- How do nuclear decay rates differ from chemical reaction rates?

- How do scientists determine the age of an object that contains carbon-14?

Vocabulary

- half-life

Reading Strategy

Identifying Details Copy the concept map below. As you read, complete it to identify details about radiocarbon dating.

Radiocarbon dating

uses the radioisotope

a. __?__

can be used to date objects as old as

b. __?__ years

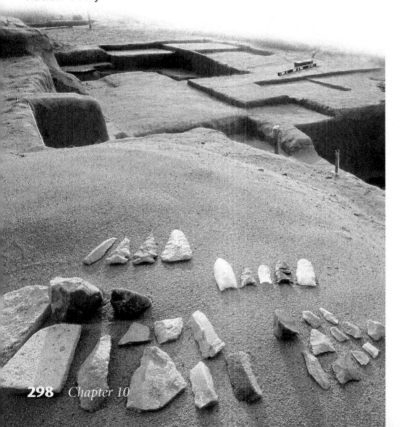

Figure 8 These stone tools from the archaeological site in Cactus Hill, Virginia, are at least 15,000 years old. Scientists estimated the age of the site based on rates of nuclear decay.

A well-known theory is that early Americans were people from Siberia who crossed the Bering Strait into Alaska about 13,000 years ago. However, this theory has been challenged by recent scientific discoveries. In the 1990s, archaeologists working at a site in Cactus Hill, Virginia, found stone tools, charcoal, and animal bones that were at least 15,000 years old. Some of the artifacts were as much as 17,000 years old. The age of these artifacts suggests that the first Americans reached the continent much earlier than formerly thought. Some archaeologists have since revised their theories on the origin of America's earliest ancestors. One possible explanation is that the first Americans were people from Europe who crossed the Atlantic Ocean by using boats.

Figure 8 shows some of the artifacts from the Cactus Hill site. They certainly look very old, but the archaeologists needed to find out *how* old. One clue that can reveal the age of an object is how many radioactive nuclei it contains. Because most materials contain at least trace amounts of radioisotopes, scientists can estimate how old they are based on rates of nuclear decay.

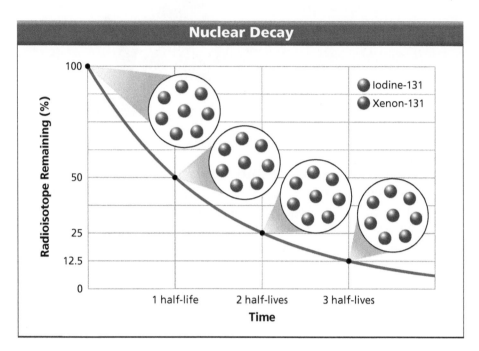

Nuclear Decay

Radioisotope Remaining (%)

100
50
25
12.5
0

1 half-life   2 half-lives   3 half-lives

Time

● Iodine-131
● Xenon-131

Figure 9 The half-life for the beta decay of iodine-131 is 8.07 days. After one half-life (8.07 days), half of a sample of iodine-131 will have decayed into xenon-131. After two half-lives (16.14 days), three quarters of the sample will have decayed.

Half-Life

A nuclear decay rate describes how fast nuclear changes take place in a radioactive substance. Every radioisotope decays at a specific rate that can be expressed as a half-life. A **half-life** is the time required for one half of a sample of a radioisotope to decay. After one half-life, half of the atoms in a radioactive sample have decayed, while the other half remain unchanged. After two half-lives, half of the remaining half decays, leaving one quarter of the original sample unchanged. Figure 9 illustrates the nuclear decay rate of iodine-131. Iodine-131 has a half-life of 8.07 days. After two half-lives, or 16.14 days, the fraction of iodine-131 remaining is one quarter. After three half-lives, or 24.21 days, the fraction of iodine-131 remaining is one half of one quarter, or one eighth.

Half-lives can vary from fractions of a second to billions of years. Figure 10 lists the half-lives of some common radioisotopes. Uranium-238, for instance, has a half-life of 4.5 billion years. This means that in 4.5 billion years, there will be half as much uranium-238 on Earth as there is today. You could also say that 4.5 billion years ago, there was twice as much uranium-238 on Earth as there is today. ⬭ **Unlike chemical reaction rates, which vary with the conditions of a reaction, nuclear decay rates are constant.** Regardless of the temperature, pressure, or surface area of a uranium-238 sample, its half-life is still 4.5 billion years.

Figure 10 Nuclear decay rates are constant. A given radioisotope decays at a specific rate, or half-life. **Calculating** *What isotope is produced by the nuclear decay of radon-222?*

Half-Lives and Radiation of Selected Radioisotopes		
Isotope	**Half-life**	**Nuclear Radiation Emitted**
Radon-222	3.82 days	α
Iodine-131	8.07 days	β
Thorium-234	24.1 days	β, γ
Radium-226	1620 years	α, γ
Carbon-14	5730 years	β
Thorium-230	75,200 years	α, γ
Uranium-235	7.04×10^8 years	α, γ
Potassium-40	1.28×10^9 years	β, γ
Uranium-238	4.47×10^9 years	α

 Reading Checkpoint *What is a half-life?*

Quick Lab

Modeling Half-Life

Procedure

1. Put 100 1-cm squares of wallpaper in a large plastic bag. Construct a data table with 2 columns and 9 blank rows. Label the columns Spill Number and Number of Squares Returned.

2. Close the bag and shake it to mix up the squares. Then, spill them onto a flat surface.

3. Remove the squares that are face-side up. Record the number of squares remaining and return them to the bag.

4. Repeat Steps 2 and 3 until there are no squares left to put back into the bag.

Analyze and Conclude

1. **Analyzing Data** How many spills were required to remove half of the squares? To remove three fourths of the squares?

2. **Using Graphs** Graph your results. Plot spill number on the horizontal axis and the number of squares remaining on the vertical axis.

3. **Using Models** If each spill represents one year, what is the half-life of the squares?

Suppose you have a one-gram sample of iridium-182, which undergoes beta decay to form osmium-182. The half-life of iridium-182 is 15 minutes. After 45 minutes, how much iridium-182 will remain in the sample? To solve this problem, you first need to calculate how many half-lives will elapse during the total time of decay.

$$\text{Half-lives elapsed} = \frac{\text{Total time of decay}}{\text{Half-life}} = \frac{45 \text{ min}}{15 \text{ min}} = 3$$

After three half-lives, the amount of iridium-182 has been reduced by half three times.

$$\frac{1}{2} \times \frac{1}{2} \times \frac{1}{2} = \frac{1}{8}$$

So after 45 minutes, $\frac{1}{8} \times 1$ gram, or 0.125 gram, of iridium-182 remains while 0.875 gram of the sample has decayed into osmium-182.

Radioactive Dating

Now suppose you have a sample that was originally iridium-182, but three quarters of it have since decayed into osmium-182. Based on the fraction of iridium-182 left (one quarter), you can calculate the age of the sample to be two half-lives, or 30 minutes old.

The artifacts from Cactus Hill were dated by measuring levels of carbon-14, which has a half-life of 5730 years. Carbon-14 is formed in the upper atmosphere when neutrons produced by cosmic rays collide with nitrogen-14 atoms. The radioactive carbon-14 undergoes beta decay to form nitrogen-14.

$$^{14}_{6}\text{C} \rightarrow ^{14}_{7}\text{N} + ^{0}_{-1}\text{e}$$

Go Online

NSTA SciLINKS

For: Links on half-life
Visit: www.SciLinks.org
Web Code: ccn-1102

Carbon reacts with oxygen in the atmosphere and forms carbon dioxide. As plants absorb carbon dioxide during photosynthesis, they maintain the same ratio of carbon-14 to carbon-12 as in the atmosphere. Likewise, animals have the same ratio of carbon isotopes as the plants they eat. When a plant or animal dies, however, it can no longer absorb carbon. From this point on, the organism's carbon-14 levels decrease as the radioactive carbon decays. 🔑 **In radiocarbon dating, the age of an object is determined by comparing the object's carbon-14 levels with carbon-14 levels in the atmosphere.** For example, if the ratio of carbon-14 to carbon-12 in a fossil is half the ratio in the atmosphere, then the organism lived about 5730 years ago.

Because atmospheric carbon-14 levels can change over time, the calculated age of the fossil is not totally accurate. To get a more accurate radiocarbon date, scientists compare the carbon-14 levels in a sample to carbon-14 levels in objects of known age. Such objects might include trees (which can be dated by counting tree rings) or artifacts from a specific historical period.

Radiocarbon dating can be used to date any carbon-containing object less than 50,000 years old, such as the artifact in Figure 11. Objects older than 50,000 years contain too little carbon-14 to be measurable. To date objects thought to be older than 50,000 years, scientists measure the amounts of radioisotopes with longer half-lives than carbon-14. Geologists, for instance, use the half-lives of potassium-40, uranium-235, and uranium-238 to date rock formations. The older the rock, the lower are the levels of the radioisotope present.

Figure 11 Radiocarbon dating has helped archaeologists learn more about ancient civilizations. Excavations in Abydos, a major archaeological site of ancient Egypt, have unearthed fascinating artifacts. This mummy case, containing the remains of a cat, is 1900 years old.

Section 10.2 Assessment

Reviewing Concepts

1. 🔑 How are nuclear decay rates different from chemical reaction rates?

2. 🔑 How can scientists determine the age of an object that contains carbon-14?

3. If a radioactive sample has decayed until only one eighth of the original sample remains unchanged, how many half-lives have elapsed?

4. What type of nuclear radiation is emitted when carbon-14 decays?

Critical Thinking

5. **Predicting** Can radiocarbon dating be used to determine the age of dinosaur fossils? Explain. (*Hint:* Dinosaurs roamed Earth more than 65 million years ago.)

6. **Inferring** All of the isotopes of radon have half-lives shorter than four days, yet radon is still found in nature. Explain why all the radon has not already decayed.

7. **Calculating** A certain isotope of technetium has a half-life of six hours. If it is given to a patient as part of a medical procedure, what fraction of the radioisotope remains in the body after one day?

Writing in Science

Explanatory Paragraph Archaeology is the study of past cultures. Explain how a concept in chemistry led to advances in archaeology.

Should Radon Testing in Schools Be Mandatory?

Radon (Rn) is a radioactive element that forms from the nuclear decay of uranium in rocks and soil. A colorless, odorless gas, radon can enter buildings through drains, cracks in the floors and walls, and even the water supply. Indoor radon levels tend to be highest in places that are close to the soil and have little ventilation, such as basements or crawl spaces.

When a person inhales radon-contaminated air, the lungs trap radioactive particles. As these particles decay, radiation is released into the lung tissue. Over time, repeated exposure to high radon levels can result in lung cancer.

The Environmental Protection Agency (EPA) identifies 4 picocuries per liter (pCi/L) of air as the national "action level" for radon. (A picocurie is a unit of radioactivity.) If an indoor space has a radon level of 4 pCi/L or higher, the EPA recommends that steps be taken to reduce it. Such steps might include installing a ventilation system and sealing cracks in the building's foundation.

The Viewpoints

Radon Testing in Schools Should Be Mandatory

The EPA estimates that indoor radon exposure contributes to 21,000 lung cancer deaths in the United States each year. After smoking, radon is the second-leading cause of lung cancer.

Students and teachers spend extended periods of time indoors at school. A nationwide survey of radon levels in schools found that nearly one in five schools has at least one classroom with radon exceeding the EPA's action level of 4 pCi/L.

Indoor radon can be easily tested. If elevated radon levels are found, they can be reduced using proven techniques. But without mandatory testing, school administrators may not be aware of the potential risk of radon exposure in their schools.

Radon Testing in Schools Should Not Be Mandatory

The EPA's radon guidelines are based mainly on studies of workers in uranium mines. Radon levels in these mines were far greater than those found in homes or schools. In addition, the miners engaged in tiring labor, resulting in heavy breathing of the surrounding air. Lastly, most of the miners were smokers. The data from these studies are appropriate for predicting the risk of radon exposure for uranium miners—but not for the general public.

The EPA's action level of 4 pCi/L is not universally accepted. In Canada and Europe, for example, radon guidelines are much less strict. Until scientists gather more data about the risk of residential radon exposures, radon testing in schools should not be mandatory.

Research and Decide

1. **Defining the Issue** In your own words, explain the issue that needs to be resolved about indoor radon.

2. **Analyzing the Viewpoints** List two arguments of those who think that radon testing should be mandatory in schools. List two arguments of those who think that radon testing should not be mandatory in schools.

3. **Forming Your Opinion** Should there be mandatory radon testing in schools? Which argument did you find more convincing?

For: More on this issue
Visit: PHSchool.com
Web Code: cch-1100

10.3 Artificial Transmutation

Reading Focus

Key Concepts
- How do artificial transmutations occur?
- How are transuranium elements produced?

Vocabulary
- transmutation
- transuranium elements
- quark

Reading Strategy
Monitoring Your Understanding Preview the Key Concepts, topic headings, vocabulary, and figures in this section. List two things you expect to learn. After reading, state what you learned about each item you listed.

What I Expect to Learn	What I Learned
a. _____?_____	b. _____?_____
c. _____?_____	d. _____?_____

During the Middle Ages, a number of people, like the ones shown in Figure 12, were obsessed with the idea of changing lead into gold. For centuries, these early scientists, known as alchemists, tried to use chemical reactions to make gold. But no matter how many recipes they tried, the alchemists only succeeded in making compounds that contained lead. What were they doing wrong?

Nuclear Reactions in the Laboratory

The alchemists were trying to achieve transmutation. **Transmutation** is the conversion of atoms of one element to atoms of another. It involves a nuclear change, not a chemical change.

Nuclear decay is an example of a transmutation that occurs naturally. Transmutations can also be artificial. **Scientists can perform artificial transmutations by bombarding atomic nuclei with high-energy particles, such as protons, neutrons, or alpha particles.**

Early experiments involving artificial transmutation led to important clues about atomic structure. In 1919, a decade after he discovered the atomic nucleus, Ernest Rutherford performed the first artificial transmutation. Rutherford had been studying the effects of nuclear radiation on various gases. When Rutherford exposed nitrogen gas to alpha particles, he found that some of the alpha particles were absorbed by the nitrogen nuclei. Each newly formed nucleus then ejected a proton, leaving behind the isotope oxygen-17.

$$^{14}_{7}\text{N} + {}^{4}_{2}\text{He} \rightarrow {}^{17}_{8}\text{O} + {}^{1}_{1}\text{H}$$

Note that ${}^{1}_{1}\text{H}$ represents a proton. Rutherford's experiment provided evidence that the nucleus contains protons.

Figure 12 This painting of an alchemist's laboratory was made around 1570. The alchemists failed in their attempts to turn lead into gold.

Modeling Transmutation

Materials

periodic table, 2 sheets of unlined white paper, 32 green beads, 32 purple beads

Procedure

1. Use the periodic table to complete the following nuclear reaction. Then, write it on one of the sheets of paper.

$$^{10}_{5}B + ^{4}_{2}He \rightarrow ^{A}_{Z}X + ^{1}_{1}H$$

2. Count the number of protons and neutrons present in each reactant and product.

3. Using the green beads to represent protons and the purple beads to represent neutrons,

make a model of each reactant and product below its symbol on the sheet of paper.

4. Repeat Steps 1 to 3 using the following nuclear reaction and the second sheet of paper.

$$^{14}_{7}N + ^{4}_{2}He \rightarrow ^{A}_{Z}X + ^{1}_{1}H$$

Analyze and Conclude

1. **Applying Concepts** What was the missing product in each of the equations? How did you know what the missing product was?

2. **Using Models** Make a model of the nuclear reaction between an alpha particle and an atom of aluminium-27. (*Hint:* One of the two products is a proton.)

Figure 13 In 1977, the National Aeronautics and Space Administration (NASA) launched two identical spacecraft, Voyager 1 and Voyager 2. These spacecraft, which are still exploring the outer solar system, are powered by the alpha decay of plutonium-238. **Inferring** *What isotope is produced by the alpha decay of plutonium-238?*

Transuranium Elements

Elements with atomic numbers greater than 92 (uranium) are called **transuranium elements.** All transuranium elements are radioactive, and they are generally not found in nature. **Scientists can synthesize a transuranium element by the artificial transmutation of a lighter element.**

Neptunium was the first transuranium element synthesized. In 1940, scientists at the University of California, Berkeley, bombarded uranium-238 with neutrons, producing uranium-239. The uranium-239 underwent beta decay to form neptunium-239.

$$^{239}_{92}U \rightarrow ^{239}_{93}Np + ^{0}_{-1}e$$

Although most transuranium elements have only been produced for research, some are synthesized for industrial or consumer use. For example, americium-241 is a transuranium element used in smoke detectors. As americium-241 decays, it emits alpha radiation. This radiation ionizes the air inside a smoke detector to allow an electric current to flow. When smoke enters the smoke detector, it disrupts the current and the alarm goes off. Another useful transuranium element is plutonium-238. Figure 13 shows a space probe that runs on electrical energy generated by the decay of plutonium-238.

Reading Checkpoint *What is a transuranium element?*

Particle Accelerators

In Rutherford's transmutation experiment, the radioactive element radium was used as a source of alpha particles. However, sometimes transmutations will not occur unless the bombarding particles are moving at extremely high speeds. In order to perform such transmutations, scientists use devices called particle accelerators. In a particle accelerator, charged particles can be accelerated to speeds very close to the speed of light. The fast-moving particles are guided toward a target, where they collide with atomic nuclei. With the help of particle accelerators, scientists have produced more than 3000 different isotopes.

Scientists also conduct collision experiments in order to study nuclear structure. Since the proton, neutron, and electron were discovered, more than 200 different subatomic particles have been detected. According to the current model of the atom, protons and neutrons are made up of even smaller particles called quarks. A **quark** is a subatomic particle theorized to be among the basic units of matter. Both protons and neutrons belong to a class of particles that are made up of three quarks. Six types of quarks are currently thought to exist. Two of these types were discovered at Fermi National Accelerator Laboratory, also known as Fermilab. Figure 14 shows one of the devices used at Fermilab to detect subatomic particles.

Figure 14 This particle detector records subatomic particles produced in the Tevatron, the most powerful particle accelerator in the United States. The Tevatron is located at Fermilab in Batavia, Illinois.

Section 10.3 Assessment

Reviewing Concepts

1. How do scientists perform artificial transmutations?

2. How are transuranium elements produced?

3. How does artificial transmutation differ from nuclear decay?

4. Write the equation for the transmutation that occurs when an alpha particle combines with an oxygen-16 atom, emitting a proton.

5. Does fermium-257 undergo nuclear decay? Explain.

Critical Thinking

6. **Predicting** Bombarding a lithium-6 atom with a neutron produces helium-4 and another particle. What is that particle?

7. **Predicting** Curium was first synthesized by bombarding a target isotope with alpha particles, which produced curium-242 and a neutron. What was the target isotope? (*Hint:* Use the symbol $_0^1n$ to represent a neutron.)

8. **Inferring** Why can't the transuranium elements be made by exposing other elements to naturally occurring alpha radiation?

Writing in Science

Summary Write a brief summary of the first artificial transmutation, performed by Ernest Rutherford. (*Hint:* Your summary should describe an example of a nuclear reaction.)

Nuclear Medicine

Exposure to nuclear radiation is often harmful to the human body. However, scientists have also found nuclear radiation to be a powerful tool in the field of medicine.

Because radioisotopes are detectable by their radiation, they can be used as tracers that map out specific locations in the body. For example, the radioisotope iodine-131 is absorbed by the thyroid gland in the throat in the same way that iodine-127 is. If iodine-131 is injected into the body, the radiation it emits will show how well the thyroid gland is functioning.

Radioactive tracers can also be used to pinpoint the location of cancer cells. Cancer cells multiply rapidly and absorb glucose much faster than normal cells. If the glucose molecules are "tagged" with a radioactive tracer, such as flourine-18, the location of the cancer cells can be found by tracking areas of high glucose concentration.

Radioisotopes with short half-lives are chosen for medical uses. These isotopes decay so rapidly that after only a day or two, practically none of the isotope remains.

PET scanner
PET (positron emission tomography) scans use radioactive tracers to examine parts of the body, such as the brain. The patient receives an injection of radioactive tracer. The tracer produces gamma rays that are detected by the scanner.

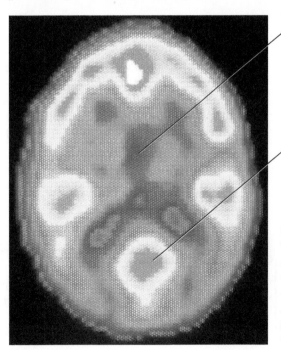

Tagged glucose is absorbed slowly in the blue areas, indicating normal tissue.

Red color shows greater glucose absorption in possibly cancerous areas.

PET scan of brain
This scan shows the level of activity in different areas of the brain. Glucose tagged with flourine-18 is absorbed more rapidly in areas of high brain activity and by cancer cells. Here, red shows the greatest activity and blue the least.

Positron

Gamma ray

Electron

Gamma rays

Gamma rays are produced when the tracer emits a positron. A positron is a particle with the mass of an electron but a charge of 1+. The positron is destroyed upon contact with an electron from a nearby atom in the body, and emits two gamma rays in opposite directions.

Gamma-ray detectors

Brain

Atom of tracer isotope

Gamma ray

Producing an image

The scanner detects the gamma rays and produces two-dimensional images like slices through the brain. The scanner's computer then constructs a three-dimensional image based on the scans.

Going Further

- Write a paragraph describing how radioactive tracers are used in medicine. Indicate what qualities make a particular radioisotope useful as a radioactive tracer in the human body.

- Take a Discovery Channel Video Field Trip by watching "Nuclear Medicine."

DISCOVERY
CHANNEL
SCHOOL
Video Field Trip

10.4 Fission and Fusion

Reading Focus

Key Concepts

- Under what conditions does the strong nuclear force overcome electric forces in the nucleus?

- What property of fission makes it so useful?

Vocabulary

- strong nuclear force
- fission
- chain reaction
- critical mass
- fusion
- plasma

Reading Strategy

Comparing and Contrasting Copy the Venn diagram below. As you read, contrast fission and fusion by listing the ways they differ.

Fission   **Fusion**

a. ? | releases large amounts of energy | c. ?
b. ? | | d. ?

Strong Nuclear Forces

Neutron

Neutron

Proton

Proton

Electric Forces

Neutron

Neutron

Proton

Proton

Figure 15 Two kinds of forces act upon particles in the nucleus. Strong nuclear forces, which are attractive, act on protons and neutrons alike. Electric forces in the nucleus are repulsive, and act only among protons.
Using Models *What atomic nucleus is represented above?*

Alternative energy sources may someday replace fossil fuels such as coal and oil. One alternative energy source that is widely used today is nuclear energy. Nuclear energy is the energy released by nuclear reactions.

Shortly after the discovery of radioactivity, scientists realized that atomic nuclei contained vast amounts of energy. By the late 1930s, scientists discovered that transmutations involved more than just the conversion of one element into another—they also involved the conversion of mass into energy.

Nuclear Forces

What holds the nucleus together? Remember that the protons in the nucleus are all positively charged, so they tend to repel one another. Clearly, there must be an attractive force that binds the particles of the nucleus. Otherwise, the protons would simply push one another away.

The **strong nuclear force** is the attractive force that binds protons and neutrons together in the nucleus. Because the strong nuclear force does not depend on charge, it acts among protons, among neutrons, and among protons and neutrons. **Over very short distances, the strong nuclear force is much greater than the electric forces among protons.** For example, at distances as short as the width of a proton, the strong nuclear force is more than 100 times greater than the electric force that repels protons. However, the strong nuclear force quickly weakens as protons and neutrons get farther apart. Figure 15 summarizes the forces acting on protons and neutrons in the nucleus.

A Nuclear Forces Acting on a Proton of a Small Nucleus

Strong nuclear forces

Electric force

B Nuclear Forces Acting on a Proton of a Large Nucleus

Strong nuclear forces

Electric forces

The Effect of Size on Nuclear Forces Electric forces in atomic nuclei depend on the number of protons. The greater the number of protons in a nucleus, the greater is the electric force that repels those protons. So in larger nuclei, the repulsive electric force is stronger than in smaller nuclei.

The effect of size on the strong nuclear force is more complicated. On one hand, the more protons and neutrons there are in a nucleus, the more possibilities there are for strong nuclear force attractions. However, as the size of the nucleus increases, the average distance between protons and neutrons increases. Because the strong nuclear force only acts over short ranges, the possibility of many attractions is never realized in a large nucleus. As a result, the strong nuclear force felt by one proton or neutron in a large nucleus is about the same as in a small nucleus, as shown in Figure 16.

Unstable Nuclei A nucleus becomes unstable, or radioactive, when the strong nuclear force can no longer overcome the repulsive electric forces among protons. While the strong nuclear force does not increase with the size of the nucleus, the electric forces do. There is, therefore, a point beyond which all elements are radioactive. All nuclei with more than 83 protons are radioactive.

Fission

In 1938, two German chemists, Otto Hahn and Fritz Strassman, performed a series of important transmutation experiments. By bombarding uranium-235 with high-energy neutrons, Hahn and Strassman hoped to produce more massive elements. Instead, their experiments produced isotopes of a smaller element, barium. Unable to explain their data, Hahn and Strassman turned to a colleague for help. In 1939, Lise Meitner, shown in Figure 17, and Otto Frisch, another physicist, offered a groundbreaking explanation for the experiments. The uranium-235 nuclei had been broken into smaller fragments. Hahn and Strassman had demonstrated nuclear fission. **Fission** is the splitting of an atomic nucleus into two smaller parts.

Figure 16 The size of a nucleus affects how strongly it is bound together. **A** In a nucleus containing two protons and two neutrons, the strong nuclear forces easily overcome the electric force between the protons. **B** In a nucleus containing many protons and neutrons, the larger number of electric forces makes the nucleus less stable.

Figure 17 Austrian physicist Lise Meitner (1878–1968), shown here, and Otto Frisch were the first scientists to describe nuclear fission. Meitner correctly predicted that fission releases large amounts of energy.

Figure 18 The fission of uranium-235 yields smaller nuclei, neutrons, and energy. The nuclear equation for this reaction can be written as follows.

$$^{235}_{92}U + ^{1}_{0}n \rightarrow$$

$$^{91}_{36}Kr + ^{142}_{56}Ba + 3^{1}_{0}n + energy$$

Comparing and Contrasting
How does fission differ from nuclear decay?

Neutron

Krypton-91
$^{91}_{36}Kr$

Energy

$^{235}_{92}U$
Uranium-235

$^{236}_{92}U$
Uranium-236
(very unstable)

$^{142}_{56}Ba$
Barium-142

Figure 18 illustrates the fission of a uranium-235 nucleus. Notice that one of the products of the reaction is energy. **In nuclear fission, tremendous amounts of energy can be produced from very small amounts of mass.** For example, the nuclear energy released by the fission of 1 kilogram of uranium-235 is equivalent to the chemical energy produced by burning more than 17,000 kilograms of coal.

Converting Mass Into Energy In the nuclear equation shown in Figure 18, the mass numbers on the left equal the mass numbers on the right. Yet when the fission of uranium-235 is carried out, about 0.1 percent of the mass of the reactants is lost during the reaction. This "lost" mass is converted into energy.

In 1905, more than 30 years before the discovery of fission, physicist Albert Einstein had introduced the mass-energy equation. It describes how mass and energy are related.

Mass–Energy Equation

$$E = mc^2$$

In the mass-energy equation, E represents energy, m represents mass, and c represents the speed of light (3.0×10^8 m/s). The conversion of a small amount of mass releases an enormous amount of energy. Likewise, a large amount of energy can be converted into a small amount of mass. The explosion of the first atomic bomb in 1945 offered a powerful demonstration of the mass-energy equation. The bomb contained 5 kilograms of plutonium-239. Fission of the plutonium produced an explosion that was equivalent to 18,600 tons of TNT.

Recall how the law of conservation of mass applied to chemical reactions. In nuclear reactions, however, the energies involved are much larger. To account for the conversion of mass into energy, a modified conservation law is used. According to the law of conservation of mass and energy, the total amount of mass and energy remains constant.

Go Online
SC/LINKS

For: Links on fission
Visit: www.SciLinks.org
Web Code: ccn-1104

Figure 19 The fission of one nucleus can trigger a chain reaction. The splitting of a uranium-235 nucleus by a neutron yields two or three neutrons, each of which can cause another fission. **Interpreting Diagrams** *Does the fission of uranium-235 always yield the same isotopes as products? Explain.*

Triggering a Chain Reaction

How fast does a rumor spread? Imagine that you started a rumor by telling it to three of your friends. Then suppose each of those friends told three more friends. If this pattern continued, the rumor would quickly spread to hundreds of people, even though it originally started with just one person, you.

Nuclear fission can follow a similar pattern, in which one reaction leads to a series of others. During the fission of uranium-235, each reactant nucleus splits into two smaller nuclei and releases two or three neutrons. If one of these neutrons is absorbed by another uranium-235 nucleus, another fission can result, releasing more neutrons, as shown in Figure 19. In a **chain reaction,** neutrons released during the splitting of an initial nucleus trigger a series of nuclear fissions.

The speed of a chain reaction can vary. In an uncontrolled chain reaction, all of the released neutrons are free to cause other fissions, resulting in a fast, intense release of energy. Nuclear weapons are designed to produce uncontrolled chain reactions. In a controlled chain reaction, some of the neutrons are absorbed by nonfissionable materials, resulting in only one new fission for each splitting of an atom. The heat from controlled chain reactions can be used to generate electrical energy. Unfortunately, another product of controlled chain reactions is radioactive waste, shown in Figure 20.

In order to sustain a chain reaction, each nucleus that is split must produce, on average, one neutron that causes the fission of another nucleus. This condition corresponds to a specific mass of fissionable material, known as a critical mass. A **critical mass** is the smallest possible mass of a fissionable material that can sustain a chain reaction.

 Reading Checkpoint *What is a chain reaction?*

Figure 20 A crane lowers drums of radioactive waste into a landfill in Hanford, Washington.

Nuclear Energy from Fission Today, nuclear power plants generate about 20 percent of the electricity in the United States. In a nuclear power plant, controlled fission of uranium-235 occurs in a vessel called a fission reactor.

Unlike power plants that burn fossil fuels, nuclear power plants do not emit air pollutants such as oxides of sulfur and nitrogen. However, nuclear power plants have their own safety and environmental issues. For example, workers in nuclear power plants need to wear protective clothing to reduce their exposure to nuclear radiation. In addition, the fission of uranium-235 produces many radioactive isotopes with half-lives of hundreds or thousands of years. This radioactive waste must be

Nuclear Chemistry

Over the last 100 years scientists have uncovered many secrets about the atomic nucleus. Developments have ranged from the synthesis of new elements to the harnessing of nuclear power as a viable energy source.

MARIE AND PIERRE CURIE AT WORK IN THEIR LABORATORY

EQUIPMENT USED BY HAHN AND STRASSMANN

HENRI BECQUEREL

1896 French scientist Antoine Henri Becquerel discovers radioactivity in uranium.

1898 Marie and Pierre Curie discover the radioactive elements radium and polonium. By making radium available to other scientists, the Curies helped advance the study of radioactivity.

1905 Albert Einstein's mass-energy equation, $E = mc^2$, provides the basis for nuclear power.

1932 First atom smasher (subatomic particle accelerator) is used by John Cockcroft and Ernest Walton.

1938 Germans Otto Hahn and Fritz Strassmann produce nuclear fission by bombarding uranium-235 atoms with neutrons.

1890　　　　　　　　　1910　　　　　　　　　1930

isolated and stored so that it cannot harm people or contaminate the environment while it decays.

Another concern about nuclear power is that the operators of the plant could lose control of the reactor. For instance, if the reactor's cooling system failed, then a meltdown might occur. During a meltdown, the core of the reactor melts and radioactive material may be released. If the structure that houses the reactor is not secure, then the environment can become contaminated. In 1986, one of the reactors at the nuclear power station in Chernobyl, Ukraine, overheated during an experiment. A partial meltdown resulted, and large amounts of radioactive material were released into the atmosphere.

Writing in Science

Summary Write a paragraph about the history of nuclear energy based on some of the events in the time line below. (*Hint:* Before you write, use a flowchart to organize the events you wish to include.)

ENRICO FERMI

ATOM BOMB TEST

IDAHO TESTING STATION

1942 The first controlled, self-sustaining nuclear chain reaction is achieved by Enrico Fermi's research group in Chicago.

1945 United States explodes first atom bomb in a test near Alamagordo, New Mexico.

1951 Electricity from nuclear fission produced at National Reactor Testing Station, Idaho.

1960 Willard Libby wins the Nobel Prize for developing carbon-14 dating. The technique became widely used in archaeology and geology.

1986 Partial meltdown occurs at Chernobyl power plant.

1950

1970

1990

Nuclear Power Station

Since the first nuclear bomb was exploded in 1945, scientists have found ways of utilizing the enormous power of nuclear fission for peaceful purposes. Nuclear power is now a major means of producing electricity. About 20 percent of electricity in the United States is generated this way. **Interpreting Diagrams**

How is water used in a nuclear power station?

Fission control
The fission reaction within the reactor core is controlled by neutron-absorbing control rods. Because they are still radioactive, the used rods are removed from the reactor core and stored in a pool, as shown above.

A Reactor core Fission reactions take place in the reactor core, releasing large amounts of heat.

B Steam generator Heat released in the reactor core is absorbed by water in the steam generator. This transfer of energy produces large amounts of high-pressure steam.

C Turbines and condenser The high-pressure steam forces the turbine to rotate at great speed. As it cools, the steam condenses to form liquid water, which is then piped back to the steam generator.

D Electric generator Here the work done by the force turning the turbines produces electrical energy.

Water pressurizer

High-strength protective shielding

High-pressure turbine

Steam condenses.

Condenser

Control rods

Pump *Fuel rods containing uranium dioxide*

Water

Cooling water exits.

Cooling water enters.

Pump

Filter

Fusion

Another type of nuclear reaction that can release huge amounts of energy is fusion. **Fusion** is a process in which the nuclei of two atoms combine to form a larger nucleus. As in fission, during fusion, a small fraction of the reactant mass is converted into energy.

On any day or night, you can detect the energy released by fusion reactions occurring far away from Earth. The sun and other stars are powered by the fusion of hydrogen into helium. Inside the sun, an estimated 600 million tons of hydrogen undergo fusion each second. About 4 million tons of this matter is converted into energy.

Matter within the sun and other stars exists as plasma. **Plasma** is a state of matter in which atoms have been stripped of their electrons. You can think of plasma as a gas containing two kinds of particles—nuclei and electrons. Although fusion occurs at millions of degrees Celsius, plasma can exist at much lower temperatures. Scientists estimate that more than 99 percent of matter in the universe is plasma.

Fusion may someday provide an efficient and clean source of electricity. Scientists envision fusion reactors fueled by two hydrogen isotopes, deuterium (hydrogen-2) and tritium (hydrogen-3). The fusion of deuterium and tritium produces helium, neutrons, and energy.

$$\,^2_1\text{H} + \,^3_1\text{H} \rightarrow \,^4_2\text{He} + \,^1_0\text{n} + \text{energy}$$

Scientists face two main problems in designing a fusion reactor. They need to achieve the high temperatures required to start the reaction, and they must contain the plasma.

Figure 21 The Tokamak Fusion Test Reactor at the Princeton Plasma Physics Laboratory in Princeton, New Jersey, was one of the very few fusion reactors that have been built. It was retired in 1997, after 15 years of experimentation.

Section 10.4 Assessment

Reviewing Concepts

1. ⬭ Under what conditions does the strong nuclear force overcome the repulsive effect of electric forces in the nucleus?

2. ⬭ What property of fission makes it a useful reaction?

3. What particles are affected by strong nuclear forces?

4. What must happen in order for a nuclear chain reaction to occur?

5. Why is a cooling system necessary in a nuclear reactor?

6. How do the products of a fusion reaction differ from the products of a fission reaction?

Critical Thinking

7. **Inferring** How does the strong nuclear force affect an atom's electrons? (*Hint:* Think about where the electrons are located in the atom.)

8. **Inferring** Why do fission chain reactions of uranium-235 not occur in underground uranium deposits?

Connecting ⊂ Concepts

Fossil Fuels Reread the description of fossil fuels in Section 9.1. Then compare fossil fuel combustion with nuclear fission.

Modeling a Chain Reaction

In a nuclear fission chain reaction, a nucleus is struck by a neutron, which causes the nucleus to split into two smaller nuclei and to release other neutrons. If these neutrons strike other nuclei, a chain reaction can occur. In this lab, you will model a nuclear fission chain reaction using dominoes.

Problem How can you make a model of a nuclear fission chain reaction?

Materials

- 20 dominoes
- watch with a second hand, or stopwatch
- metric ruler

Skills Observing, Using Models

Procedure

1. Stand 15 dominoes in a single straight row in such a way that the distance between them is about one half of their height. Knock over the first domino. Measure and record the time it takes for all the dominoes to fall.

2. Repeat Step 1 two more times. Then, average the three time measurements to get a more accurate time.

3. Arrange 15 dominoes as shown below so that each domino will knock over two others. Observe what happens when you knock over the first domino. Measure and record how long it takes for the whole set of dominoes to fall over.

4. Repeat Step 3 two more times. Average the three time measurements to get a more accurate time.

5. Set up 15 dominoes again as you did in Step 3. This time, however, hold a metric ruler on end, in the middle of the arrangement of dominoes, as shown in the photograph on the next page. Knock over the first domino. Observe what happens.

6. Set up 15 dominoes as you did in Step 3, but this time, place 5 additional dominoes behind and at right angles to 5 randomly chosen dominoes for support, as shown below. The 5 supported dominoes represent atoms of a different isotope that must be struck with more energy to undergo fission.

7. Knock over the first domino. Measure and record the time it takes for the dominoes to fall and how many dominoes fall.

8. Repeat Steps 6 and 7 two more times. Then, average the three time measurements to get a more accurate time.

9. Repeat Steps 6 through 8, but this time, place supporting dominoes behind only 3 dominoes.

10. Repeat Steps 6 through 8, but this time, place a supporting domino behind only 1 domino.

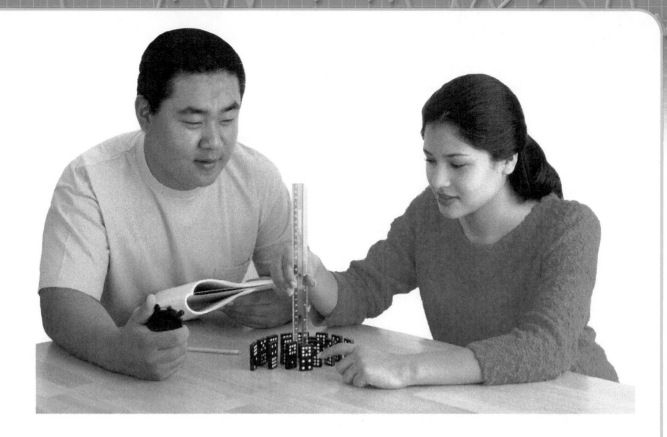

Analyze and Conclude

1. **Calculating** What was the average fall time for the arrangement of dominoes in Steps 1 and 2? In Steps 3 and 4?

2. **Applying Concepts** What type of reaction was modeled in Steps 3 and 4?

3. **Using Models** In your falling-dominoes model of nuclear fission chain reactions, what did a standing domino represent? What did the fall of a domino represent?

4. **Using Models** In your falling-dominoes model of nuclear fission chain reactions, what did the striking of one domino by another represent? What did the metric ruler represent?

5. **Analyzing Data** Before a sample of an easily fissionable isotope is used, it is refined by removing less fissionable isotopes of the same element. On the basis of your observations in Steps 6 through 10, explain why this refinement is necessary.

6. **Inferring** What factors do you think would affect the rate of a nuclear fission chain reaction?

7. **Drawing Conclusions** What do you think would happen to a nuclear fission chain reaction if control rods were not present?

8. **Evaluating and Revising** What are some of the limitations of using falling dominoes to model a nuclear fission chain reaction? Suggest how you might revise this model to make it more representative of a chain reaction.

Go Further Visit the library and find out about the Manhattan Project and how it made history. Use what you have learned from the falling-dominoes model to help you understand the scientific discoveries related to controlled and uncontrolled nuclear chain reactions.

10.1 Radioactivity

🔑 Key Concepts

- During nuclear decay, atoms of one element can change into atoms of a different element altogether.
- Common types of nuclear radiation include alpha particles, beta particles, and gamma rays.
- Nuclear radiation can ionize atoms.
- Devices that are used to detect nuclear radiation include Geiger counters and film badges.

Vocabulary

radioactivity, *p. 292;* radioisotope, *p. 292;* nuclear radiation, *p. 293;* alpha particle, *p. 293;* beta particle, *p. 294;* gamma ray, *p. 294;* background radiation, *p. 296*

10.2 Rates of Nuclear Decay

🔑 Key Concepts

- Unlike chemical reaction rates, which vary with the conditions of a reaction, nuclear decay rates are constant.
- In radiocarbon dating, the age of an object is determined by comparing the object's carbon-14 levels with carbon-14 levels in the atmosphere.

Vocabulary

half-life, *p. 299*

10.3 Artificial Transmutation

🔑 Key Concepts

- Scientists can perform artificial transmutations by bombarding atomic nuclei with high-energy particles such as protons, neutrons, or alpha particles.
- Scientists can synthesize a transuranium element by the artificial transmutation of a lighter element.

Vocabulary

transmutation, *p. 303;* transuranium elements, *p. 304;* quark, *p. 305*

10.4 Fission and Fusion

🔑 Key Concepts

- Over very short distances, the strong nuclear force is much greater than the electric forces among protons.
- In nuclear fission, tremendous amounts of energy can be produced from very small amounts of mass.

Vocabulary

strong nuclear force, *p. 308;* fission, *p. 309;* chain reaction, *p. 311;* critical mass, *p. 311;* fusion, *p. 315;* plasma, *p. 315*

Thinking Visually

Concept Map Use information from the chapter to complete the concept map below.

Reviewing Content

Choose the letter that best answers the questions or completes the statement.

1. An alpha particle is identical to
   - **a.** a neutron.
   - **b.** a helium nucleus.
   - **c.** an electron.
   - **d.** a hydrogen nucleus.

2. When a beta particle is emitted, the mass number of a nucleus
   - **a.** increases by one.
   - **b.** decreases by one.
   - **c.** decreases by four.
   - **d.** remains the same.

3. The most penetrating form of nuclear radiation is
   - **a.** an alpha particle.
   - **b.** a beta particle.
   - **c.** a gamma ray.
   - **d.** an electron.

4. The half-life of cobalt-60 is 5.3 years. What fraction of a sample remains after 21.2 years?
   - **a.** one half
   - **b.** one quarter
   - **c.** one eighth
   - **d.** one sixteenth

5. Which of the following is a radioisotope commonly used in dating archeological artifacts?
   - **a.** nitrogen-14
   - **b.** carbon-12
   - **c.** uranium-235
   - **d.** carbon-14

6. Transmutation does not occur in which of these nuclear processes?
   - **a.** nuclear fission
   - **b.** nuclear fusion
   - **c.** alpha decay
   - **d.** gamma decay

7. Based on its location on the periodic table, an element that is not naturally occurring is
   - **a.** terbium (Tb).
   - **b.** curium (Cm).
   - **c.** holmium (Ho).
   - **d.** lutetium (Lu).

8. Nuclear particles are held together by
   - **a.** the strong nuclear force.
   - **b.** electrical attraction.
   - **c.** quarks.
   - **d.** electrical repulsion.

9. Nuclear power plants generate electricity from
   - **a.** nuclear fusion.
   - **b.** nuclear fission.
   - **c.** combustion.
   - **d.** radioactivity.

10. The primary reaction inside stars changes
    - **a.** hydrogen to helium.
    - **b.** helium to hydrogen.
    - **c.** uranium to plutonium.
    - **d.** nitrogen to carbon.

Understanding Concepts

11. How do radioisotopes of an element differ from other isotopes?

12. What is the effect on the mass number and charge of a nucleus when it loses an alpha particle?

13. How do the mass number and charge of a nucleus change when it emits a gamma ray?

14. Which type of radiation—alpha, beta, or gamma— is most dangerous to living things? Explain.

15. Why does a Geiger counter occasionally click even if no artificial radioisotopes are nearby?

16. How does raising the temperature affect the rate of nuclear decay?

17. Why can't carbon-14 be used to determine the age of fossils that are several hundred thousand years old?

18. Write the equation for the transmutation that occurs when an alpha particle combines with a nitrogen-14 atom, emitting a proton.

19. Compare and contrast the processes of fission and fusion.

20. What is necessary to sustain a nuclear chain reaction?

21. Why do nuclear reactions produce more energy per mass of matter than chemical reactions?

22. The diagram below shows a nuclear reactor, including control rods. What is the function of a control rod in a nuclear power plant?

Assessment (continued)

Critical Thinking

Use the figure below to answer Questions 23 and 24.

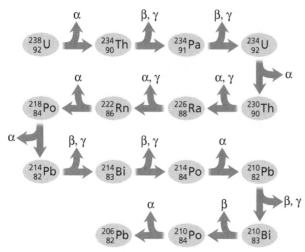

Stable isotope

23. **Classifying** In the illustrated uranium-238 decay sequence, classify the type of radiation released in each of the transmutations from uranium-238 to radon-222.

24. **Making Generalizations** Study the sequence of decay from radon-222 to lead-206. Make a generalization as to what type of decay lead, polonium, and bismuth undergo until stable lead-206 is formed.

25. **Inferring** A film badge consists of a piece of film wrapped in a piece of dark plastic or paper. Doses of what kinds of radiation can be measured with this simple piece of equipment? Explain.

26. **Calculating** The first sample of californium was made by bombarding a target isotope with alpha particles. In addition to californium-245, the reaction produced a neutron. What was the target isotope?

Math Skills

27. **Calculating** After 36.9 years, a sample of hydrogen-3 contains one eighth of the amount it contained originally. What is the half-life of the isotope?

28. **Calculating** The half-life of iron-59 is 44.5 days. After 133.5 days, 2.76 g of iron-59 remains. What was the mass of the original sample?

29. **Inferring** The beta emissions from a bone that was found buried in a cave indicate that there are 4.6 carbon-14 decays per gram of carbon per minute. A chicken bone from a fast-food restaurant shows 18.4 emissions per gram of carbon per minute. How old is the bone from the cave?

Concepts in Action

30. **Inferring** Radioisotopes are commonly used in medical tests to diagnose diseases. Do the radioisotopes used for this purpose have long half-lives or short half-lives? Explain.

31. **Applying Concepts** Americium-241 and radon-222 both emit alpha particles. Americium is found in almost every home as a component of smoke detectors. But radon is considered a health hazard. Why is radon more hazardous?

32. **Making Judgments** If a fusion power plant could be constructed, why might it be a better source of energy than a fission plant?

33. **Writing in Science** Write a paragraph explaining how radon gas can collect in buildings. (*Hint:* The first sentence in your paragraph should state the paragraph's main idea.)

Performance-Based Assessment

Evaluating Many transuranium elements were named for the scientists who synthesized them or the location in which they were produced. Choose such a transuranium element, find out how it was created, and evaluate its importance. Write a pamphlet informing your classmates about the element you chose.

For: Self-grading assessment
Visit: PHSchool.com
Web Code: cca-1100

Standardized Test Prep

Test-Taking Tip

Evaluating and Revising
Frequently, a scientifically accurate answer choice may not answer the question that is being asked. Keep these tips in mind:

- Verify what the question is asking.
- Determine if an answer choice is a true statement or not.
- Determine if a true answer choice actually answers the question.
- Be cautious with inserted or deleted words that make a false statement seem accurate.

Practice using these tips in Question 5.

Choose the letter that best answers the question or completes the statement.

1. Which equation correctly shows beta decay?
   - (A) $^{210}_{82}Pb \rightarrow ^{209}_{81}Tl + ^{0}_{-1}e + \gamma$
   - (B) $^{210}_{82}Pb \rightarrow ^{209}_{83}Bi + ^{0}_{-1}e + \gamma$
   - (C) $^{210}_{82}Pb \rightarrow ^{210}_{83}Tl + ^{0}_{-1}e + \gamma$
   - (D) $^{210}_{82}Pb \rightarrow ^{210}_{83}Bi + \gamma$
   - (E) $^{210}_{82}Pb \rightarrow ^{210}_{83}Bi + ^{0}_{-1}e + \gamma$

2. The half-life of radon-222 is 3.8 days. If a sample currently has 3.1 grams of radon-222, how much radon-222 did this sample have 15.2 days ago?
   - (A) 12.4 grams
   - (B) 47.1 grams
   - (C) 49.6 grams
   - (D) 57.8 grams
   - (E) 92.7 grams

3. Radioactive decay of nuclei often involves several decays before a stable nucleus is formed. This is called a decay chain. What stable isotope is formed when radon-222 undergoes a decay chain of four alpha decays followed by four beta decays?
   - (A) tungsten-206
   - (B) platinum-206
   - (C) lead-206
   - (D) tungsten-214
   - (E) lead-214

4. Which nucleus balances the following nuclear equation for the fission of uranium-235?
   $$^{235}_{92}U + ^{1}_{0}n \rightarrow ^{90}_{38}Sr + ^{A}_{Z}X + 2^{1}_{0}n + \gamma$$
   - (A) $^{146}_{54}Xe$
   - (B) $^{146}_{52}Te$
   - (C) $^{144}_{52}Te$
   - (D) $^{144}_{54}Xe$
   - (E) $^{142}_{50}Sn$

5. Uranium-238 is less stable than oxygen-16. What accounts for this difference?
   - (A) Uranium is a solid, while oxygen is a gas.
   - (B) Unlike oxygen-16, uranium-238 has a nucleus in which repulsive electric forces surpass the strong nuclear forces.
   - (C) Oxygen-16 has fewer electrons than uranium-238.
   - (D) Uranium-238 has fewer neutrons than oxygen-16.
   - (E) Unlike uranium-238, oxygen-16 has a nucleus in which the strong nuclear forces are overcome by repulsive electric forces.

6. The primary source of energy in stars is the fusion of hydrogen into helium. However, another reaction is believed to occur simultaneously. It is called the carbon-nitrogen-oxygen (CNO) cycle. In the diagram below, the symbol $^{0}_{+1}e$ represents a positron. A positron is a particle that has the same mass as an electron but a charge of 1+.

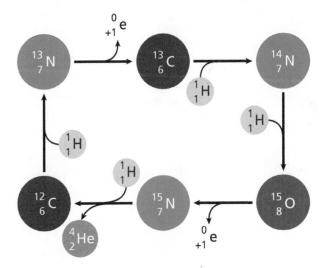

Which equation describes the CNO cycle?
   - (A) $^{1}_{1}H \rightarrow ^{4}_{2}He + ^{0}_{+1}e$
   - (B) $4^{1}_{1}H \rightarrow ^{4}_{2}He + 2^{0}_{+1}e$
   - (C) $^{2}_{1}H + ^{3}_{1}H \rightarrow ^{4}_{2}He + ^{1}_{0}n$
   - (D) $^{12}_{6}C \rightarrow ^{12}_{6}C + ^{4}_{2}He$
   - (E) $^{12}_{6}C + ^{1}_{1}H \rightarrow ^{12}_{6}C + ^{4}_{2}He$

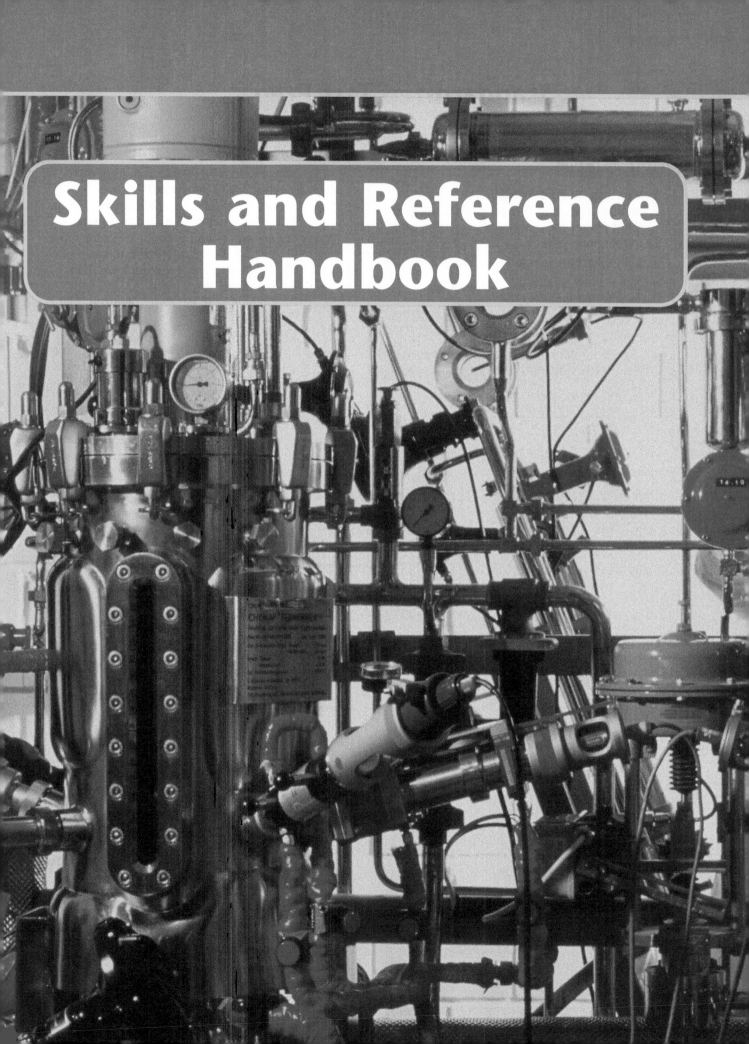

Skills and Reference Handbook

Science Skills

Basic Process Skills

During a physical science course, you often carry out some short lab activities as well as more detailed experiments. Here are some skills that you will use as you work.

Observing

In every science activity, you make a variety of observations. **Observing** is using one or more of the five senses to gather information. Many observations involve the senses of sight, hearing, touch, and smell.

Sometimes you will use tools that increase the power of your senses or make observations more precise. For example, hand lenses enable you to see things in greater detail. Tools may help you eliminate personal opinions or preferences.

In science it is customary to record your observations at the time they are made, usually by writing or drawing in a notebook. You may occasionally make records by using computers, cameras, videotapes, and other tools. As a rule, scientists keep complete accounts of their observations, often using tables to help organize their observations in a regular way.

Inferring

In science as in everyday life, observations are usually followed by inferences. **Inferring** is interpreting an observation or statement based on prior knowledge. For example, you can make several observations using the strobe photograph below. You can observe that the

ball is moving. Based on the motion of the ball, you might infer that the ball was thrown downward at an angle by an experimenter. In making that inference, you would use your knowledge about the motion of projectiles. Someone who knew more about projectile motion might infer that the ball loses energy with each bounce. That is why the height decreases with each bounce.

Notice that an inference is an act of reasoning, not a fact. That means an inference may be logical but not true. It is often necessary to gather further information before you can be confident that an inference is correct. For scientists, that information may come from further observations or from research into the work done by others.

Comparing Observations and Inferences

Sample Observation	Sample Inference
The ball moves less and less vertical distance in the time between each flash of the strobe light.	Gravity is slowing down the ball's upward motion.
The ball moves the same distance to the right in the time between each flash of the strobe light.	Air resistance is so small that it does not slow down the ball's horizontal motion.

Predicting

People often make predictions, but their statements about the future could be either guesses or inferences. In science, a **prediction** is an inference about a future event based on evidence, experience, or knowledge. For example, you can say, *On the first day next month, it will be sunny all day.* If your statement is based on evidence of weather patterns in the area, then the prediction is scientific. If the statement was made without considering any evidence, it's just a guess.

Predictions play a major role in science because they offer scientists a way to test ideas. If scientists understand an event or the properties of a particular object, they should be able to make accurate predictions about that event or object. Some predictions can be tested simply by making observations. For others, carefully designed experiments are needed.

Measuring

Measurements are important in science because they provide specific information and help observers avoid bias. **Measuring** is comparing an object or process to a standard. Scientists use a common set of standards, called the International System of Units, abbreviated as SI (for its French name, *Système International d'Unités*).

What distance does the ball travel in each time interval in the strobe photograph? You can make measurements on the photograph to make more precise statements about the ball's motion.

Calculating

Once scientists have made measurements, calculations are a very important part of analyzing data. How fast is a ball moving? You could directly measure the speed of a ball using probeware such as a motion sensor. But you can also calculate the speed using distance and time measurements. **Calculating** is a process in which a person uses mathematical operations to manipulate numbers and symbols.

Classifying

Classifying is grouping items according to some organizing idea or system. Classifying occurs in every branch of science but it's especially important in chemistry because there are so many different ways that elements can combine to form compounds.

Sometimes you place objects into groups using an established system. Other times you create a system by observing a variety of objects and identifying their properties. For example, you could group household cleaners into those that are abrasive and those that are not. Or you could categorize cleaners as toxic or nontoxic. Ammonia is toxic, whereas vinegar is not.

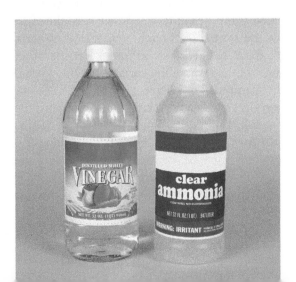

Using Tables and Graphs

Scientists represent and organize data in tables and graphs as part of experiments and other activities. Organizing data in tables and graphs makes it easier to see patterns in data. Scientists analyze and interpret data tables and graphs to determine the relationship of one variable to another and to make predictions based on the data.

Space-filling model   Electron dot model

Using Models

Some cities refuse to approve new tall buildings if they would cast shadows on existing parks. As architects plan buildings in such locations, they use models to show where a proposed building's shadow will fall at any time of day at any season of the year. A **model** is a mental or physical representation of an object, process, or event. In science, models are usually made to help people understand natural objects and the processes that affect these objects.

Models can be varied. Mental models, such as mathematical equations, can represent some kinds of ideas or processes. For example, the equation for the surface area of a sphere can model the surface of Earth, enabling scientists to determine its size. Models can be two-dimensional (flat) or three-dimensional (having depth). In chemistry, for example, there are several ways to model the arrangement of atoms in a molecule. Two models for a water molecule are shown above. The electron dot model is two-dimensional. It has the advantage of clearly showing how electrons are shared among atoms in the molecule. The space-filling model cannot show the number of electrons inside the atoms or between atoms, but it does show the arrangement of atoms in space.

Experimental Methods

A science experiment is a procedure designed so that there is only one logical explanation for the results. Some types of experiments are fairly simple to design. Others may require ingenious problem solving.

Posing Questions

As a gardener harvested corn in her vegetable garden, she noticed that on one side of the garden the plants produced very few ears of corn. The gardener wondered, *Why didn't the plants on one side of the garden produce as much corn?*

An experiment may begin when someone like the gardener asks a specific question or wants to solve a particular problem. Sometimes the original question leads directly to an experiment, but often researchers need to restate the problem before they can design an appropriate experiment. The gardener's question about the corn, for example, is too broad to be tested by an experiment, since there are so many possible different answers. To narrow the topic, the gardener might think about several related questions: *Were the seeds the same on both sides of the garden? Was the sunlight the same? Is there something different about the soil?*

Formulating Hypotheses

In science, a question about an event is answered by developing a possible explanation called a **hypothesis**. The hypothesis may be developed after long thought and research or come to a scientist "in a flash." To be useful, a hypothesis must lead to predictions that can be tested.

In this case, the gardener decided to focus on the quality of the soil on each side of her garden. She did some tests and discovered that the soil had a lower pH on the side where the plants did not produce well. That led her to propose this hypothesis: *If the pH of the soil is too low, the plants will produce less corn.* The next step is to make a prediction based on the hypothesis, for example, *If the pH of the soil is increased using lime, the plants will yield more corn.* Notice that the prediction suggests the basic idea for an experiment.

Designing Experiments

A carefully designed experiment can test a prediction in a reliable way, ruling out other possible explanations. As scientists plan their experimental procedures, they pay particular attention to the variables that must be controlled and the procedures that must be defined.

The gardener decided to study three groups of plants:
Group 1—20 plants on the side of the garden with a low pH;
Group 2—20 plants on the side of the garden with a low pH, but with lime added; and
Group 3—20 plants on the side of the garden with a high pH.

Controlling Variables

As researchers design an experiment, they identify the **variables**, factors that can change. Some common variables include mass, volume, time, temperature, light, and the presence or absence of specific materials. An experiment involves three categories of variables. The factor that scientists purposely change is called the **manipulated variable**. The factor that may change because of the manipulated variable and that scientists want to observe is called the **responding variable**. And the factors that scientists purposely keep the same are called the **controlled variables**. Controlling variables helps make researchers confident that the observed changes in the responding variable are due to changes in the manipulated variable.

For the gardener, the manipulated variable is the pH of the soil. The responding variable is the number of ears of corn produced by the plants. Among the variables that must be controlled are the amount of sunlight received each day, the time of year when seeds are planted, and the amount of water the plants receive.

Forming Operational Definitions

In an experiment, it is often necessary to define one or more variables explicitly so that any researcher could measure or control the variable in exactly the same way. An **operational definition** describes how a particular variable is to be measured or how a term is to be defined. In this context, the term *operational* means "describing what to do."

The gardener, for example, has to decide exactly how much lime to add to the soil. Can lime be added after the seeds are planted or only before planting? At what pH should no more lime be added to the soil? In this case, the gardener decided to add lime only before planting, and to add enough lime to make the pH equal in Groups 2 and 3.

Analyzing Data

The observations and measurements that are made in an experiment are called **data**. Scientists customarily record data in an orderly way. When an experiment is done, the researcher analyzes the data for trends or patterns, often by doing calculations or making graphs, to determine whether the results support the hypothesis.

For example, the gardener regularly measured and recorded data such as the soil moisture, daily sunlight, and pH of the soil. She found that the soil pH in Groups 2 and 3 started the same, but after two months the soil pH for Group 3 was a little higher than the soil pH for Group 2.

After harvesting the corn, the gardener recorded the numbers of ears of corn produced by each plant. She totaled the number of ears for each group. Her results were the following.

Group 1: 67 ears of corn
Group 2: 102 ears of corn
Group 3: 126 ears of corn

The overall trend was clear: The gardener's prediction was correct.

Drawing Conclusions

Based on whether the results confirm or refute the hypothesis, researchers make a final statement that summarizes the experiment. That final statement is called the **conclusion**. For example, the gardener's conclusion was, *Adding lime to soil with a low pH will improve the production of corn plants.*

Communicating Results

When an experiment has been completed, one or more events may follow. Researchers may repeat the experiment to verify the results. They may publish the experiment so that others can evaluate and replicate their procedures. They may compare their conclusion with the discoveries made by other scientists. And they may raise new questions that lead to new experiments. For example, *Why does the pH level decrease over time when soil is treated with lime?*

Evaluating and Revising

Scientists must be flexible about the conclusions drawn from an experiment. Further research may help confirm the results of the experiment or make it necessary to revise the initial conclusions. For example, a new experiment may show that lime can be effective only when certain microbes are present in the soil. Scientists continuously evaluate and revise experiments based on the findings in new research.

Science Skills

Science Safety

Laboratory work can be exciting, but it can be dangerous if you don't follow safety rules. Ask your teacher to explain any rules you don't understand. Always pay attention to safety symbols and **CAUTION** statements.

General Safety Rules and First Aid

1. Read all directions for an experiment several times. Follow the directions exactly as they are written. If you are in doubt, ask your teacher for assistance.
2. Never perform unauthorized or unsupervised labs, or handle equipment without specific permission.
3. When you design an experiment, do not start until your teacher has approved your plan.
4. If a lab includes physical activity, use caution to avoid injuring yourself or others. Tell your teacher if there is a reason that you should not participate.
5. Never eat, drink, or bring food into the laboratory.
6. Report all accidents to your teacher immediately.
7. Learn the correct ways to deal with a burn, a cut, and acid splashed in your eyes or on your skin.
8. Be aware of the location of the first-aid kit. Your teacher should administer any required first aid.
9. Report any fire to your teacher immediately. Find out the location of the fire extinguisher, the fire alarm, and the phone where emergency numbers are listed.

Dress Code

10. Always wear safety goggles to protect your eyes when working in the lab. Avoid wearing contact lenses. If you must wear contact lenses, ask your teacher what precautions you should take.
11. Wear a laboratory apron to protect your skin and clothing from harmful chemicals or hot materials.
12. Wear disposable plastic gloves to protect yourself from contact with chemicals that can be harmful. Keep your hands away from your face. Dispose of gloves according to your teacher's instructions.
13. Tie back long hair and loose clothing. Remove any jewelry that could contact chemicals or flames.

Heating and Fire Safety

14. Hot plates, hot water, and hot glassware can cause burns. Never touch hot objects with your bare hands. Use an oven mitt or other hand protection.
15. Use a clamp or tongs to hold hot objects. Test an object by first holding the back of your hand near it. If you feel heat on the back of your hand, the object may be too hot to handle.
16. Tie back long hair and loose clothing, and put on safety goggles before using a burner. Follow instructions from your teacher for lighting and extinguishing burners. If the flame leaps out of a burner as you are lighting it, turn the gas off. Never leave a flame unattended or reach across a flame. Make sure your work area is not cluttered with materials.
17. If flammable materials are present, make sure there are no flames, sparks, or exposed sources of heat.
18. Never heat a chemical without your teacher's permission. Chemicals that are harmless when cool can be dangerous when heated. When heating a test tube, point the opening away from you and others in case the contents splash or boil out of the test tube.
19. Never heat a closed container. Expanding hot gases may cause the container to explode.

Using Electricity Safely

20. To avoid an electric shock, never use electrical equipment near water, or when the equipment or your hands are wet. Use ground fault circuit interrupter (GFCI) outlets if you or your equipment may come into contact with moisture.
21. Use only sockets that accept a three-prong plug. Never use two-prong extension cords or adapters. When removing an electrical plug from a socket or extension cord, grasp the plug, not the cord.
22. Disconnect equipment that is not in use. Be sure cords are untangled and cannot trip anyone.
23. Do not use damaged electrical equipment. Look for dangerous conditions such as bare wires or frayed cords. Report damaged equipment immediately.

Using Glassware Safely

24. Handle fragile glassware, such as thermometers, test tubes, and beakers, with care. Do not touch broken glass. Notify your teacher if glassware breaks. Never use chipped or cracked glassware.
25. Never force glass tubing into a stopper. Your teacher will demonstrate the proper methods.
26. Never heat glassware that is not thoroughly dry. Use a wire screen to protect glassware from flames.
27. Hot glassware may not appear hot. Never pick up glassware without first checking to see if it is hot.
28. Never eat or drink from laboratory glassware.

Using Chemicals Safely

29. Do not let any corrosive or poisonous chemicals get on your skin or clothing, or in your eyes. When working with poisonous or irritating vapors, work in a well-ventilated area and wash your hands thoroughly after completing the activity.

30. Never test for an odor unless instructed by your teacher. Avoid inhaling a vapor directly. Use a wafting motion to direct vapor toward your nose.

31. Never mix chemicals "for the fun of it." You might produce a dangerous, possibly explosive substance.

32. Never touch, taste, or smell a chemical that you do not know for certain to be harmless.

33. Use only those chemicals listed in an investigation. Keep the lids on the containers when chemicals are not being used. To avoid contamination, never return chemicals to their original containers.

34. Take extreme care not to spill any chemicals. If a spill occurs, immediately ask your teacher about the proper cleanup procedure. Dispose of all chemicals as instructed by your teacher.

35. Be careful when working with acids or bases. Pour these chemicals over the sink, not over your workbench. If an acid or base gets on your skin or clothing, rinse it off with plenty of cold water. Immediately notify your teacher about an acid or base spill.

36. When diluting an acid, pour the acid into water. Never pour water into the acid.

Using Sharp Instruments

37. Use sharp instruments only as directed. Scissors, scalpels, pins, and knives are sharp and can cut or puncture your skin. Always direct sharp edges and points away from yourself and others.

38. Notify your teacher immediately if you cut yourself when in the laboratory.

End-of-Experiment Rules

39. All chemicals and any other materials used in the laboratory must be disposed of safely. Follow your teacher's instructions.

40. Clean up your work area and return all equipment to its proper place. Thoroughly clean glassware before putting it away.

41. Wash your hands thoroughly with soap, or detergent, and warm water. Lather both sides of your hands and between your fingers. Rinse well.

42. Check that all burners are off and the gas supply for the burners is turned off.

Safety Symbols

 General Safety Awareness
Follow all safety instructions.

 Physical Safety
Use caution in physical activities.

 Safety Goggles
Always wear goggles in the laboratory.

 Lab Apron
Always wear a lab apron in the laboratory.

 Plastic Gloves
Protect your hands from unsafe chemicals.

 Heating
Be careful using sources of heat.

 Heat-Resistant Gloves
Do not touch hot objects with bare hands.

 Flames
Work carefully around open flames.

 No Flames
Flammable materials may be present.

 Electric Shock
Take precautions to avoid electric shock.

 Fragile Glassware
Handle glassware carefully.

 Corrosive Chemical
Work carefully with corrosive chemicals.

 Poison
Avoid contact with poisonous chemicals.

 Fumes
Avoid inhaling dangerous vapors.

 Sharp Object
Use caution with sharp or pointed tools.

 Disposal
Follow instructions for disposal.

 Hand Washing
Wash your hands before leaving the lab.

Reading and Study Skills

At the beginning of each section, you will find a reading strategy to help you study. Each strategy uses a graphic organizer to help you stay organized. The following strategies and graphic organizers are used throughout the text.

Reading Strategies

Using Prior Knowledge
This strategy helps you think about your own experience before you read a section. Research has shown that you learn new material better if you can relate it to something you already know.

Previewing
Previewing a lesson can give you a sense of how the textbook is organized and what lies ahead. One technique is to look at the section topics (in green and blue type). You also can preview by reading captions. Sometimes previewing helps you simply because you find out a topic isn't as hard as you thought it might be.

Predicting
You can preview a section and then make a prediction. For example, you might predict the meaning of an important concept. Then, as you read, check to see if your prediction was correct. Often you find out that you knew more about a topic than you realized.

Building Vocabulary
Start building new vocabulary by previewing a section and listing boldface terms you don't recognize. Then look for each term as you read. Writing a sentence with a term, and defining a term in your own words are two techniques that will help you remember definitions.

Identifying the Main Idea
The key symbols next to boldface sentences identify the main ideas in a section. You can use topic sentences to find the main idea in a paragraph. Often, a topic sentence is the first or second sentence in a paragraph.

Identifying Cause and Effect
Cause-and-effect relationships are very important in science. A flowchart will help you identify cause-and-effect relationships as you read about a process.

Comparing and Contrasting
Comparing and contrasting can help you understand how concepts are related. Comparing is identifying both similarities and differences, while contrasting focuses on the differences. Compare-and-contrast tables and Venn diagrams work best with this strategy.

Sequencing
When you sequence events, it helps you to visualize the steps in a process and to remember the order in which they occur. Sequences often involve cause-and-effect relationships. Use flowcharts for linear sequences and cycle diagrams for repeating sequences.

Relating Text and Figures
You can use diagrams and photographs to focus on the essential concepts in a section. Then find text that extends the information in the figures. You can also reinforce concepts by comparing different figures.

Summarizing
Summarizing requires you to identify key ideas and state them briefly in your own words. You will remember the content of an entire section better even if you summarize only a portion of the section.

Outlining
You can quickly organize an outline by writing down the green and blue headings in a section. Then add phrases or sentences from the boldface sentences to expand the outline with the most important concepts.

Monitoring Your Understanding
You can evaluate your progress with graphic organizers such as a Know-Write-Learn (KWL) table. To make a KWL table, construct a table with three columns, labeled K, W, and L. Before you read, write what you already know in the first column (K). In the middle column, write what you want to learn (W). After you read, write what you learned (L).

Graphic Organizers

Concept Maps and Web Diagrams

A **concept map** is a diagram that contains concept words in ovals and connects the ovals with linking words. Often the most general concept is placed at the top of the map. The content of the other ovals becomes more specific as you move away from the main concept. Linking words are written on a line between two ovals.

A **web diagram** is a type of concept map that shows how several ideas relate to one central idea. Each subtopic may also link to subtopics, creating the visual effect of a spider web. Linking words are usually not included.

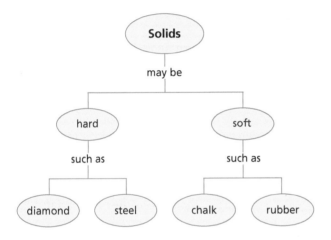

Compare-and-Contrast Tables

A **compare-and-contrast table** is a way of showing the similarities and differences between two or more objects or processes. The table provides an organized framework for making comparisons based on specific characteristics.

The items to be compared are usually column headings across the top of the table. Characteristics for comparison are listed in the first column. You complete the table by filling in information for each item.

Compare-and-Contrast Table		
Contents	**Book**	**CD-ROM**
Paper pages	Yes	No
Photographs	Yes	Yes
Videos	No	Yes

Venn Diagrams

A **Venn diagram** consists of two or more ovals that overlap. Each oval represents a particular object or idea. Unique characteristics are shown in the part of each oval that does not overlap. Shared characteristics are shown in the area of overlap.

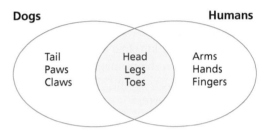

Flowcharts

A **flowchart** is used to represent the order in which a set of events occurs. Each step in the sequence is described in a box. Each box is linked to the next box with an arrow. The flowchart shows a sequence from beginning to end.

Cycle Diagrams

A **cycle diagram** shows boxes representing a cyclical sequence of events. As in a flowchart, boxes are linked with arrows, but the sequence does not have a beginning or end. The boxes are usually arranged in a clockwise circle.

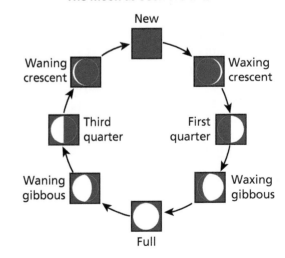

Math Skills

Throughout your study of physical science, you will often need to solve math problems. This appendix is designed to help you quickly review the basic math skills you will use most often.

Fractions

Adding and Subtracting Fractions

To add or subtract fractions that have the same denominator, add or subtract the numerators, and then write the sum or difference over the denominator. Express the answer in lowest terms.

Examples

$$\frac{3}{10} + \frac{1}{10} = \frac{3+1}{10} = \frac{4}{10} = \frac{2}{5}$$

$$\frac{5}{7} - \frac{2}{7} = \frac{5-2}{7} = \frac{3}{7}$$

To add or subtract fractions with different denominators, find the least common denominator. Write an equivalent fraction for each fraction using the least common denominator. Then add or subtract the numerators. Write the sum or difference over the least common denominator and express the answer in lowest terms.

Examples

$$\frac{1}{3} + \frac{3}{5} = \frac{5}{15} + \frac{9}{15} = \frac{5+9}{15} = \frac{14}{15}$$

$$\frac{7}{8} - \frac{1}{4} = \frac{7}{8} - \frac{2}{8} = \frac{7-2}{8} = \frac{5}{8}$$

Multiplying Fractions

When multiplying two fractions, multiply the numerators to find the product's numerator. Then multiply the denominators to find the product's denominator. It helps to divide any numerator or denominator by the greatest common factor before multiplying. Express the answer in lowest terms.

Examples

$$\frac{3}{5} \times \frac{2}{7} = \frac{3 \times 2}{5 \times 7} = \frac{6}{35}$$

$$\frac{4}{14} \times \frac{6}{9} = \frac{2 \times 2}{7 \times 2} \times \frac{2 \times 3}{3 \times 3} = \frac{2 \times 2}{7 \times 3} = \frac{4}{21}$$

Dividing Fractions

To divide one fraction by another, invert and multiply. Express the answer in lowest terms.

Examples

$$\frac{2}{5} \div \frac{3}{4} = \frac{2}{5} \times \frac{4}{3} = \frac{2 \times 4}{5 \times 3} = \frac{8}{15}$$

$$\frac{9}{16} \div \frac{5}{8} = \frac{9}{16} \times \frac{8}{5} = \frac{9 \times 1}{2 \times 5} = \frac{9}{10}$$

Ratios and Proportions

A ratio compares two numbers or quantities. A ratio is often written as a fraction expressed in lowest terms. A ratio also may be written with a colon.

Examples

The ratio of 3 to 4 is written as 3 to 4, $\frac{3}{4}$, or 3 : 4.

The ratio of 10 to 5 is written as $\frac{10}{5} = \frac{2}{1}$, or 2 : 1.

A proportion is a mathematical sentence that states that two ratios are equivalent. To write a proportion, place an equal sign between the two equivalent ratios.

Examples

The ratio of 6 to 9 is the same as the ratio of 8 to 12.

$$\frac{6}{9} = \frac{8}{12}$$

The ratio of 2 to 4 is the same as the ratio of 7 to 14.

$$\frac{2}{4} = \frac{7}{14}$$

You can set up a proportion to determine an unknown quantity. Use x to represent the unknown. To find the value of x, cross multiply and then divide both sides of the equation by the number that comes before x.

Example

Two out of five students have blue notebooks. If this same ratio exists in a class of twenty students, how many students in the class have blue notebooks?

$$\frac{2}{5} = \frac{x}{20} \quad \leftarrow \textbf{Cross multiply.}$$
$$2 \times 20 = 5x \quad \leftarrow \textbf{Divide.}$$
$$8 = x$$

Percents and Decimals

Calculating Percents

A percent is a ratio that compares a number to 100. The word *percent* (%) means "parts of 100" or "per 100 parts." Another way to think of a percent is as a part of a whole expressed in hundredths. Thus, the number 0.41 ("41 hundredths") can also be expressed as 41%, or "41 per 100 parts."

$$0.41 = \frac{41}{100} = 41\%$$

You can calculate a percent by multiplying the ratio of the part to the whole by 100%.

$$\text{Percent} = \frac{\text{Part}}{\text{Whole}} \times 100\%$$

Examples

The fraction $\frac{7}{10}$ is equivalent to 70%.

The fraction $\frac{5}{8}$ is equivalent to 62.5%.

The fraction $\frac{15}{200}$ is equivalent to 7.5%.

You have probably seen data expressed in the form of a percent. For instance, nutrition labels on packaged foods include a column titled "% Daily Value." In this column, the nutrients (such as fat, cholesterol, and fiber) contained in a single serving are compared to the recommended daily intake. You also encounter percents when you go shopping (items on sale might be labeled "20% off") or when you receive test scores.

Example

A student answers 34 questions correctly on a 40-question exam. What is the student's score expressed as a percent?

$$\text{Percent} = \frac{\text{Part}}{\text{Whole}} \times 100\%$$

$$= \frac{\text{Number of correct answers}}{\text{Number of questions asked}} \times 100\%$$

$$= \frac{34}{40} \times 100\%$$

$$= 85\%$$

Converting Between Percents and Decimals

To convert a percent to a decimal value, write the number without the percent sign and move the decimal point two places to the left. Add a zero before the decimal point.

Examples

$$38\% = 0.38$$
$$13.92\% = 0.1392$$

You can convert a decimal value to a percent value by moving the decimal point two places to the right and adding the percent sign.

Examples

$$0.46 = 46\%$$
$$0.8215 = 82.15\%$$

Converting between percents and decimals is often necessary when solving word problems involving composition or concentration.

Example

A nighttime cold medicine is 22% alcohol by volume. How many milliliters of alcohol are in a 250-mL bottle of this medicine?

$22\% = 0.22$ ← **Convert percent to a decimal.**

$$\frac{\text{Part}}{\text{Whole}} = \frac{\text{Part}}{250 \text{ mL}} = 0.22$$

$$\text{Part} = 250 \text{ mL} \times 0.22$$

$$\text{Part} = 55 \text{ mL}$$

Example

During a flu epidemic, 28% of the students at a school were absent. If 238 students were absent, what was the school's enrollment?

$28\% = 0.28$ ← **Convert percent to a decimal.**

$$\frac{\text{Part}}{\text{Whole}} = \frac{238 \text{ students}}{\text{Whole}} = 0.28$$

$$\text{Whole} = \frac{238 \text{ students}}{0.28}$$

$$\text{Whole} = 850 \text{ students}$$

Math Skills

Exponents

A base is a number that is used as a factor. An exponent is a number that tells how many times the base is to be used as a factor.

Example

$$2^5 = 2 \times 2 \times 2 \times 2 \times 2 = 32$$

A power is any number that can be expressed as a product in which all of the factors are the same. Any number raised to the zero power is 1. Any number raised to the first power is that number. The only exception is the number 0, which is zero regardless of the power it is raised to.

Exponents	
Powers of 2	**Powers of 10**
$2^4 = 16$	$10^4 = 10,000$
$2^3 = 8$	$10^3 = 1000$
$2^2 = 4$	$10^2 = 100$
$2^1 = 2$	$10^1 = 10$
$2^0 = 1$	$10^0 = 1$
$2^{-1} = \frac{1}{2}$	$10^{-1} = \frac{1}{10}$
$2^{-2} = \frac{1}{4}$	$10^{-2} = \frac{1}{100}$
$2^{-3} = \frac{1}{8}$	$10^{-3} = \frac{1}{1000}$
$2^{-4} = \frac{1}{16}$	$10^{-4} = \frac{1}{10,000}$

Multiplying With Exponents

To multiply exponential expressions with the same base, add the exponents. The general expression for exponents with the same base is $x^a \times x^b = x^{a+b}$.

Example

$$3^2 \times 3^4 = (3 \times 3) \times (3 \times 3 \times 3 \times 3) = 3^6 = 729$$

To raise a power to a power, keep the base and multiply the exponents. The general expression is $(x^a)^b = x^{ab}$.

Example

$$(3^2)^3 = (3^2) \times (3^2) \times (3^2) = 3^6 = 729$$

To raise a product to a power, raise each factor to the power. The general expression is $(xy)^n = x^n y^n$.

Example

$$(3 \times 9)^2 = 3^2 \times 9^2 = 9 \times 81 = 729$$

Dividing With Exponents

To divide exponential expressions with the same base, keep the base and subtract the exponents. The general expression is

$$\frac{x^a}{x^b} = x^{a-b}$$

Example

$$\frac{5^6}{5^4} = 5^{6-4} = 5^2 = 25$$

When the exponent of the denominator is greater than the exponent of the numerator, the exponent of the result is negative. A negative exponent follows the general expression

$$x^{-n} = \frac{1}{x^n}$$

Example

$$2^3 \div 2^5 = 2^{3-5} = 2^{-2} = \frac{1}{2^2} = \frac{1}{4}$$

Metric conversions often involve multiplication or division of exponential expressions. Make sure to keep track of the sign of the exponent when performing operations with exponential expressions.

Example

Convert 3.49×10^2 μm to meters. (1 μm = 10^{-6} m)

Based on the equivalence 1 μm = 10^{-6} m, you can write the ratio 1 μm/10^{-6} m, which equals one.

$$3.49 \times 10^2 \, \mu\text{m} \times \frac{10^{-6} \text{ m}}{1 \, \mu\text{m}} = 3.49 \times 10^2 \times 10^{-6} \text{ m}$$

$$= 3.49 \times 10^{2-6} \text{ m}$$

$$= 3.49 \times 10^{-4} \text{ m}$$

Scientific Notation

Very large and very small numbers are often expressed in scientific notation. In scientific notation, a number is written as the product of two numbers: a coefficient that is greater than or equal to one and less than ten, and 10 raised to a power. For example, the number 710,000 written in scientific notation is 7.1×10^5. The coefficient in this number is 7.1. The power of ten, or the exponent, is 5. The exponent indicates how many times the coefficient must be multiplied by 10 to equal the number 710,000.

To convert a large number to scientific notation, move the decimal point to the left until it is located just to the right of the first nonzero number. The number of places that you move the decimal point becomes the positive exponent of 10.

Example

$18{,}930{,}000 = 1.893 \times 10^7$

To write a number less than 1 in scientific notation, move the decimal point just to the right of the first nonzero number. Use the number of places you moved the decimal point as the negative exponent of 10.

Example

$0.0027 = \dfrac{2.7}{10 \times 10 \times 10} = 2.7 \times 10^{-3}$

When you convert a number to scientific notation, remember that you are not changing the value of the number. You are only changing the way that it is written.

Examples

$500{,}000 = 5 \times 10^5$

$0.000\,000\,042 = 4.2 \times 10^{-8}$

$0.030\,06 = 3.006 \times 10^{-2}$

$285.2 = 2.852 \times 10^2$

$0.0002 = 2 \times 10^{-4}$

$83{,}700{,}000 = 8.37 \times 10^7$

Adding and Subtracting

To add or subtract numbers in scientific notation, the exponents must be the same. If they are different, rewrite one of the numbers to make the exponents the same. Then write the answer so that only one number is to the left of the decimal point.

Examples

$$(3.20 \times 10^3) + (5.1 \times 10^2) = (32.0 \times 10^2) + (5.1 \times 10^2)$$
$$= 37.1 \times 10^2$$
$$= 3.71 \times 10^3$$

$$(3.42 \times 10^{-5}) - (2.5 \times 10^{-6})$$
$$= (34.2 \times 10^{-6}) - (2.5 \times 10^{-6})$$
$$= 31.7 \times 10^{-6}$$
$$= 3.17 \times 10^{-5}$$

Multiplying and Dividing

To multiply or divide numbers in scientific notation, the exponents are added or subtracted.

Examples

$$(1.2 \times 10^3) \times (3.4 \times 10^4) = (4.1 \times 10^{3+4})$$
$$= 4.1 \times 10^7$$

$$(5.0 \times 10^9) \div (2.5 \times 10^6) = (2.0 \times 10^{9-6})$$
$$= 2.0 \times 10^3$$

$$\frac{(1.2 \times 10^{-3})^2}{(10^{-2})^3 \times (2.0 \times 10^{-3})} = \frac{1.2^2 \times (10^{-3})^2}{(10^{-6}) \times (2.0 \times 10^{-3})}$$

$$= \frac{1.44 \times 10^{-6}}{2.0 \times 10^{-6+3(-3)}}$$

$$= \frac{1.44 \times 10^{-6}}{2.0 \times 10^{-9}}$$

$$= 0.72 \times 10^{-6-(-9)}$$

$$= 0.72 \times 10^3$$

$$= 7.2 \times 10^2$$

Math Skills

Significant Figures

When measurements are combined in calculations, the uncertainty of each measurement must be correctly reflected in the final result. The digits that are accurate in the answer are called significant figures. When the result of a calculation has more significant figures than needed, the result must be rounded off. If the first digit after the last significant digit is less than 5, round down. If the first digit after the last significant digit is 5 or more, round up.

Examples

1577 rounded to three significant figures is 1580.
1574 rounded to three significant figures is 1570.
2.458462 rounded to three significant figures is 2.46.
2.458462 rounded to four significant figures is 2.458.

Examples

Each of the measurements listed below has three significant figures. The significant figures are underlined.

456 mL
0.305 g
70.4 mg
0.000457 g
5.64 × 10³ km
444,000 ng
1.30 × 10⁻² m
0.004 06 dm

Adding and Subtracting

In addition and subtraction, the number of significant figures in the answer depends on the number with the largest uncertainty.

Example

$$
\begin{array}{r}
25.34 \text{ g} \\
152 \text{ g} \\
+ \quad 4.009 \text{ g} \\
\hline
181 \text{ g}
\end{array}
$$

The measurement with the largest uncertainty is 152 g, and it is measured to the nearest gram. Therefore, the answer is given to the nearest gram.

Example

$189.427 \text{ g} - 19.00 \text{ g} = 170.427 \text{ g} \approx 170.43 \text{ g}$

The measurement with the larger uncertainty is 19.00 g, which is measured to the nearest hundredth of a gram. Therefore, the answer is given to the nearest hundredth of a gram.

Multiplying and Dividing

In multiplication and division, the measurement with the smallest number of significant figures determines the number of significant figures in the answer.

Example

$(5.3 \text{ m}) \times (1.54 \text{ m}) = 8.162 \text{ m}^2 \approx 8.2 \text{ m}^2$

Because 5.3 m has only two significant figures, the answer must be rounded to two significant figures.

Example

$$
\begin{aligned}
\text{Density} &= \frac{\text{Mass}}{\text{Volume}} \\
&= \frac{20.79 \text{ g}}{5.5 \text{ mL}} \\
&= 3.78 \text{ g/mL} \\
&\approx 3.8 \text{ g/mL}
\end{aligned}
$$

Because 5.5 mL has only two significant figures, the answer must be rounded to two significant figures.

Example

Calculate the perimeter [(2 × length) + (2 × width)] and the area (length × width) of a rectangular garden plot that measures 32.8 m by 16 m. Round each answer to the correct number of significant figures.

$$
\begin{aligned}
\text{Perimeter} &= (2 \times 32.8 \text{ m}) + (2 \times 16 \text{ m}) \\
&= 65.6 \text{ m} + 32 \text{ m} \\
&= 97.6 \text{ m} \\
&\approx 98 \text{ m}
\end{aligned}
$$

$\text{Area} = 32.8 \text{ m} \times 16 \text{ m} = 524.8 \text{ m}^2 \approx 5.2 \times 10^2 \text{ m}^2$

Formulas and Equations

An equation is a mathematical sentence that contains one or more variables and one or more mathematical operators (such as $+$, $-$, $\div$, $\times$, and $=$). An equation expresses a relationship between two or more quantities.

A formula is a special kind of equation. A formula such as $V = l \times w \times h$ states the relationship between unknown quantities represented by the variables V, l, w, and h. The formula means that volume (of a rectangular solid) equals length times width times height. Some formulas have numbers that do not vary, such as the formula for the perimeter of a square: $P = 4s$. In this formula, the number 4 is a constant.

To solve an equation or formula for an unknown quantity, first rearrange the equation so that the unknown is on one side of the equation, and all the known quantities are on the other side. Then substitute known values for the variables. Be sure to include units.

Example

An airplane travels in a straight line at a speed of 600 km/h. How far does it fly in 3.5 hours?

Write the formula that relates speed, distance, and time.

$$\text{Speed} = \frac{\text{Distance}}{\text{Time}}$$

$$v = \frac{d}{t}$$

To solve for distance, multiply both sides of the equation by t.

$$v = \frac{d}{t}$$

$$v \times t = \frac{d}{t} \times t$$

$$v \times t = d$$

Substitute in the known values.

$$600 \text{ km/h} \times 3.5 \text{ h} = d$$
$$2100 \text{ km} = d$$

Example

What is the volume of 642 g of gold if the density of gold is 19.3 g/cm^3?

Write the formula that relates density, mass, and volume.

$$\text{Density} = \frac{\text{Mass}}{\text{Volume}}$$

$$d = \frac{m}{v}$$

First solve the equation for the unknown quantity, volume (v).

$$d = \frac{m}{v}$$

$$v \times d = m$$

$$v = \frac{m}{d}$$

Then substitute in the known values for m and d.

$$v = \frac{642 \text{ g}}{19.3 \text{ g/cm}^3}$$

$$v = 33.2645 \text{ cm}^3$$

$$v \approx 33.3 \text{ cm}^3$$

Example

A gas has a volume of 5.0 L at a temperature of 200 K. The temperature of the gas is increased under constant pressure until the final volume of the gas is 15 L. What is the final temperature of the gas?

Write the formula that describes how the volume of a gas changes with temperature if the pressure and number of particles are constant.

$$\frac{V_1}{T_1} = \frac{V_2}{T_2}$$

First solve the equation for the unknown quantity, T_2.

$$\frac{V_1}{T_1} = \frac{V_2}{T_2}$$

$$T_2 = \frac{V_2 \times T_1}{V_1}$$

Now substitute the known values for V_1, V_2, and T_1.

$$T_2 = \frac{15 \text{ L} \times 200 \text{ K}}{5 \text{ L}}$$

$$T_2 = 600 \text{ K}$$

Math Skills

Conversion Factors

Many problems involve converting measurements from one unit to another. You can convert units by using an equation that shows how units are related. For example, 1 in. = 2.54 cm relates inches and centimeters.

To write a conversion factor, divide both sides of the equation by 1 in.

$$\frac{1\ \text{in.}}{1\ \text{in.}} = \frac{2.54\ \text{cm}}{1\ \text{in.}}$$

$$1 = 2.54\ \text{cm/in.}$$

Because the conversion factor is equal to 1, you can multiply one side of an equation by it and preserve equality. You can make a second conversion factor by dividing both sides of the equation by 2.54 cm.

$$\frac{1\ \text{in.}}{2.54\ \text{cm}} = \frac{2.54\ \text{cm}}{2.54\ \text{cm}} = 1$$

One conversion factor converts inches to centimeters and the other converts centimeters to inches. Choose the conversion factor that cancels out the unit that you have a measurement for.

Example

Convert 25 inches to centimeters. Use the conversion factor 2.54 cm/in. so that the inches units cancel.

$$25\ \text{in.} \times \frac{2.54\ \text{cm}}{1\ \text{in.}} \approx 64\ \text{cm}$$

Some conversions are more complicated and require multiple steps.

Example

Convert 23°F to a Celsius temperature. The conversion formula is °F = ($\frac{9}{5}$ × °C) + 32°F.

First solve the equation for °C.

$$°F = (\tfrac{9}{5} \times °C) + 32°F$$

$$°F - 32°F = \tfrac{9}{5} \times °C$$

$$\tfrac{5}{9}(°F - 32°F) = °C$$

Now substitute in 23°F.

$$°C = \tfrac{5}{9}(23°F - 32°F) = \tfrac{5}{9}(-9) = -5$$

Thus, 23°F is equivalent to −5°C.

Example

A grocer is selling oranges at a price of 3 for $1.00. How much would 10 oranges cost?

Use the equality 3 oranges = $1.00 to write a conversion factor. The desired conversion factor should have dollars in the numerator so that the oranges units cancel.

$$10\ \text{oranges} \times \frac{\$1.00}{3\ \text{oranges}} = \$3.33$$

Example

Water runs through a hose at a rate of 2.5 gallons per minute. What is the rate of water flow in gallons per day?

To convert gal/min to gal/d, you must use conversion factors based on the following equalities.

$$60\ \text{min} = 1\ \text{h}$$

$$24\ \text{h} = 1\ \text{d}$$

$$\frac{2.5\ \text{gal}}{\text{min}} \times \frac{60\ \text{min}}{1\ \text{h}} \times \frac{24\ \text{h}}{1\ \text{d}} = 3600\ \text{gal/d}$$

Example

The density of nitrogen gas is 1.17 g/L. What is the density of nitrogen expressed in micrograms per deciliter (μg/dL)?

Derive the needed conversion factors from the following equalities.

$$10^6\ \mu\text{g} = 1\ \text{g}$$

$$10\ \text{dL} = 1\ \text{L}$$

$$\frac{1.17\ \text{g}}{\text{L}} \times \frac{10^6\ \mu\text{g}}{1\ \text{g}} \times \frac{1\ \text{L}}{10\ \text{dL}} = 1.17 \times 10^5\ \mu\text{g/dL}$$

Data Tables

Data tables help to organize data and make it easier to see patterns in data. If you plan data tables before doing an experiment, they will help you record observations in an orderly fashion.

The data table below shows United States immigration data for the year 2001. Always include units of measurement so people can understand the data.

Immigration to the United States, 2001	
Place of Origin	Number of Legal Immigrants
Africa	53,948
Asia	349,776
Europe	175,371
North America	407,888
South America	68,888

Bar Graphs

To make a bar graph, begin by placing category labels along the bottom axis. Add an overall label for the axis *Place of Origin*. Decide on a scale for the vertical axis. An appropriate scale for the data in the table is 0 to 500,000. Label the vertical axis *Number of People*. For each continent, draw a bar whose height corresponds to the number of immigrants. You will need to round off the values. For example, the bar for Africa should correspond to 54,000 people. Add a graph title to make it clear what the graph shows.

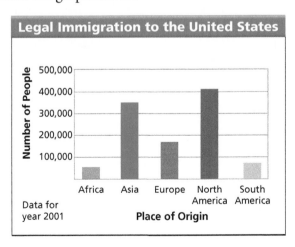

Circle Graphs

Use the total number to calculate percentages. For example, the percentage of immigrants from Africa in 2001 was 53,948 ÷ 1,061,984 = 0.051 ≈ 5%. Multiply each percent by 360° to find the central angle of each wedge. For Africa, the central angle is 18°. Use a protractor to draw each central angle. Color and label the wedges and finish your graph with a title.

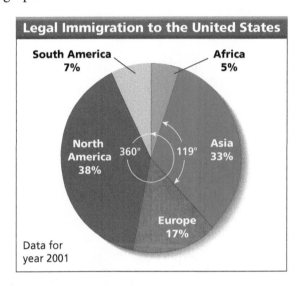

Line Graphs

The slope of a straight-line graph equals the "rise over the run." The rise is the change in the y values and the run is the change in the x values. Using points A and B on the graph below gives

$$\text{Slope} = \frac{\text{Rise}}{\text{Run}} = \frac{5-3}{9-3} = \frac{2}{6} = 0.33$$

21st Century Skills

The Partnership for 21st Century Skills is the leading advocacy organization focused on infusing skills for the 21st century into education. The organization brings together the business community, education leaders, and policy makers to define a powerful vision for 21st century education to ensure every child's success as citizens and workers by providing tools and resources to help facilitate and drive change.

Today's students will spend their adult lives in a multitasking, multifaceted, technology-driven, diverse, vibrant world—and they must arrive equipped to do so. The goal of 21st Century Learning is to bridge the gap between how students live and how they learn. A way to bridge the gap is summarized in the diagram below.

The arches of the rainbow represent student outcomes. These are the skills, knowledge, and expertise students will need to master to succeed in work and life in the 21st century. The pools at the base of the rainbow represent the 21st Century Support Systems that must be present in order for students to master the skills described in the rainbow.

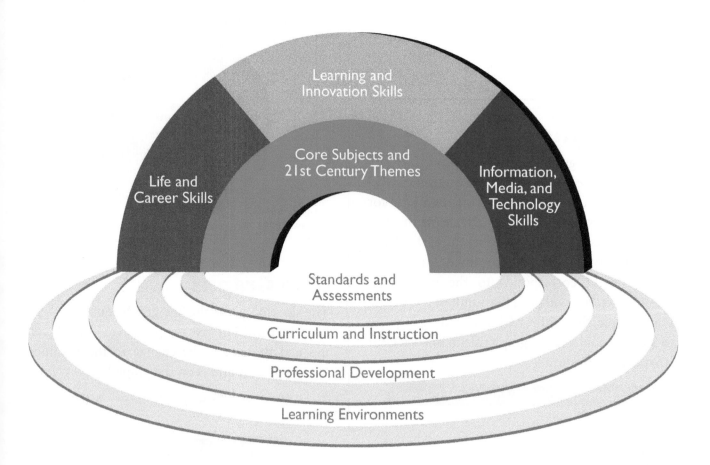

Core Subjects and 21st Century Themes

Let's start with the green section of the rainbow: Core Subjects and 21st Century Themes. Today's students will still need to master core subjects such as English (reading or language arts), world languages, arts, mathematics, economics, sciences, geography, history, government, and civics. However, they can move beyond basic competence to higher levels of understanding if schools weave into those subjects such themes as global awareness; financial, economic, business, and entrepreneurial literacy; civic literacy; and health literacy.

Learning and Innovation Skills

The yellow section, Learning and Innovation Skills, prepares students for increasingly complex life and work environments. Skills such as creativity and innovation allow students to implement, analyze, refine, and evaluate new ideas. Critical thinking and problem-solving skills allow students to make their way through the multistep process required to find solutions—be they conventional or innovative—to non-familiar problems. Communication and collaboration skills will be key to success in today's global, interconnected, multicultural world.

Information, Media, and Technology Skills

The 21st century is a technology- and media-suffused environment that requires mastery of the skills in the blue section—Information, Media, and Technology Skills. These skills include information literacy, media literacy, and ICT (information, communications, and technology) literacy. Students must learn to access, evaluate, and use information from a wide variety of sources. They will need to know how to recognize, understand, and create media messages. In order to function in the new knowledge economy, today's students will need to use digital devices, communication and networking tools, and social networks professionally as well as personally.

Life and Career Skills

The ultimate goal is to prepare students for success beyond the classroom with Life and Career Skills. This is a globally competitive information age with complex life and work environments. These environments require such skills as flexibility and adaptability, initiative and self-direction, social and cross-cultural skills, productivity and accountability, and leadership and responsibility.

Adapted from Partnership for 21st Century Skills, 177 N. Church Avenue, Suite 305, Tucson, AZ 85701, 520-623-2466; www.21stcenturyskills.org.

21st Century Learning

Communication Skills

Why is soil acidity important in gardening?

In order for their plants to thrive, gardeners and farmers need to be mindful of the acidity of the soil. Suppose you are planning a small garden for your neighborhood. Use the library or Internet to find out the typical soil acidity for your area and how this affects the variety of plant life. Talk to a local gardener, farmer, or plant nursery worker to find out how soil acidity is measured and maintained. Then write a paragraph that outlines your plan for the garden, making sure to discuss soil pH considerations.

Using Technology

Prentice Hall provides references in your textbook to a variety of technology options for enhancing your learning experiences. They include the Interactive Textbook, probeware versions of textbook labs, Sci-Links®, PHSchool.com, Science News®, Planet Diary, and Active Art.

The Interactive Textbook is a resource that expands your learning with a variety of interactive opportunities.
- **Entire text online and on CD-ROM**
- **Multimedia activities** With engaging video, audio, and interactive features, the Interactive Textbook makes learning a multimedia experience. All of the interactive features can be accessed with a single click.
- **Additional assessment opportunities with instant feedback** You don't have to wait to receive feedback—you'll know immediately whether you're on track.

 Probeware Labs

Ten of the textbook labs have an alternate probeware version in the Probeware Lab Manual. Probeware labs have several advantages over traditional labs.
- **Instant feedback** Your data are displayed immediately, so you know right away if the lab is working.
- **Graphing and data analysis** Built-in tools let you immediately focus on science concepts instead of getting bogged down in generating graphs and tables.
- **Encourage creativity** With probeware labs, you can ask (and answer) what-if questions.

The National Science Teachers Association manages the SciLinks® Service, a project that blends the best of the two main educational resources—textbooks and the Internet. Under each SciLinks icon that appears in this book, you'll find the SciLinks URL (www.scilinks.org) and a code. Go to the SciLinks Web site, sign in, type the code from the page you are reading, and you'll receive a list of URLs that are selected by science educators.

Go Online opportunities appear throughout the textbook to alert you to interactive opportunities at the Prentice Hall Web site.
- **Data-Sharing Labs** Share and compare data with students from across the country.
- **Background for Issues** Access more detailed information about issues featured in the textbook.
- **Self-Assessments** Take self-tests with instant feedback to monitor your own progress and stay on track.

Stay current with articles from Science News. Use the keyword links to quickly find relevant articles written for a high school audience.

Planet Diary features weekly reports on environmental news and natural phenomena such as earthquakes, tornadoes, and hurricanes.

The Active Art resources feature interactive simulations that help you practice skills and understand content.

Standardized Test Prep

The strategies listed here will help you learn how to apply test-taking skills in a logical fashion. Once you know how to prepare for a test, you can improve your chances for getting the right answer. You'll be able to approach a test with confidence and tell yourself, "I will do well."

Preparing for a Standardized Test

- **Be well rested.** Get plenty of sleep the night before the test. You will perform better if you are not tired.
- **Eat a good breakfast.** The brain works better when it has fuel.
- **Bring a sweater or sweatshirt.** You will want to be comfortable, no matter how warm or cool the testing room is.
- **Wear a watch.** Be aware of how many questions you have to answer and the amount of time you are given.
- **Remember your supplies.** You will likely need several sharp #2 pencils and a good eraser. Bring a calculator if it is permitted.
- **Allow plenty of time to get to the test site.** You will be more relaxed if you arrive early.

Taking a Standardized Test

- **Read the directions first.** Then start answering the questions.
- **Read all of the answers.** Then make your choice.
- **Underline important words and phrases.**
- **Cross out choices you know are wrong.**
- **Do the easy questions first.** Don't get stuck on difficult questions. You can come back to them.
- **Record your answers properly.** Be sure to put your answers in the right place. Fill in the marks completely.
- **Answer every question.**
- **Stay relaxed.** If you get nervous, stop and take a few deep breaths.
- **Change your body position.** Once in a while, shift your position to keep comfortable.
- **Stick with your first choice.** Change an answer only when you are SURE your first choice is wrong.
- **Review your answers if you have time.**

Question Strategies

Multiple Choice

- **Read the question thoroughly and carefully.**
- **Know what the question wants from you.** Are you expected to provide all possible answers, or the best answer? Do you have to find all responses that apply, or one that does not apply?
- **Anticipate the answer.** If you know the answer even before you read the list of responses, look for an answer that is similar to the one you are thinking of.
- **Skip the question if you get stuck.** Don't lose precious time. You can always go back to it later.
- **Read all answers.** Even when you think you have found the correct answer right away, you may find a better answer.
- **If you find two correct answers, keep reading!** You may discover an "All of the above" option. Or the question may ask for the "best" answer.
- **Eliminate responses you know are wrong.** If you have fewer options to choose from, you are more likely to choose the correct response.

Constructed Response (Short Answer)

- **Know which question(s) to answer.** Do you have to answer all of them or only some? If you can choose, answer the ones you are most familiar with.
- **Notice action words.** Do you have to "draw" a diagram? "Create" a list? "Write" a paragraph?
- **Make notes.** Write down names, dates, facts, and figures that come to mind. Don't waste time; write only as much as you need to jog your memory.
- **Make a brief outline.** Plan how to approach the response. Then stick to it; don't get sidetracked.
- **Write legibly.** Neatness counts. Don't lose points just because the evaluator couldn't read your response.
- **Use key terms and vocabulary.** Your answer will be more precise and sound more credible.
- **Be thorough.** But don't waste time on unnecessary details or long explanations.
- **Always provide an answer.** Partial credit is better than no credit. If time is short, outline or list the remaining information.
- **Leave space.** You can add information you may think of later.

SI *(Système International d'Unités)* is a revised version of the metric system, which was originally developed in France in 1791. SI units of measurement are used by scientists throughout the world. The system is based on multiples of ten. Each unit is ten times larger or ten times smaller than the next unit. The most commonly used SI units are given below.

You can use conversion factors to convert between SI and non-SI units. Try the following conversions. How tall are you in meters? What is your weight in newtons? What is your normal body temperature in degrees Celsius?

Metric ruler

Commonly Used Metric Units

Length — The distance from one point to another

meter (m)	A meter is slightly longer than a yard.
	1 meter = 1000 millimeters (mm)
	1 meter = 100 centimeters (cm)
	1000 meters = 1 kilometer (km)

Volume — The amount of space an object takes up

liter (L)	A liter is slightly more than a quart.
	1 liter = 1000 milliliters (mL)

Mass — The amount of matter in an object

gram (g)	A gram has a mass equal to about one paper clip.
	1000 grams = 1 kilogram (kg)

Temperature — The measure of hotness or coldness

degrees Celsius (°C)	0°C = freezing point of water at sea level
	100°C = boiling point of water at sea level

Metric–Customary Equivalents

2.54 centimeters (cm) = 1 inch (in.)
1 meter (m) = 39.37 inches (in.)
1 kilometer (km) = 0.62 miles (mi)
1 liter (L) = 1.06 quarts (qt)
250 milliliters (mL) = 1 cup (c)
9.8 newtons (N) = 2.2 pounds (lb)
$°C = 5/9 \times (°F - 32)$

Triple-Beam Balance

Thermometer

Graduated cylinder

The laboratory balance is an important tool in scientific investigations. You can use a balance to determine the masses of materials that you study or experiment with in the laboratory.

Different kinds of balances are used in the laboratory. One kind of balance is the triple-beam balance. The balance that you may use in your science class is probably similar to the balance illustrated. To use the balance properly, you should learn the name, location, and function of each part of the balance you are using.

The Triple-Beam Balance

The triple-beam balance is a single-pan balance with three beams The back, or 100-gram, beam is divided into ten units of 10 grams. The middle, or 500-gram, beam is divided into five units of 100 grams. The front, or 10-gram, beam is divided into ten major units, each of which is 1 gram. Each 1-gram unit is further divided into units of 0.1 gram. What is the largest mass you could measure with a triple-beam balance?

The following procedure can be used to find the mass of an object with a triple-beam balance.
1. When no object is on the pan, and the riders are at zero, make sure the pointer is at zero. If it is not, use the adjustment screw to zero the balance.
2. Place the object on the pan.
3. Move the rider on the middle beam notch by notch until the horizontal pointer drops below zero. Move the rider back one notch.
4. Move the rider on the back beam notch by notch until the pointer again drops below zero. Move the rider back one notch.
5. Slowly slide the rider along the front beam until the pointer stops at zero. The mass of the object is the sum of the readings on the three beams.

Triple-Beam Balance

Element	Symbol	Atomic Number	Atomic Mass[†]	Element	Symbol	Atomic Number	Atomic Mass[†]
Actinium	Ac	89	(277)	Neodymium	Nd	60	144.24
Aluminum	Al	13	26.982	Neon	Ne	10	20.179
Americium	Am	95	(243)	Neptunium	Np	93	(237)
Antimony	Sb	51	121.75	Nickel	Ni	28	58.71
Argon	Ar	18	39.948	Niobium	Nb	41	92.906
Arsenic	As	33	74.922	Nitrogen	N	7	14.007
Astatine	At	85	(210)	Nobelium	No	102	(259)
Barium	Ba	56	137.33	Osmium	Os	76	190.2
Berkelium	Bk	97	(247)	Oxygen	O	8	15.999
Beryllium	Be	4	9.0122	Palladium	Pd	46	106.4
Bismuth	Bi	83	208.98	Phosphorus	P	15	30.974
Bohrium	Bh	107	(264)	Platinum	Pt	78	195.09
Boron	B	5	10.81	Plutonium	Pu	94	(244)
Bromine	Br	35	79.904	Polonium	Po	84	(209)
Cadmium	Cd	48	112.41	Potassium	K	19	39.098
Calcium	Ca	20	40.08	Praseodymium	Pr	59	140.91
Californium	Cf	98	(251)	Promethium	Pm	61	(145)
Carbon	C	6	12.011	Protactinium	Pa	91	231.04
Cerium	Ce	58	140.12	Radium	Ra	88	(226)
Cesium	Cs	55	132.91	Radon	Rn	86	(222)
Chlorine	Cl	17	35.453	Rhenium	Re	75	186.21
Chromium	Cr	24	51.996	Rhodium	Rh	45	102.91
Cobalt	Co	27	58.933	Roentgenium	Rg	111	(272)
Copernicium	Cn	112	(277)	Rubidium	Rb	37	85.468
Copper	Cu	29	63.546	Ruthenium	Ru	44	101.07
Curium	Cm	96	(247)	Rutherfordium	Rf	104	(261)
Darmstadtium	Ds	110	(269)	Samarium	Sm	62	150.4
Dubnium	Db	105	(262)	Scandium	Sc	21	44.956
Dysprosium	Dy	66	162.50	Seaborgium	Sg	106	(263)
Einsteinium	Es	99	(252)	Selenium	Se	34	78.96
Erbium	Er	68	167.26	Silicon	Si	14	28.086
Europium	Eu	63	151.96	Silver	Ag	47	107.87
Fermium	Fm	100	(257)	Sodium	Na	11	22.990
Fluorine	F	9	18.998	Strontium	Sr	38	87.62
Francium	Fr	87	(223)	Sulfur	S	16	32.06
Gadolinium	Gd	64	157.25	Tantalum	Ta	73	180.95
Gallium	Ga	31	69.72	Technetium	Tc	43	(98)
Germanium	Ge	32	72.59	Tellurium	Te	52	127.60
Gold	Au	79	196.97	Terbium	Tb	65	158.93
Hafnium	Hf	72	178.49	Thallium	Tl	81	204.37
Hassium	Hs	108	(265)	Thorium	Th	90	232.04
Helium	He	2	4.0026	Thulium	Tm	69	168.93
Holmium	Ho	67	164.93	Tin	Sn	50	118.69
Hydrogen	H	1	1.0079	Titanium	Ti	22	47.90
Indium	In	49	114.82	Tungsten	W	74	183.85
Iodine	I	53	126.90	Uranium	U	92	238.03
Iridium	Ir	77	192.22	Vanadium	V	23	50.941
Iron	Fe	26	55.847	Xenon	Xe	54	131.30
Krypton	Kr	36	83.80	Ytterbium	Yb	70	173.04
Lanthanum	La	57	138.91	Yttrium	Y	39	88.906
Lawrencium	Lr	103	(262)	Zinc	Zn	30	65.38
Lead	Pb	82	207.2	Zirconium	Zr	40	91.22
Lithium	Li	3	6.941				
Lutetium	Lu	71	174.97				
Magnesium	Mg	12	24.305				
Manganese	Mn	25	54.938				
Meitnerium	Mt	109	(268)				
Mendelevium	Md	101	(258)				
Mercury	Hg	80	200.59				
Molybdenum	Mo	42	95.94				

[†] Number in parentheses gives the mass number of the most stable isotope

*Name not officially assigned

Appendix D | PROBLEM BANK

The following problems provide additional practice for solving equations and word problems. If you need help, look at the Math Skills Boxes on the referenced pages, where you will find solutions to similar problems.

Using Scientific Notation
(See Math Skills, page 15.)

1. The floor of a room measures 7.5 m by 6.0 m.
   a. What area of carpeting (in m^2) would you need to cover the entire floor? Express your answer in scientific notation.
   b. What would the area be in cm^2? (*Hint:* $10^4 \ cm^2 = 1 \ m^2$).
   c. Suppose you want to tile the floor with square tiles that measure 30.5 cm on a side. How many tiles would you need? (*Hint:* Divide the total floor area by the area of a single tile.)
2. A mercury thermometer exchange program collected 1045 mercury thermometers in a month.
   a. If each thermometer contains 0.70 g of mercury, what is the total mass of mercury? Express your answer in scientific notation.
   b. A hazardous waste container holds 100.0 cm^3. Can this container hold all of the mercury? (*Hint:* Find the volume by dividing the mass by the density of mercury, 11.3 g/cm^3.)

The Combined Gas Law
(See Math Skills, page 80.)

1. The air in a bicycle tire is at a temperature of 11.0°C and a pressure of 542 kPa. What is the pressure in the tire if the temperature increases to 29.0°C while you ride the bicycle? Assume the volume of the tire does not change.

2. A helium tank holds 20.0 L of helium at a pressure of 3050 kPa. How many balloons can the tank fill if each balloon holds 2.0 L of gas at a pressure of 105 kPa? The balloons and the tank are both at room temperature. (*Hint:* Find the volume the helium in the tank would expand to if its pressure were reduced to 105 kPa. Then divide by the volume of one balloon.)

Formulas and Names for Compounds
(See Math Skills, page 174.)

1. Write the formulas for the ionic compounds lead(II) sulfide and lithium nitrate.
2. Name the molecular compounds with these formulas: NBr_3, SCl_2, and CCl_4.
3. Write the names for the ionic compounds $FeCl_2$ and $FeCl_3$.

Balancing Chemical Equations
(See Math Skills, page 195.)
Balance the following equations.

1. $H_2 + Cl_2 \rightarrow HCl$
2. $Ca(OH)_2 + HCl \rightarrow CaCl_2 + H_2O$
3. $Fe + O_2 \rightarrow Fe_3O_2$
4. $C_2H_4 + O_2 \rightarrow CO_2 + H_2O$

Balancing Nuclear Equations
(See Math Skills, page 295.)

1. Write a balanced nuclear equation for the beta decay of bismuth-210.
2. Write a balanced nuclear equation for the alpha decay of polonium-214.
3. Determine the product for the alpha decay of uranium-234.
4. What is the product of the beta decay of phosphorus-30?

Measuring Speed
(See Math Skills, page 333.)

1. A runner travels 3.0 kilometers in 24 minutes, then another 2.5 kilometers in 27 minutes, and finally 1.2 kilometers in 15 minutes. What is the runner's average speed?
2. A bus travels 140 km in 3.0 hours and then stops for a 30-minute rest stop. The bus then travels 120 km in 2.0 hours. What is the average speed for the entire trip?
3. A plane's average speed for a 300.0-km trip is 550 km/h. How long did the flight take?

Measuring Acceleration
(See Math Skills, page 346.)

1. During a crash, a bicycle racer moving at 17 m/s comes to a complete stop in 1.5 seconds. Calculate the bicycle's deceleration.
2. A ball is thrown straight up into the air. It comes to a rest at the highest point after 2.0 seconds. How fast was it going when it was thrown upward?

Newton's Second Law
(See Math Skills, page 367.)

1. A truck with a mass of 2200 kg accelerates when the traffic light turns green. If the net force on the truck is 3500 N in the forward direction, what is the truck's acceleration?
2. A bicycle with its rider has a total mass of 95 kg. If the bicycle accelerates at a rate of 2.0 m/s^2, what is the net force acting on the bicycle?
3. What net force is needed to accelerate a 9000-kg truck at the rate of 2.0 m/s^2?

Calculating Power
(See Math Skills, page 415.)

1. While lifting a box 0.75 m straight up, you exert an upward force of 320 N on the box. How much work do you do on the box? What is the power if you take 2.0 s to lift the box?

2. A dog sled is pulled at a constant horizontal speed of 8.0 m/s by a team of dogs. What is the power of the dogs if they are applying a constant horizontal force of 200.0 N to the sled? (*Hint:* Calculate the work done in one second).

3. How much work can a 500-watt engine do in 1.0 hour?

Calculating IMA and AMA
(See Math Skills, page 425.)

1. A crowbar is 0.75 m long and the fulcrum is located 10.0 cm from the end of the bar. What is the ideal mechanical advantage of the crowbar?

2. A person changing a tire exerts a force of 520 N on a car jack to apply a lifting force of 12,000 N. What is the actual mechanical advantage of the car jack?

3. A pair of pliers has an actual mechanical advantage of 3.5. If you were to squeeze the handles together with a force of 3.0 N, how much force would the jaws of the pliers exert?

4. If a machine has an efficiency of 35%, and you do 1500 J of work on the machine, what will be the work output of the machine?

Kinetic Energy
(See Math Skills, page 448.)

1. A 13,000-kg automobile moves at 28 m/s. What is the automobile's kinetic energy?

2. Two birds fly at the same speed, 4.0 m/s. One bird has a mass of 0.25 kg and the other has a mass of 0.75 kg. What is the kinetic energy of each bird?

Conservation of Energy
(See Math Skills, page 458.)

1. An 80.0-kg diver climbs a ladder up to a high-dive platform 10.0 meters above the ground.
a. How much gravitational potential energy does the diver gain?
b. After diving, what is the diver's speed at the water? Assume all of the potential energy has been converted to kinetic energy.

2. A 4.0-kg bowling ball returns to a bowler along a horizontal track at a speed of 5.0 m/s. At the end of the track, the ball must rise up an incline to a height of 1.0 m. Show that the ball has enough energy to make it to the top of the ramp. Assume friction can be ignored.

Specific Heat
(See Math Skills, page 477.)

1. How much heat is needed to raise the temperature of a plastic beaker by 10.0°C? The beaker's mass is 24.4 g and the specific heat of the plastic is 1.90 J/g•°C.

2. Tin has a specific heat of 0.23 J/g•°C. How much heat is needed to raise the temperature of 550 g of tin from 65°C to 125°C?

3. What mass of water will change its temperature by 10.0°C when 500.0 J of heat is added to it?

Speed of Mechanical Waves
(See Math Skills, page 506.)

1. A wave on a rope has a wavelength of 1.5 m and a frequency of 3.0 Hz. What is the speed of the wave?

2. A motorboat in a lake makes a surface wave with a frequency of 13 Hz and a wavelength of 0.15 m. What is the speed of the wave?

3. Seven ocean wave crests pass by a pier in 28.0 s. If the wave speed is 11 m/s, what is the wavelength of the waves?

Calculating Wave Speed
(See Math Skills, page 535.)

1. A cell phone transmits a carrier wave at a frequency 1900 MHz. What is the wavelength of the wave? (Assume the wave moves at the speed of light in a vacuum.)

2. A carrier wave from an FM station has a frequency 94.5 MHz. What is the wavelength?

3. A light-emitting diode (LED) emits light with a wavelength of 630 nanometers. What is the frequency of the light and what color is the LED?

Power, Voltage, and Current
(See Math Skills, page 611.)

1. A flashlight uses a 6.0-W light bulb connected to 3.6-V nickel-cadmium battery. How much current does the bulb use?

2. A hair dryer has a power rating of 1600 W. If it is connected to a 120-volt line, how much current does it draw?

Answers to even-numbered Math Practice and Section Assessment questions that involve calculations are given below. Use these answers to check your work.

Chapter 1

Math Practice, page 15
2. Distance = 2.6×10^{13} m
Section 1.3 Assessment, page 21
8. 1.5×10^{-4} cm^3

Chapter 3

Math Practice, page 80
2. $T_2 = 580$ K
Section 3.2 Assessment, page 81
10. $P_2 = 281$ kPa

Chapter 6

Math Practice, page 174
2. Cu_2S
4. sodium hydroxide
Section 6.3 Assessment, page 175
8. lithium chloride, barium oxide, sodium nitride, lead sulfate
10. K_2S

Chapter 7

Math Practice, page 195
2. a. $2H_2O_2 \rightarrow 2H_2O + O_2$
   b. $Mg + 2HCl \rightarrow H_2 + MgCl_2$
Section 7.1 Assessment, page 198
10. $2Mg + O_2 \rightarrow 2MgO$

Chapter 10

Math Practice, page 295

2. $^{14}_{6}C \rightarrow {}^{14}_{7}N + {}^{0}_{-1}e$

4. $^{90}_{38}Sr \rightarrow {}^{90}_{39}Y + {}^{0}_{-1}e$
Section 10.1 Assessment, page 297

10. $^{226}_{88}Ra \rightarrow {}^{222}_{86}Rn + {}^{4}_{2}He$

Chapter 11

Math Practice, page 333
2. $v = 62$ km/h
Math Practice, page 346
2. $(v_f - v_i) = 36$ m/s
4. $v_i = -25$ m/s
Section 11.3 Assessment, page 348
8. $a = 0.83$ m/s^2

Chapter 12

Math Practice, page 367
2. $a = 2$ m/s^2
4. $m = 50$ kg
Section 12.2 Assessment, page 369
6. Deceleration = 11 m/s^2

Chapter 14

Math Practice, page 415
2. Power = 7.5 W
Section 14.1 Assessment, page 416
8. Power = 50 W
Math Practice, page 425
2. IMA = 10
Section 14.3 Assessment, page 426
8. Efficiency = 80%

Chapter 15

Math Practice, page 448
2. 440 kJ
Section 15.1 Assessment, page 452
8. PE = 44 kJ
Math Practice, page 458
2. PE = 2100 J; $v = 7.7$ m/s
Section 15.2 Assessment, page 459
10. $h = 0.20$ m

Chapter 16

Math Practice, page 477
2. $Q = 34$ kJ
4. $\Delta T = 10.0°C$
Section 16.1 Assessment, page 478
10. $Q = 7.8$ kJ

Chapter 17

Math Practice, page 506
2. Speed = 0.4 m/s
4. Wavelength = 0.5 km
Section 17.2 Assessment, page 507
10. Period = 0.5 s

Chapter 18

Math Practice, page 535
2. Wavelength = 440 m
Section 18.1 Assessment, page 538
10. Wavelength = 0.190 m

Chapter 20

Math Practice, page 611
2. $I = 0.32$ amps
Section 20.3 Assessment, page 613
8. $I = 0.85$ amps

Glossary

A

absolute zero a temperature of 0 kelvins (pp. 78, 475)

acceleration the rate at which velocity changes (p. 342)

accuracy the closeness of a measurement to the true value of what is measured (p. 19)

acid a compound that produces hydronium ions (H_3O^+) when dissolved in water; a proton donor (p. 241)

actual mechanical advantage the ratio of the output force to the input force in a machine (p. 422)

air resistance fluid friction acting on an object moving through the air (p. 360)

alkali metals the elements in Group 1A of the periodic table, not including hydrogen (p. 140)

alkaline earth metals the elements in Group 2A of the periodic table (p. 141)

alloy a mixture of two or more elements, at least one of which is a metal, that has the characteristic properties of a metal (p. 178)

alpha particle a positively charged particle, emitted by certain radioactive nuclei, made up of two protons and two neutrons; a helium nucleus (p. 293)

alternating current (AC) a flow of electric charge that regularly reverses its direction (p. 604)

amino acids compounds that contain both carboxyl and amino functional groups (p. 280)

amplitude the maximum displacement of a medium from the rest position (p. 507)

amplitude modulation (AM) a method of transmitting a radio signal in which the amplitude of the carrier wave varies while its frequency remains the same (p. 541)

analog signal a smoothly varying signal produced by continuously changing the voltage or current in a circuit (p. 619)

angle of incidence the angle an incident ray makes with a line perpendicular to a surface it strikes (p. 570)

angle of reflection the angle a reflected ray makes with a line perpendicular to a surface it strikes (p. 570)

angle of refraction the angle a light ray makes with the normal after it enters a new medium at an angle (p. 575)

anion an ion with a negative charge (p. 160)

antinode a point of maximum displacement midway between two nodes in a standing wave (p. 512)

Archimedes' principle the equivalence of the buoyant force on an object and the weight of the fluid displaced by the object (p. 401)

aromatic hydrocarbons hydrocarbons that contain a ring structure similar to benzene (p. 266)

astigmatism an eye condition in which objects at any distance appear blurry because of the distorted shape of the cornea (p. 592)

astronomy the study of the universe beyond Earth (p. 4)

atom the smallest particle of an element (p. 39)

atomic mass unit (amu) one twelfth the mass of a carbon-12 atom (p. 134)

atomic number a unique number for each element that equals the number of protons in an atom of that element (p. 110)

average speed the total distance traveled divided by the time it takes to travel that distance (p. 333)

B

background radiation nuclear radiation that occurs naturally in the environment (p. 296)

base a compound that produces hydroxide ions (OH^-) when dissolved in water; a proton acceptor (p. 242)

battery a device that converts chemical energy into electrical energy (p. 606)

beta particle an electron emitted by an unstable nucleus (p. 294)

biology the study of life and life processes (p. 4)

biomass energy the chemical energy stored in living things (p. 464)

boiling point the temperature at which a substance boils; the temperature at which vapor pressure is equal to atmospheric pressure (p. 47)

Boyle's law the inverse variation of the volume of a gas with its pressure if the temperature and the number of particles are constant (p. 79)

buffer a solution that is resistant to large changes in pH (p. 248)

buoyancy the ability of a fluid to exert an upward force on an object placed in it (p. 400)

buoyant force an upward force acting on an object in a fluid (p. 400)

C

calorimeter instrument used to measure thermal energy released or absorbed during a chemical or physical change (p. 478)

camera an optical instrument that records an image of an object (p. 582)

carbohydrate a compound composed of carbon, hydrogen, and oxygen in which the ratio of hydrogen to oxygen atoms is 2 : 1 (p. 278)

catalyst a substance that affects the rate of a chemical reaction without being used up in the reaction (p. 215)

cation an ion with a positive charge (p. 160)

central heating system a heating system that heats many rooms from one central location (p. 489)

centripetal force a force that continuously changes the direction of an object to make it move in a circle (p. 381)

chain reaction a series of fission reactions triggered by neutrons released during the fission of a nucleus (p. 311)

Charles's law the direct proportion of the volume of a gas to its temperature (in kelvins) if the pressure and the number of particles of the gas are constant (p. 78)

chemical bond the force that holds atoms or ions together as a unit (p. 160)

chemical change change that occurs when a substance reacts and forms one or more new substances (p. 56)

chemical energy the energy stored in chemical bonds (pp. 206, 451)

chemical equation a representation of a chemical reaction in which the reactants and products are expressed as formulas (p. 193)

chemical formula notation that shows what elements a compound contains and the ratio of the atoms or ions of these elements in the compound (p. 161)

chemical property any property that produces a change in the composition of matter (p. 54)

chemistry the study of the composition, structure, properties, and reactions of matter (p. 4)

circuit breaker a switch that opens when the current in a circuit is too high (p. 612)

coefficients numbers that appear before a formula in a chemical equation to show the relative proportions of each reactant and product (p. 194)

coherent light light waves having the same wavelength, with the crests and troughs lined up (p. 560)

colloid a mixture that contains some particles that are intermediate in size between the small particles in a solution and the larger particles in a suspension (p. 44)

combustion reaction a chemical reaction in which a substance reacts rapidly with oxygen, often producing heat and light (p. 204)

complementary colors of light any two colors of light that combine to form white light (p. 552)

complementary colors of pigments any two colors of pigments that combine to make black pigment (p. 553)

compound a substance that is made from two or more simpler substances and can be broken down into those simpler substances (p. 40)

compound machine a combination of two or more simple machines that operate together (p. 435)

compression an area of a longitudinal wave where the particles of the medium are close together (p. 502)

computer a programmable device that can store and process information (p. 622)

concave lens a lens that is curved inward at the center and is thickest at the outside edges (p. 576)

concave mirror a mirror that is curved inward (p. 572)

concentration the amount of solute dissolved in a certain amount of solvent (p. 238)

condensation the phase change in which a substance changes from a gas or vapor to a liquid (p. 90)

conduction the transfer of thermal with no overall transfer of matter, within a material or between materials that are touching (p. 479); the transfer of electric charge by direct contact with a conductor (p. 602)

conductivity a material's ability to allow heat or electric charges to flow (p. 46)

cones light-sensitive neurons in the retina that detect color (p. 589)

constant acceleration a steady change in velocity (p. 345)

constructive interference the interaction among two or more waves in which displacements combine to produce a wave with a larger displacement (p. 511)

controlled experiment an experiment in which only one variable, the manipulated variable, is deliberately changed at a time (p. 8)

convection the transfer of thermal energy when particles of a fluid move from one place to another (p. 480)

convection current circulation of a fluid in a loop as the fluid alternately heats up and cools down (p. 481)

conversion factor a ratio of equivalent measurements that is used to convert a quantity from one unit to another (p. 18)

convex lens a lens that is curved outward at the center and is thinnest at the outside edges (p. 576)

convex mirror a mirror that is curved outward (p. 573)

cornea the transparent outer coating of the eye (p. 588)

covalent bond a chemical bond in which two atoms share a pair of valence electrons (p. 166)

crest the highest point of a transverse wave (p. 501)

critical angle the angle of incidence that produces an angle of refraction equal to 90 degrees (p. 578)

critical mass the smallest possible mass of a fissionable material that can sustain a chain reaction (p. 311)

crystals solids whose particles are arranged in a lattice structure (p. 162)

D

decibel a unit that compares the intensities of different sounds (p. 515)

decomposition reaction a chemical reaction in which a compound breaks down into two or more simpler substances (p. 200)

density the ratio of a material's mass to its volume (p. 17)

deposition the phase change in which a gas or vapor changes directly into a solid without first changing into a liquid (p. 91)

Glossary

destructive interference the interaction among two or more waves in which displacements combine to produce a wave with a smaller displacement (p. 511)

diffraction the bending of a wave as it moves around an obstacle or passes through a narrow opening (p. 510)

diffuse reflection reflection that occurs when parallel light waves strike a rough, uneven surface and reflect in many different directions (p. 547)

digital signal a signal that encodes information as a string of 1's and 0's (p. 619)

diode a solid-state component with an n-type semiconductor joined to a p-type semiconductor (p. 621)

direct current (DC) a flow of electric charge in only one direction (p. 604)

direct proportion a relationship between two variables in which their ratio is constant (p. 23)

dispersion the process of dissolving by breaking into smaller pieces (p. 230), the process in which white light separates into colors (p. 551)

dissociation the separation of ions in an ionic compound as the compound dissolves (p. 229)

distance the length of the path between two points (p. 329)

distillation a process that separates the substances in a solution based on their boiling points (p. 50)

Doppler effect a change in sound frequency caused by motion of the sound source, motion of the listener, or both (p. 516)

double-replacement reaction a chemical reaction in which two compounds exchange positive ions and form two new compounds (p. 203)

E

efficiency the percentage of the work input that becomes work output in a machine (p. 425)

elastic potential energy the potential energy of an object that is stretched or compressed (p. 450)

electric charge a property that causes subatomic particles such as protons and electrons to attract or repel one another (p. 600)

electric circuit a complete path through which electric charge can flow (p. 609)

electric current a continuous flow of electric charge (p. 604)

electric field a field in a region of space that exerts electric forces on charged particles; a field produced by electric charges or by changing magnetic fields (pp. 533, 602)

electric force the attraction or repulsion between electrically charged objects (p. 601)

electric motor a device that uses an electromagnet to turn an axle (p. 639)

electric power the rate at which electrical energy is converted to another form of energy (p. 611)

electrical conductor a material through which electric charge can flow easily (p. 605)

electrical energy the energy associated with electric charges (p. 452)

electrical insulator a material through which charge cannot flow easily (p. 605)

electrolyte a compound that produces ions when it dissolves (p. 249)

electromagnet a solenoid with a ferromagnetic core (p. 637)

electromagnetic energy a form of energy consisting of changing electric and magnetic fields (p. 452)

electromagnetic force a force associated with charged particles, which has two aspects, electric force and magnetic force (pp. 378, 635)

electromagnetic induction the process of generating a current by moving an electrical conductor relative to a magnetic field (p. 642)

electromagnetic radiation the transfer of energy by electromagnetic waves (p. 533)

electromagnetic spectrum the full range of electromagnetic radiation (p. 540)

electromagnetic wave a transverse wave consisting of changing electric and changing magnetic fields (p. 533)

electron a negatively charged subatomic particle that is found in the space outside the nucleus of an atom (p. 108)

electron cloud a visual model of the most likely locations for the electrons in an atom (p. 116)

electron configuration the arrangement of electrons in the orbitals of an atom (p. 118)

electron dot diagram a diagram of an atom, ion or molecule in which each dot represents a valence electron (p. 158)

electronics the science of using electric currents to process or transmit information (p. 618)

electronic signal information sent as patterns in the controlled flow of electrons through a circuit (p. 618)

element a substance that cannot be broken down into simpler substances (p. 39)

endothermic a description of a change in which a system absorbs engergy from its surroundings (p. 86)

endothermic reaction a chemical reaction that absorbs energy from its surroundings (p. 209)

energy the ability to do work (p. 447)

energy conservation the practice of finding ways to use less energy or to use energy more efficiently (p. 466)

energy conversion the process of changing energy from one form to another (p. 454)

energy levels the possible energies that electrons in an atom can have (p. 114)

enzyme a protein that acts as a catalyst for reactions in cells (p. 284)

equilibrium a state in which the forward and reverse paths of a physical or chemical change take place at the same rate (p. 216)

evaporation the process that changes a substance from a liquid to a gas at temperatures below the substance's boiling point (p. 89)

exothermic a description of a change in which a system releases energy to its surroundings (p. 86)

exothermic reaction a chemical reaction that releases energy to its surroundings (p. 208)

external combustion engine a heat engine in which the fuel burns outside the engine (p. 486)

F

farsightedness an eye condition that causes nearby objects to be blurry (p. 592)

ferromagnetic material a material that can be magnetized because it contains magnetic domains (p. 632)

filtration a process that separates materials based on the size of their particles (p. 50)

fission a nuclear reaction in which an atomic nucleus is split into two smaller parts (p. 309)

flammability a material's ability to burn in the presence of oxygen (p. 54)

fluid a substance or mixture that flows and has no shape of its own (p. 391)

fluid friction a friction force that opposes the motion of an object through a fluid (p. 360)

fluorescence a process in which phosphorescent material converts radiation into visible light (p. 559)

focal point the point at which light rays parallel to the axis of a mirror or lens meet or appear to meet (p. 572)

force a push or a pull that acts on an object (p. 356)

fossil fuels rich deposits of hydrocarbon mixtures that formed from the remains of organisms (p. 267, p. 462)

frame of reference a system of objects that are not moving with respect to one another (p. 328)

free fall the movement of an object toward Earth because of gravity (p. 343)

frequency the number of complete cycles per unit time for a periodic motion (p. 504)

frequency modulation (FM) a method of transmitting a radio signal in which the frequency of the carrier wave varies while its amplitude remains the same (p. 541)

friction a force that opposes the motion of objects that touch as they move past each other (p. 359)

fulcrum the fixed point a lever rotates around (p. 428)

functional group an atom or group of atoms that determines the properties of an organic compound. (p. 272)

fuse a device that prevents overheating due to current overload in a circuit (p. 612)

fusion a nuclear reaction in which the nuclei of two atoms combine to form a larger nucleus (p. 315)

G

galvanometer a device that uses an electromagnet to measure small amounts of current (p. 638)

gamma ray a penetrating form of radiation emitted by an unstable nucleus (p. 294)

gas the state of matter in which a material has neither a definite shape nor a definite volume (p. 70)

generator a device that converts mechanical energy into electrical energy by the relative motion of a coil of wire with respect to a magnetic field (p. 643)

geology the study of the origin, history, and structure of Earth (p. 4)

geothermal energy thermal energy beneath Earth's surface (p. 464)

gravitational force an attractive force that acts between any two objects (p. 380)

gravitational potential energy potential energy that depends upon an object's height above a reference point (p. 449)

gravity the attraction between any two objects because of their masses (p. 361)

ground state a state in which all the electrons in an atom have the lowest possible energies (p. 118)

grounding the transfer of excess charge through a conductor to Earth (p. 613)

group a column of elements in a periodic table (p. 131)

H

half-life the time required for one half of a sample of a radioactive isotope to decay (p. 299)

halogens the elements in Group 7A of the periodic table (p. 144)

heat the transfer of thermal energy from one object to another because of a difference in temperature (p. 474)

heat engine any device that converts thermal energy into work (p. 483)

heat of fusion the energy a substance must absorb in order to change from a solid to a liquid (p. 86)

heat of vaporization the energy a substance must absorb in order to change from a liquid to a gas (p. 88)

heat pump a device that uses work to transfer thermal energy from a colder area to a warmer area (p. 490)

hertz (Hz) the unit of measure for frequency, equal to one cycle per second (p. 504)

Glossary

heterogeneous mixture a type of mixture in which the parts of the mixture are noticeably different from one another (p. 41)

homogeneous mixture a type of mixture in which the substances are so evenly distributed that it is difficult to distinguish one substance in the mixture from another (p. 42)

horsepower (hp) a common unit of power, equal to about 746 watts (p. 416)

hydraulic system a device that uses a pressurized fluid acting on pistons of different sizes to increase force (p. 395)

hydrocarbon an organic compound that contains only the elements hydrogen and carbon (p. 264)

hydroelectric energy energy obtained from flowing water (p. 463)

hydrogen fuel cell a cell that generates electricity from a controlled reaction between hydrogen and oxygen (p. 608)

hypothesis a proposed answer to a question (p. 8)

I

ideal mechanical advantage (IMA) the mechanical advantage of a machine in the absence of friction (p. 423)

image a copy of an object formed by reflected or refracted rays of light (p. 547)

incandescent a description of an object hot enough to glow (p. 558)

inclined plane a slanted surface along which a force moves an object to a different elevation (p. 431)

index of refraction the ratio of the speed of light in a vacuum to the speed of light in a medium (p. 575)

indicator a substance that changes color in the presence of an acid or a base (p. 241)

induction the transfer of charge without contact between materials (p. 603)

inertia the tendency of an object to resist a change in its motion (p. 364)

input arm the distance between the fulcrum in a lever and the input force (p. 428)

input distance the distance through which the input force acts in a machine (p. 419)

input force the force exerted on a machine (p. 419)

instantaneous speed the rate at which an object is moving at a given moment in time (p. 334)

integrated circuit a thin slice of silicon that contains many solid-state components; a microchip (p. 622)

intensity the rate at which a wave's energy flows through a given unit of area (pp. 515, 538)

interference the interaction of two or more waves that combine in a region of overlap (p. 510)

internal combustion engine a heat engine in which the fuel burns inside the engine (p. 487)

inverse proportion a relationship in which the product of two variables is a constant when all other variables are held constant (p. 23)

ion an atom or group of atoms that has a positive or negative charge (p. 159)

ionic bond the force that holds cations and anions together (p. 160)

ionization the process by which neutral molecules gain or lose electrons (p. 230)

iris the colored part at the front of the eye, which expands and contracts to control the amount of light entering the eye (p. 589)

isomers organic compounds with the same molecular formula but with different structural formulas (p. 265)

isotopes atoms of a given element that have different numbers of neutrons and different mass numbers (p. 112)

J

joule (J) the SI unit of work, equal to 1 newton-meter (p. 414)

K

kinetic energy the energy an object has due to its motion (pp. 71, 447)

L

laser a device that generates a beam of coherent light (p. 560)

law of conservation of charge law stating that the total electric charge in an isolated system is constant; electric charge is never created or destroyed (p. 602)

law of conservation of momentum law stating that the total momentum of a system does not change if no net force acts on the system (p. 376)

length the straight-line distance between two points (p. 16)

lens an object made of any thin, transparent material that has one or two curved surfaces that can refract light (p. 576)

lever a rigid bar that is free to move around a fixed point (p. 428)

lift an upward force due to a pressure difference between the top and bottom of a wing (p. 396)

linear graph a graph in which the displayed data form a straight line (p. 347)

liquid the state of matter in which a material has a definite volume but not a definite shape (p. 69)

longitudinal wave a wave in which the vibration of the medium is parallel to the direction the wave travels (p. 502)

loudness a physical response to the intensity of sound, modified by physical factors (p. 515)

luminous a description of an object that gives off its own light (p. 558)

M

machine a device that changes a force (p. 417)

magnetic domain a region that has a large number of atoms with aligned magnetic fields (p. 632)

magnetic field a field in a region of space that exerts magnetic forces; a field produced by magnets, by changing electric fields, or by moving charges (pp. 533, 631)

magnetic force the force a magnetic field exerts on a magnet, on a ferromagnetic material, or on a moving electric charge (p. 630)

magnetic pole a region on a magnet where the force produced by the magnet is strongest (p. 630)

magnetosphere the area surrounding Earth that is influenced by Earth's magnetic field (p. 632)

malleability the ability of a solid to be hammered without shattering (p. 46)

manipulated variable the variable that causes a change in another variable (p. 8)

mass the amount of matter in an object (p. 16); a measure of the inertia of an object, which depends on the amount of matter the object contains (p. 365)

mass number the sum of the number of protons and neutrons in the nucleus of an atom (p. 110)

mechanical advantage the number of times that a machine increases an input force (p. 421)

mechanical energy the energy associated with the motion and position of everyday objects (p. 450)

mechanical wave a disturbance in matter that carries energy from one place to another (p. 500)

medium the material through which a wave travels (p. 500)

melting point the temperature at which a substance changes from solid to liquid (p. 47)

metals elements that are good conductors of heat and electric current (p. 135)

metallic bond the attraction between a metal cation and the shared electrons that surround it (p. 176)

metalloids elements with properties that fall between those of metals and nonmetals (p. 136)

microscope an optical instrument that uses lenses to provide enlarged images of very small, near objects (p. 584)

mirage a false or distorted image (p. 548)

model a representation of an object or event (p. 10)

molarity the number of moles of a dissolved solute per liter of solution (p. 239)

molar mass the mass of one mole of a substance (p. 196)

mole an amount of a substance that contains approximately 6.02×10^{23} particles of the substance (p. 195)

molecule a neutral group of atoms that are joined together by one or more covalent bonds (p. 166)

momentum the product of an object's mass and its velocity (p. 374)

monomer a small organic molecule that joins with other monomers to form a polymer (p. 275)

N

nearsightedness an eye condition in which distant objects are blurry (p. 590)

net force the overall force acting on an object after all the forces are combined (p. 357)

network solid a solid in which all the atoms are linked by covalent bonds (p. 263)

neutralization a chemical reaction between an acid and a base (p. 244)

neutron a neutral subatomic particle that is found in the nucleus of an atom (p. 109)

newton (N) the SI unit for force, equal to the force that causes a 1-kilogram mass to accelerate at a rate of 1 meter per second squared ($1 \text{ N} = 1 \text{ kg} \cdot \text{m/s}^2$) (p. 357)

noble gases the elements in Group 8A of the periodic table (p. 145)

node a point on a standing wave that has no displacement from the rest position (p. 512)

nonlinear graph a graph in which the displayed data form a curved line (p. 348)

nonmetals elements that are poor conductors of heat and electric current (p. 136)

nonrenewable energy resource a source of energy that exists in limited quantities and, once used, cannot be replaced except over the course of millions of years (p. 462)

nuclear energy the energy stored in atomic nuclei (p. 452)

nuclear radiation charged particles and electromagnetic waves that are emitted from the nuclei of radioisotopes (p. 293)

nucleic acid a large, nitrogen-containing polymer, found mainly in the nuclei of cells (p. 279)

nucleus the dense, positively charged mass located in the center of an atom (p. 105)

Glossary

O

observation information obtained through the senses (p. 8)

Ohm's law the relationship of voltage, current, and resistance: $V = IR$ (p. 607)

opaque a description of a material that either absorbs or reflects all of the light that strikes it so nothing can be seen through it (p. 547)

orbital a region of space around the nucleus where an electron is likely to be found (p. 117)

organic compounds compounds that contain carbon and hydrogen, often combined with a few other elements such as oxygen or nitrogen (p. 262)

output arm the distance between the fulcrum in a lever and the output force (p. 428)

output distance the distance an output force acts through in a machine (p. 420)

output force the force exerted by a machine (p. 420)

oxidation-reduction (redox) reaction a chemical reaction in which electrons are transferred from one reactant to another (p. 204)

P

parallel circuit an electric circuit with two or more paths through which charge can flow (p. 610)

pascal (Pa) the SI unit of pressure, equal to 1 newton per square meter (N/m^2) (p. 391)

period a row in a periodic table of elements (p. 131); the time required for one complete cycle of a periodic motion (p. 504)

periodic law the pattern of repeating properties displayed by elements in the periodic table (p. 131)

periodic motion any motion that repeats at regular time intervals (p. 504)

periodic table an arrangement of elements in columns, based on a set of properties that repeat from row to row (p. 127)

pH a measure of the hydronium ion concentration of a solution (p. 247)

phase change a reversible physical change that occurs when a substance changes from one state of matter to another (p. 84)

phosphor a solid material that emits light by fluorescence (p. 559)

photoelectric effect the emission of electrons from a metal caused by light striking the metal (p. 537)

photon a packet of electromagnetic energy (p. 537)

photosynthesis a process in which plants chemically combine carbon dioxide and water into carbohydrates, a process requiring light and chlorophyll (p. 282)

physical change a change that occurs when some properties of a material change, but the substances in the material stay the same (p. 51)

physical property any characteristic of a material that can be observed or measured without changing the composition of the substances in the material (p. 45)

physics the study of matter and energy and the interactions between the two through forces and motion (p. 4)

pigment a material that selectively absorbs certain colors of light and reflects other colors (p. 553)

pitch the frequency of a sound as a listener perceives it (p. 515)

plane mirror a mirror with a flat surface (p. 571)

plasma a state of matter in which atoms have been stripped of their electrons (p. 315)

polar covalent bond a covalent bond in which electrons are not shared equally (p. 168)

polarized light a type of light including light with waves that vibrate in only one plane (p. 548)

polyatomic ion a covalently bonded group of atoms that has a positive or negative charge and acts as a unit (p. 172)

polymer a large molecule formed when many smaller molecules are linked together by covalent bonds (p. 275)

potential difference voltage, or the difference in electrical potential energy between two places in an electric field (p. 606)

potential energy energy that is stored as a result of position or shape (p. 448)

power the rate of doing work (p. 414)

precipitate a solid that forms and separates from a liquid mixture (p. 57)

precision a gauge of how exact a measurement is (p. 19)

pressure the result of a force distributed over an area (pp. 75, 390)

primary colors three specific colors that can be combined in varying intensities to create millions of colors (p. 552)

products new substances formed as a result of a chemical reaction (p. 192)

projectile motion the curved path of an object in free fall after it is given an initial forward velocity (p. 362)

protein a long polymer that forms when amino acids bond together (p. 280)

proton a positively charged subatomic particle that is found in the nucleus of an atom (p. 108)

pulley a simple machine that consists of a rope that fits into a groove in a wheel (p. 432)

pupil the opening that allows light to enter the eye (p. 589)

pure substance matter that always has exactly the same composition; an element or compound (p. 39)

Q

quark a subatomic particle theorized to be among the basic units of matter (p. 305)

R

radiation the transfer of energy by waves moving through space (p. 481)

radioactivity the process in which an unstable atomic nucleus emits charged particles and energy (p. 292)

radioisotope an isotope with an unstable nucleus (p. 292)

rarefaction an area of a longitudinal wave where the particles of the medium are spread out (p. 502)

ray diagram a diagram that shows how light rays change direction when they strike mirrors and pass through lenses (p. 570)

reactant a substance that undergoes change in a chemical reaction (p. 192)

reaction rate the rate at which reactants change into products over time (p. 212)

reactivity the property that describes how readily a substance combines chemically with other substances (p. 55)

real image a copy of an object formed at the point where light rays actually meet (p. 572)

reflecting telescope a telescope that uses mirrors and convex lenses to collect and focus light (p. 581)

reflection the interaction that occurs when a wave bounces off a surface that it cannot pass through (p. 508)

refracting telescope a telescope that uses only lenses to collect and focus light (p. 581)

refraction the bending of a wave as it enters a new medium at an angle (p. 509)

refrigerant a fluid that vaporizes and condenses inside the tubing of a heat pump (p. 490)

regular reflection a reflection that occurs when parallel light waves strike a surface and all reflect in the same direction (p. 547)

relative motion movement in relation to a frame of reference (p. 329)

renewable energy resource a source of energy that can be replaced in a relatively short period of time (p. 463)

resistance the opposition to the flow of electric charges in a material (p. 605)

resonance the response of a standing wave to another wave of the same frequency, with dramatic increase in amplitude of the standing wave (p. 521)

responding variable a variable that changes in response to a change in the manipulated variable (p. 8)

resultant vector the vector sum of two or more vectors (p. 331)

retina the inner surface of the back of the eye, containing light-sensitive nerve endings (p. 589)

reversible reaction a chemical reaction in which the conversion of reactants into products and the conversion of products into reactants happens at the same time (p. 217)

rods light-sensitive neurons in the retina that detect low-intensity light and distinguish black, white, and gray (p. 589)

rolling friction a friction force that acts on rolling objects, caused by the change in shape at the point of rolling contact (p. 360)

S

salt an ionic compound formed when an acid reacts with a base (p. 244)

saturated hydrocarbon a hydrocarbon in which all of the bonds are single bonds (p. 264)

saturated solution a solution that contains as much solute as the solvent can normally hold at a given temperature (p. 236)

scattering a process by which light is redirected as it passes through a medium (p. 549)

science a system of knowledge about the natural world and the methods used to find that knowledge (p. 3)

scientific law a statement that summarizes a pattern found in nature (p. 9)

scientific method an organized plan used for gathering, organizing, and communicating information (p. 7)

scientific notation a way of expressing a value as the product of a number between 1 and 10 and a power of 10 (p. 14)

scientific theory a well-tested explanation for a set of observations or experimental results (p. 9)

screw an inclined plane wrapped around a cylinder (p. 431)

secondary color new color that results when any two of the primary colors are combined (p. 552)

semiconductor a crystalline solid that conducts electric current only under certain conditions (p. 621)

series circuit an electric circuit with only one path through which charge can flow (p. 610)

significant figures all the digits in a measurement that are directly measured, plus the last digit, which is estimated (p. 19)

single-replacement reaction a chemical reaction in which one element takes the place of another element in a compound (p. 202)

sliding friction a friction force that opposes the motion of an object as it slides over a surface (p. 359)

Glossary

slope the steepness of a line, equal to the ratio of a vertical change to the corresponding horizontal change (pp. 23, 334)

solar energy sunlight that is converted into usable energy (p. 464)

solenoid a coil of current-carrying wire that produces a magnetic field (p. 637)

solid the state of matter in which materials have a definite shape and a definite volume (p. 69)

solubility the maximum amount of solute that normally dissolves in a given amount of solvent at a certain temperature (p. 235)

solute a substance whose particles are dissolved in a solution (p. 229)

solution a mixture that forms when substances dissolve and form a homogeneous mixture (p. 42)

solvent a substance in which a solute dissolves (p. 229)

sonar a technique for determining the distance to an object under water (p. 516)

sound wave a longitudinal wave consisting of compressions and rarefactions, which travels through a medium (p. 514)

specific heat the amount of heat needed to raise the temperature of one gram of a material by one degree Celsius (p. 476)

speed the ratio of the distance an object moves to the amount of time the object moves (p. 332)

standing wave a wave that appears to stay in one place and does not seem to move through a medium (p. 512)

static electricity the study of the behavior of electric charges, including how charge is transferred between objects (p. 602)

static friction a friction force that acts on objects that are not moving (p. 359)

strong nuclear force the powerful attractive force that binds protons and neutrons together in the nucleus (pp. 308, 379)

sublimation the phase change in which a substance changes from a solid to a gas or vapor without changing to a liquid first (p. 91)

substance matter that always has exactly the same composition; an element or compound (p. 39)

substituted hydrocarbon a hydrocarbon in which one or more hydrogen atoms have been replaced, or substituted (p. 272)

superconductor a material that has almost zero resistance when it is cooled to low temperatures (p. 605)

supersaturated solution a solution that contains more solute than the solvent can normally hold at a given temperature (p. 236)

surface wave a wave that travels along a surface separating two media (p. 503)

suspension a heterogeneous mixture that separates into layers over time (p. 43)

synthesis reaction a chemical reaction in which two or more substances react to form a single substance (p. 200)

T

technology the use of scientific knowledge to solve practical problems (p. 3)

telescope an optical instrument that uses lenses (or lenses and mirrors) to collect and focus light from distant objects (p. 580)

temperature a measure of how hot or cold an object is compared to a reference point (p. 475)

terminal velocity the constant velocity of a falling object when the force of air resistance equals the force of gravity (p. 361)

thermal conductor a material that conducts thermal energy well (p. 480)

thermal energy the total potential and kinetic energy related to the motion of all the particles in an object (p. 451)

thermal expansion the increase in volume of a material when its temperature increases (p. 476)

thermal insulator a material that conducts thermal energy poorly (p. 480)

thermodynamics the study of conversions between thermal energy and other forms of energy (p. 482)

thermogram a color-coded picture using variations in infrared radiation to show variations in temperature (p. 543)

thermometer an instrument that measures temperature (p. 20)

total internal reflection the complete reflection of a light ray back into its original medium when the angle of incidence is greater than the critical angle of refraction (p. 578)

transformer a device that increases or decreases the voltage of two linked AC circuits (p. 644)

transistor a solid-state component with three layers of semiconductor material, used to turn current on or off or to increase the strength of electronic signals (p. 621)

transition metals elements that form a bridge between elements on the left and right sides of the periodic table (p. 136)

translucent a description of a material that scatters light that passes through it (p. 547)

transmutation the conversion of one element to another through a nuclear reaction (p. 303)

transparent a description of a material that allows most of the light that strikes it to pass through (p. 546)

transuranium elements elements with atomic numbers greater than 92 (p. 304)

transverse wave a wave that causes a medium to vibrate at right angles to the direction in which the wave travels (p. 501)

trough the lowest point of a transverse wave (p. 501)

turbine a device with fanlike blades that turn when pushed, for example, by water or steam (p. 646)

U

unsaturated hydrocarbon a hydrocarbon that contains one or more double or triple bonds (p. 265)

unsaturated solution a solution in which more solute can be dissolved at a given temperature (p. 236)

V

valence electron an electron that is in the highest occupied energy level of an atom (p. 139)

vaporization the phase change in which a substance changes from a liquid into a gas (p. 88)

vapor pressure the pressure caused by the collisions of particles in a vapor with the walls of a container (p. 89)

vector a quantity that has a direction associated with it (p. 330)

velocity the speed and direction an object is moving, measured relative to a reference point (p. 336)

virtual image a copy of an object formed at the point from which light appears to be coming (p. 571)

viscosity the tendency of a liquid to keep from flowing; resistance to flowing (p. 45)

vitamin an organic compound that organisms need in small amounts, but cannot produce (p. 284)

voltage potential difference, the difference in electrical potential energy between two places in an electric field (p. 606)

volume the amount of space taken up by an object (p. 16)

W

waste heat thermal energy discharged into an area at a lower temperature without being converted into useful work (p. 483)

watt (W) the SI unit of power, equal to one joule per second (p. 415)

wavelength the distance between a point on a wave and the same point on the next cycle of the wave (p. 505)

weak nuclear force a powerful attractive force that acts over a short range (p. 380)

wedge a V-shaped object whose sides are two inclined planes sloped toward each other (p. 431)

weight the force of gravity acting on an object (p. 367)

wheel and axle a simple machine that consists of two rigidly attached disks or cylinders, each one with a different radius (p. 430)

work the product of distance and the force in the direction an object moves (p. 412)

work input the work done on a machine as the input force acts through the input distance (p. 419)

work output the work done by a machine as the output force acts through the output distance (p. 420)

Spanish Glossary

A

absolute zero / cero absoluto una temperatura de 0 kelvin (págs. 78, 475)

acceleration / aceleración la tasa a la cual cambia la velocidad (pág. 342)

accuracy / exactitud la cercanía de una medida al valor real de lo que se mide (pág. 19)

acid / ácido un compuesto que produce iones hidronios (H_3O^+) cuando se disuelve en agua; un donante de protones (pág. 241)

actual mechanical advantage / ventaja mecánica real la relación de la fuerza desarrollada con respecto a la fuerza aplicada en una máquina (pág. 422)

air resistance / resistencia del aire fricción de un fluido que actúa sobre un objeto que se mueve a través del aire (pág. 360)

alkali metals / metales alcalinos los elementos del Grupo 1A de la tabla periódica, sin incluir el hidrógeno (pág. 10)

alkaline earth metals / metales terreo-alcalinos los elementos del Grupo 2A de la tabla periódica (pág. 141)

alloy / aleación una mezcla de dos o más elementos, de los cuales al menos uno es un metal, que tiene las propiedades características de un metal (pág. 178)

alpha particle / partícula alfa una partícula de carga positiva que es emitida por algunos núcleos radiactivos y está formada por dos protones y dos neutrones; un núcleo de helio (pág. 293)

alternating current (AC) / corriente alterna (CA) un flujo de energía eléctrica que cambia de positiva a negativa a intervalos regulares (pág. 604)

amino acids / aminoácidos compuestos que contienen los grupos funcionales carboxilo y amino (pág. 280)

amplitude / amplitud el máximo desplazamiento de un determinado medio desde su posición de reposo (pág. 507)

amplitude modulation (AM) / amplitud modulada (AM) un método para la transmisión de señales de radio en el que la amplitud de la onda transmisora varía mientras que la frecuencia permanece estable (pág. 541)

analog signal / señal análoga una señal de variación gradual que se produce al cambiar continuamente el voltaje o corriente en un circuito (pág. 619)

angle of incidence / ángulo de incidencia el ángulo que forma un rayo incidente con una línea perpendicular a la superficie sobre la que impacta (pág. 570)

angle of reflection / ángulo de reflexión el ángulo que forma un rayo reflejado con una línea perpendicular a la superficie sobre la que impacta (pág. 570)

angle of refraction / ángulo de refracción el ángulo que forma un rayo de luz con el normal después de ingresar a un nuevo medio a un ángulo determinado (pág. 575)

anion / anión un ión de carga negativa (pág. 160)

antinode / antinodo un punto de máximo desplazamiento a mitad de camino entre dos nodos y una onda estacionaria (pág. 512)

Archimedes' principle / principio de Arquímedes la equivalencia de la fuerza de flotación de un objeto y el peso del fluido desplazado por el objeto (pág. 401)

aromatic hydrocarbons / hidrocarburos aromáticos hidrocarburos que contienen una estructura de anillos similar al benceno (pág. 26)

astigmatism / astigmatismo condición de los ojos en la que los objetos situados a cualquier distancia aparecen borrosos debido a la forma distorsionada de la córnea (pág. 592)

astronomy / astronomía el estudio del Universo más allá de la Tierra (pág. 4)

atom / átomo la partícula más pequeña de un elemento (pág. 39)

atomic mass unit (amu) / unidad de masa atómica (uma) una doceava parte de la masa que tiene un átomo de carbono-12 (pág. 134)

atomic number / número atómico un único número por cada elemento que equivale al número de protones en un átomo de ese elemento (pág. 110)

average speed / rapidez media la distancia total recorrida dividida por el tiempo que se necesita para recorrer esa distancia (pág. 333)

B

background radiation / radiación de fondo radiación nuclear que se produce naturalmente en el ambiente (pág. 296)

base / base un compuesto que produce iones hidróxidos (OH^-) cuando se disuelve en agua; un receptor de protones (pág. 242)

battery / batería un artefacto que convierte la energía química en energía eléctrica (pág. 606)

beta particle / partícula beta un electrón emitido por un núcleo inestable (pág. 294)

biology / biología el estudio de la vida y los procesos vitales (pág. 4)

biomass energy / energía de la biomasa la energía química que se almacena en las cosas vivas (pág. 464)

boiling point / punto de ebullición la temperatura a la cual hierve una sustancia; la temperatura a la cual la presión del vapor es igual a la presión atmosférica (pág. 47)

Boyle's law / ley de Boyle la variación inversa del volumen de un gas y su presión si la temperatura y el número de partículas son constantes (pág. 79)

buffer / búfer una solución que es resistente a grandes cambios en su pH (pág. 248)

buoyancy / flotación la capacidad que tiene un fluido de ejercer una fuerza ascendente en los objetos colocados en él (pág. 400)

buoyant force / fuerza de flotación una fuerza ascendente que actúa sobre un objeto colocado en un fluido (pág. 400)

C

calorimeter / calorímetro instrumento que sirve para medir la energía térmica que se libera o absorbe durante un cambio químico o físico (pág. 478)

camera / cámara fotográfica un instrumento óptico que registra la imagen de un objeto (pág. 582)

carbohydrate / carbohidrato un compuesto de carbono, hidrógeno y oxígeno en el cual la relación de los átomos de hidrógeno respecto de los átomos de oxígeno es de 2:1 (pág. 278)

catalyst / catalizador una sustancia que afecta la velocidad de una reacción química sin que sea usada en la reacción (pág. 215)

cation / catión un ión con carga positiva (pág. 160)

central heating system / sistema de calefacción central un sistema de calefacción que calienta varias habitaciones desde una ubicación central (pág. 489)

centripetal force / fuerza centrípeta una fuerza que cambia continuamente la dirección de un objeto para hacerlo moverse en un círculo (pág. 381)

chain reaction / reacción en cadena una serie de reacciones de fisión disparadas por neutrones liberados durante la fisión de un núcleo (pág. 311)

Charles's law / ley de Charles la proporción directa del volumen de un gas con respecto a su temperatura (en kelvins), si la presión y el número de partículas del gas son constantes (pág. 78)

chemical bond / enlace químico la fuerza que mantiene los átomos e iones juntos como una unidad (pág. 160)

chemical change / cambio químico cambio que se produce cuando una sustancia reacciona y forma una o más sustancias nuevas (pág. 56)

chemical energy / energía química la energía almacenada en los enlaces químicos (págs. 206, 451)

chemical equation / ecuación química una representación de una reacción química en la cual los reactantes y los productos se expresan como fórmulas (pág. 193)

chemical formula / fórmula química notación que muestra los elementos que contienen un compuesto y la relación de los átomos o iones de estos elementos en el compuesto (pág. 161)

chemical property / propiedad química toda propiedad que produce un cambio en la composición de la materia (pág. 54)

chemistry / química el estudio de la composición, estructura, propiedades y reacciones de la materia (pág. 4)

circuit breaker / interruptor de circuito un interruptor que se abre cuando la corriente en un circuito es demasiado alta (pág. 612)

coefficients / coeficientes los números que aparecen antes de una fórmula en una ecuación química para mostrar las proporciones relativas de cada reactante y producto (pág. 194)

coherent light / luz coherente ondas de luz que tienen la misma longitud de onda, con sus crestas y valles alineados (pág. 560)

colloid / coloide una mezcla que contiene algunas partículas que son de tamaño intermedio entre las partículas pequeñas de una solución y las partículas grandes de una suspensión (pág. 44)

combustion reaction / reacción de combustión una reacción química en la que una sustancia reacciona rápidamente con el oxígeno, produciendo a menudo calor y luz (pág. 204)

complementary colors of light / colores complementarios de la luz dos colores cualesquiera de luz que se combinan para formar luz blanca (pág. 552)

complementary colors of pigments / colores complementarios de pigmentos dos colores cualesquiera de pigmentos que se combinan para formar un pigmento negro (pág. 553)

compound / compuesto una sustancia que está formada por dos o más sustancias más simples y que se puede descomponer en esas sustancias más simples (pág. 40)

compound machine / máquina compuesta una combinación de dos o más máquinas simples que operan juntas (pág. 435)

compression / compresión un área en una onda longitudinal en la cual las partículas de ese medio están juntas entre sí (pág. 502)

computer / computadora un artefacto programable que puede almacenar y procesar información (pág. 622)

concave lens / lente cóncava lente curvada hacia dentro en el centro y que tiene mayor grosor en los bordes exteriores (pág. 576)

concave mirror / espejo cóncavo un espejo que se curva hacia dentro (pág. 572)

concentration / concentración la cantidad de soluto disuelto en una determinada cantidad de solvente (pág. 238)

Spanish Glossary

condensation / condensación el cambio de fase en el que una sustancia cambia de gas o vapor a líquido (pág. 90)

conduction / conducción la transferencia de energía térmica sin transferencia significativa de materia, dentro de un material o entre materiales en contacto (pág. 479); la transferencia de carga eléctrica por contacto directo con un conductor (pág. 602)

conductivity / conductividad la capacidad que tiene un material de permitir que fluyan el calor o las cargas eléctricas (pág. 46)

cones / conos las neuronas sensibles a la luz de la retina que detectan el color (pág. 589)

constant acceleration / aceleración constante un cambio continuo en la velocidad (pág. 345)

constructive interference / interferencia constructiva la interacción entre dos o más ondas en las que los desplazamientos se combinan para formar una onda con un desplazamiento más amplio (pág. 511)

controlled experiment / experimento controlado experimento en el que una sola variable, la variable manipulada, se cambia deliberadamente en un momento determinado (pág. 8)

convection / convección transferencia de energía térmica cuando las partículas de un fluido se mueven de un lugar a otro (pág. 480)

convection current / corriente de convección circulación de un fluido en un circuito cuando el fluido se calienta y se enfría alternativamente (pág. 481)

conversion factor / factor de conversión una razón de medidas equivalentes que se usan para convertir una determinada cantidad de una unidad a otra (pág. 18)

convex lens / lente convexa lente curvada hacia fuera en el centro y más delgada en los bordes exteriores (pág. 576)

convex mirror / espejo convexo espejo curvado hacia afuera (pág. 573)

cornea / córnea capa externa y transparente del ojo (pág. 588)

covalent bond / enlace covalente enlace químico en el que dos átomos comparten un par de electrones de valencia (pág. 166)

crest / cresta el punto más alto de una onda transversal (pág. 501)

critical angle / ángulo crítico el ángulo de incidencia que produce un ángulo de refracción igual a 90 grados (pág. 578)

critical mass / masa crítica la masa más pequeña posible de un material fisionable que puede generar una reacción en cadena (pág. 311)

crystals / cristales sólidos cuyas partículas se encuentran dispuestas en una estructura reticular (pág. 162)

D

decibel / decibelio una unidad que compara las intensidades de diferentes sonidos (pág. 515)

decomposition reaction / reacción de descomposición una reacción química en la que un compuesto se separa en dos o más sustancias más simples (pág. 200)

density / densidad la relación entre el volumen y la masa de un material (pág. 17)

deposition / deposición cambio de fase en el que un gas o vapor cambia directamente al estado sólido sin pasar primero por el estado líquido (pág. 91)

destructive interference / interferencia destructiva la interacción entre dos o más ondas cuyos desplazamientos se combinan para producir una onda con un desplazamiento menor (pág. 511)

diffraction / difracción la curvatura de una onda que se mueve alrededor de un obstáculo o pasa a través de una abertura estrecha (pág. 510)

diffuse reflection / reflexión difusa la reflexión que se produce cuando ondas de luz paralelas chocan contra una superficie áspera y desigual, y se reflejan en muchas direcciones diferentes (pág. 547)

digital signal / señal digital una señal que codifica la información como una secuencia de unos y ceros (pág. 619)

diode / diodo un componente de estado sólido con un semiconductor de tipo n unido a un semiconductor de tipo p (pág. 621)

direct current (DC) / corriente directa (CD) el flujo de carga eléctrica que corre en una sola dirección (pág. 604)

direct proportion / proporción directa una relación entre dos variables cuya proporción es constante (pág. 23)

dispersion / dispersión el proceso de disolución por rotura en partes pequeñas (pág. 230); proceso en el que la luz blanca se separa en colores (pág. 551)

dissociation / disociación separación de iones en un compuesto iónico a medida que éste se disuelve (pág. 229)

distance / distancia longitud de la trayectoria entre dos puntos (pág. 329)

distillation / destilación el proceso que separa las sustancias en una solución según sus puntos de ebullición (pág. 50)

Doppler effect / efecto Doppler un cambio en la frecuencia de sonido provocada por el movimiento de la fuente de sonido, movimiento de la persona que escucha o de ambos (pág. 516)

double-replacement reaction / reacción de sustitución doble una reacción química en la que dos componentes intercambian iones positivos y forman otros dos nuevos compuestos (pág. 203)

E

efficiency / eficiencia porcentaje de trabajo de entrada que se transforma en trabajo de salida en una máquina (pág. 425)

elastic potencial energy / energía elástica potencial energía potencial de un objeto al ser estirado o comprimido (pág. 450)

electric charge / carga eléctrica una propiedad que provoca atracción o rechazo entre partículas subatómicas como los protones y electrones (pág. 600)

electric circuit / circuito eléctrico recorrido completo a través del cual puede fluir la carga eléctrica (pág. 609)

electric current / corriente eléctrica un flujo continuo de carga eléctrica (pág. 604)

electric field / campo eléctrico campo en una región del espacio que ejerce fuerzas eléctricas sobre partículas cargadas; campo generado por cargas eléctricas o por campos magnéticos variables (págs. 533, 602)

electric force / fuerza eléctrica la atracción o rechazo entre objetos con carga eléctrica (pág. 601)

electric motor / motor eléctrico un aparato que utiliza un electroimán para mover o rotar un eje (pág. 639)

electric power / potencia eléctrica la velocidad a la que la energía eléctrica se convierte en otro tipo de energía (pág. 611)

electrical conductor / conductor eléctrico un material a través del cual la carga eléctrica puede fluir fácilmente (pág. 605)

electrical energy / energía eléctrica energía asociada con las cargas eléctricas (pág. 452)

electrical insulator / aislante eléctrico un material a través del cual la carga eléctrica no puede fluir fácilmente (pág. 605)

electrolyte / electrolito un compuesto que produce iones al ser disuelto (pág. 249)

electromagnet / electroimán un solenoide con núcleo ferromagnético (pág. 637)

electromagnetic energy / energía electromagnética una forma de energía que consiste en campos eléctricos y magnéticos variables (pág. 452)

electromagnetic force / fuerza electromagnética una fuerza asociada con las partículas cargadas, la cual tiene dos aspectos, fuerza eléctrica y fuerza magnética (págs. 378, 635)

electromagnetic induction / inducción electromagnética el proceso de generación de corriente en el que un conductor eléctrico se mueve en relación a un campo magnético (pág. 642)

electromagnetic radiation / radiación electromagnética la transferencia de energía por medio de ondas electromagnéticas (pág. 533)

electromagnetic spectrum / espectro electromagnético rango completo de radiación electromagnética (pág. 540)

electromagnetic wave / onda electromagnética onda transversal formada por campos eléctricos y campos magnéticos variables (pág. 533)

electron / electrón una partícula subatómica con carga negativa que se encuentra en el espacio fuera del núcleo de un átomo (pág. 108)

electron cloud / nube de electrones modelo visual de las ubicaciones más probables de los electrones en un átomo (pág. 116)

electron configuration / configuración de electrones la disposición de los electrones en las órbitas de un átomo (pág. 118)

electron dot diagram / diagrama de puntos de electrones diagrama de un átomo, ión o molécula en el que cada punto representa la valencia de un electrón (pág. 158)

electronics / electrónica la ciencia que utiliza corrientes eléctricas para procesar o transmitir información (pág. 618)

electronic signal / señal electrónica información enviada en forma de patrones en el flujo controlado de electrones a través de un circuito (pág. 618)

element / elemento sustancia que no puede ser descompuesta en sustancias más simples (pág. 39)

endothermic / endotérmico la descripción de un cambio en el que un sistema absorbe energía de su entorno (pág. 86)

endothermic reaction / reacción endotérmica una reacción química que absorbe energía del entorno (pág. 209)

energy / energía capacidad de realizar un trabajo (pág. 447)

energy conservation / conservación de la energía práctica para encontrar formas de utilizar menos energía o de utilizarla en forma más eficiente (pág. 466)

energy conversion / conversión de la energía el proceso de cambiar energía de una forma a otra (pág. 454)

energy levels / niveles energéticos energías posibles que pueden tener los electrones de un átomo (pág. 114)

enzyme / enzima una proteína que actúa como catalítico para las reacciones en las células (pág. 284)

equilibrium / equilibrio estado en el que las trayectorias hacia delante y hacia atrás de un cambio físico o químico se realizan a la misma velocidad (pág. 216)

evaporation / evaporación el proceso por el cual una sustancia en estado líquido se transforma en gas a temperaturas por debajo del punto de ebullición de esa sustancia (pág. 89)

exothermic / exotérmico descripción de un cambio en el que el sistema libera energía hacia su entorno (pág. 86)

Spanish Glossary

exothermic reaction / reacción exotérmica una reacción química que libera energía hacia el entorno (pág. 208)

external combustion engine / motor de combustión externa un motor térmico en el que el combustible se quema fuera de él (pág. 486)

F

farsightedness / hipermetropía condición de los ojos que provoca una visión borrosa de los objetos cercanos (pág. 592)

ferromagnetic material / material ferromagnético un material que puede ser magnetizado por su contenido de dominios magnéticos (pág. 632)

filtration / filtración proceso que separa los materiales de acuerdo al tamaño de sus partículas (pág. 50)

fission / fisión una reacción nuclear en que el núcleo de un átomo se separa en dos partes pequeñas (pág. 309)

flammability / flamabilidad capacidad que tiene un material de quemarse en presencia de oxígeno (pág. 54)

fluid / fluido sustancia o mezcla que fluye y que no tiene forma definida (pág. 391)

fluid friction / fricción de fluido una fuerza de fricción que se opone al movimiento de un objeto dentro de un fluido (pág. 360)

fluorescence / fluorescencia proceso en el que un material fosforescente convierte la radiación en luz visible (pág. 559)

focal point / punto de enfoque punto en el que se encuentran o parecen encontrarse los rayos de luz paralelos al eje de un espejo o lente (pág. 572)

force / fuerza la atracción o rechazo que actúa sobre un objeto (pág. 356)

fossil fuels / combustibles fósiles mezclas de depósitos ricos en hidrocarburos que se formaron a partir de restos de organismos (pág. 267)

frame of reference / marco de referencia un sistema de objetos que no se mueve con respecto a otro (pág. 328)

free fall / caída libre movimiento de un objeto hacia la Tierra por causa de la gravedad (pág. 343)

frequency / frecuencia cantidad de ciclos completos en una unidad de tiempo para producir un movimiento periódico (pág. 504)

frequency modulation (FM) / frecuencia modulada (FM) método de transmisión de una señal de radio en el que varía la frecuencia de la onda portadora mientras su amplitud permanece igual (pág. 541)

friction / fricción fuerza que se opone al movimiento de los objetos que se tocan a medida que cada uno de ellos se mueve con respecto al otro (pág. 359)

fulcrum / fulcro punto fijo alrededor del cual gira una palanca (pág. 428)

functional group / grupo funcional átomo o grupo de átomos que determina las propiedades de un compuesto orgánico (pág. 272)

fuse / fusible dispositivo que evita el sobrecalentamiento de un circuito por sobrecarga (pág. 612)

fusion / fusión una reacción nuclear en la que se combinan los núcleos de dos átomos para formar un núcleo más grande (pág. 315)

G

galvanometer / galvanómetro un aparato que utiliza un electroimán para medir pequeñas cantidades de corriente (pág. 638)

gamma ray / rayo gamma una forma penetrante de radiación que emite un núcleo inestable (pág. 294)

gas / gas estado de la materia en el que un material no tiene forma ni volumen definidos (pág. 70)

generator / generador un aparato que convierte la energía mecánica en energía eléctrica por el movimiento relativo de una bobina de alambre respecto de un campo magnético (pág. 643)

geology / geología estudio del origen, historia y estructura de la Tierra (pág. 4)

geothermal energy / energía geotérmica energía térmica existente debajo de la superficie de la Tierra (pág. 464)

gravitational force / fuerza gravitatoria una fuerza de atracción que actúa entre dos objetos cualesquiera (pág. 380)

gravitational potential energy / energía potencial gravitacional energía potencial que depende de la altura de un objeto por encima de un punto de referencia (pág. 449)

gravity / gravedad atracción entre dos objetos cualesquiera por efecto de sus masas (pág. 361)

ground state / estado basal estado en el que todos los electrones de un átomo tienen la mínima energía posible (pág. 118)

grounding / conexión a tierra la transferencia del exceso de carga a través de un conductor a Tierra (pág. 613)

group / grupo columna de elementos en una tabla periódica (pág. 131)

H

half-life / vida media tiempo que requiere la mitad de una muestra de un isótopo radiactivo para descomponerse (pág. 299)

halogens / halógenos los elementos del Grupo 7A de la tabla periódica (pág. 144)

heat / calor transferencia de energía térmica de un objeto a otro debido a la diferencia de temperatura (pág. 474)

heat engine / motor térmico todo artefacto que transforma la energía térmica en trabajo (pág. 483)

heat of fusion / calor de fusión la energía que debe absorber una sustancia para pasar del estado sólido al líquido (pág. 86)

heat of vaporization / calor de vaporización la energía que debe absorber una sustancia para pasar del estado líquido al gaseoso (pág. 88)

heat pump / bomba térmica dispositivo que utiliza el trabajo para transferir energía térmica de un área más fría a un área más cálida (pág. 490)

hertz (Hz) / hercios (Hz) unidad para medir la frecuencia que equivale a un ciclo por segundo (pág. 504)

heterogeneous mixture / mezcla heterogénea tipo de mezcla en la que sus partes son notoriamente diferentes unas de otras (pág. 41)

homogeneous mixture / mezcla homogénea tipo de mezcla en la que las sustancias están distribuidas en forma tan pareja que es difícil distinguir una de otra (pág. 42)

horsepower (hp) / caballo de potencia (hp) unidad de potencia que equivale aproximadamente a 746 vatios (pág. 416)

hydraulic system / sistema hidráulico dispositivo que utiliza la acción de un fluido presurizado sobre pistones de diferentes tamaños para aumentar la fuerza (pág. 395)

hydrocarbon / hidrocarburo compuesto orgánico que solamente contiene hidrógeno y carbono (pág. 264)

hydroelectric energy / energía hidroeléctrica energía que se obtiene a partir del agua en movimiento (pág. 463)

hydrogen fuel cell / pila de combustible de hidrógeno pila que genera electricidad a partir de una reacción controlada entre hidrógeno y oxígeno (pág. 608)

hypothesis / hipótesis una respuesta propuesta ante una pregunta (pág. 8)

I

ideal mechanical advantage (IMA) / ventaja mecánica ideal (VMI) ventaja mecánica de una máquina en ausencia de fricción (pág. 423)

image / imagen copia de un objeto formada por rayos de luz que se reflejan o refractan (pág. 547)

incandescent / incandescente descripción de un objeto lo suficientemente caliente como para brillar (pág. 558)

inclined plane / plano inclinado superficie inclinada a lo largo de la cual una fuerza mueve un objeto hacia una elevación diferente (pág. 431)

index of refraction / índice de refracción la relación entre la velocidad de la luz en un vacío y la velocidad de la luz en un medio (pág. 575)

indicator / indicador una sustancia que cambia de color en presencia de un ácido o una base (pág. 241)

induction / inducción transferencia de carga entre materiales, sin entrar en contacto (pág. 603)

inertia / inercia la tendencia de un objeto a resistir un cambio en su movimiento (pág. 364)

input arm / brazo de entrada distancia entre el fulcro en una palanca y la fuerza aplicada (pág. 428)

input distance / distancia de entrada distancia a través de la cual la fuerza aplicada actúa en una máquina (pág. 419)

input force / fuerza aplicada fuerza que se ejerce sobre una máquina (pág. 419)

instantaneous speed / rapidez instantánea velocidad a la que se mueve un objeto en un momento dado en el tiempo (pág. 334)

integrated circuit / circuito integrado delgada capa de silicio que contiene muchos componentes; microchip (pág. 622)

intensity / intensidad velocidad a la que fluye la energía de una onda a través de una determinada unidad de espacio (págs. 515, 538)

interference / interferencia la interacción de dos o más ondas que se combinan en una zona en común (pág. 510)

internal combustion engine / motor de combustión interna máquina térmica en la que el combustible se quema dentro de la máquina (pág. 487)

inverse proportion / proporción inversa la relación en la que el producto de dos variables es una constante cuando todas las demás variables permanecen constantes (pág. 23)

ion / ión un átomo o grupo de átomos que tiene carga positiva o negativa (pág. 159)

ionic bond / enlace iónico fuerza que mantiene unidos a cationes y aniones (pág. 160)

ionization / ionización proceso por el cual las moléculas neutrales ganan o pierden electrones (pág. 230)

iris / iris parte coloreada del frente del ojo que se expande y contrae para controlar la cantidad de luz que penetra en él (pág. 589)

isomers / isómeros compuestos orgánicos con la misma fórmula molecular pero con diferente fórmula estructural (pág. 265)

isotopes / isótopos átomos de un determinado elemento que posee diferentes cantidades de neutrones y diferentes cantidades de masa (pág. 112)

J

joule (J) / julio (J) unidad del trabajo de SI que equivale a 1 newton por metro (pág. 414)

Spanish Glossary

K

kinetic energy / energía cinética la energía que tiene un objeto debido a su movimiento (págs. 71, 447)

L

laser / láser un dispositivo que genera un haz de luz coherente (pág. 560)

law of conservation of charge / ley de la conservación de la carga ley que establece que la carga eléctrica total en un sistema aislado se mantiene constante; la carga eléctrica nunca se crea ni se destruye (pág. 602)

law of conservation of momentum / ley de la conservación del momento ley que establece que el momento total de un sistema no cambia si no hay fuerza neta que actúe sobre el sistema (pág. 376)

length / longitud la distancia en línea recta entre dos puntos (pág. 16)

lens / lente un objeto hecho con material transparente y delgado que tiene una o dos superficies curvas que pueden refractar luz (pág. 576)

lever / palanca una barra rígida que puede moverse libremente alrededor de un punto fijo (pág. 428)

lift / fuerza de elevación una fuerza hacia arriba creada por la diferencia de presión entre la parte superior y la parte inferior de un ala (pág. 396)

linear graph / gráfica lineal una gráfica en la que los datos mostrados forman una línea recta (pág. 347)

liquid / líquido el estado de la materia en el que un material tiene un volumen definido pero no una forma definida (pág. 69)

longitudinal wave / onda longitudinal una onda en la que la vibración del medio es paralela a la dirección en que viaja la onda (pág. 502)

loudness / volumen una respuesta física a la intensidad del sonido, modificada por factores físicos (pág. 515)

luminous / luminoso la descripción de un objeto que emite su propia luz (pág. 558)

M

machine / máquina un dispositivo que cambia una fuerza (pág. 417)

magnetic domain / dominio magnético una región que tiene muchos átomos con campos magnéticos alineados (pág. 632)

magnetic field / campo magnético un campo en una región del espacio que ejerce fuerzas magnéticas; un campo producido por imanes, por campos eléctricos variables o por cargas en movimiento (págs. 533, 631)

magnetic force / fuerza magnética la fuerza que un campo magnético ejerce sobre un imán, sobre un material ferromagnético o sobre una carga eléctrica en movimiento (pág. 630)

magnetic pole / polo magnético una región de un imán en donde la fuerza es mayor (pág. 630)

magnetosphere / magnetosfera el área que rodea la Tierra y que está bajo la influencia del campo magnético (pág. 632)

malleability / maleabilidad la capacidad que tiene un sólido de ser golpeado sin quebrarse (pág. 46)

manipulated variable / variable manipulada la variable que causa un cambio en otra variable (pág. 8)

mass / masa la cantidad de materia que tiene un objeto (pág. 16); medida de la inercia de un objeto que depende de la cantidad de materia que contiene el mismo (pág. 365)

mass number / número de masa la suma del número de protones y neutrones del núcleo de un átomo (pág. 110)

mechanical advantage / ventaja mecánica la cantidad de veces que una máquina aumenta la fuerza aplicada (pág. 421)

mechanical energy / energía mecánica la energía relacionada con el movimiento y la posición de objetos cotidianos (pág. 450)

mechanical wave / onda mecánica la perturbación en la materia que lleva energía de un lugar a otro (pág. 500)

medium / medio el material a través del cual viajan las ondas (pág. 500)

melting point / punto de fusión temperatura a la cual una sustancia cambia de sólida a líquida (pág. 47)

metals / metales elementos que son buenos conductores de calor y corriente eléctrica (pág. 135)

metallic bond / enlace metálico la atracción existente entre un catión metálico y los electrones compartidos que lo rodean (pág. 176)

metalloids / metaloides elementos con propiedades que están entre las de los metales y los no metales (pág. 136)

microscope / microscopio instrumento óptico que usa lentes para agrandar la imagen de objetos cercanos y muy pequeños (pág. 584)

mirage / espejismo imagen falsa o distorsionada (pág. 548)

model / modelo representación de un objeto o evento (pág. 10)

molarity / molaridad el número de moles de un soluto disuelto por litro de solución (pág. 239)

molar mass / masa molar masa de un mol de una sustancia (pág. 196)

mole / mol cantidad de una sustancia que contiene aproximadamente 6.02×10^{23} partículas de la sustancia (pág. 195)

molecule / molécula un grupo neutro de átomos, unidos entre sí por uno o más enlaces covalentes (pág. 166)

momentum / momento producto de la masa de un objeto y su velocidad (pág. 374)

monomer / monómero una pequeña molécula orgánica que se une con otros monómeros para formar un polímero (pág. 275)

N

nearsightedness / miopía una condición ocular que hace que los objetos distantes aparezcan borrosos (pág. 590)

net force / fuerza neta la fuerza total que actúa sobre un objeto después que todas las fuerzas se combinan (pág. 357)

network solid / sólido reticulado un sólido que tiene todos sus átomos unidos por enlaces covalentes (pág. 263)

neutralization / neutralización la reacción química entre un ácido y una base (pág. 244)

neutron / neutrón una partícula subatómica neutra que se encuentra en el núcleo de un átomo (pág. 109)

newton (N) / newton (N) la unidad de fuerza del SI que equivale a la fuerza que hace que 1 kilogramo de masa se acelere a razón de 1 metro por segundo cuadrado ($1 N = 1 kg \cdot m/s^2$) (pág. 357)

noble gases / gases nobles elementos en el Grupo 8A de la tabla periódica (pág. 145)

node / nodo un punto de una onda que no presenta desplazamiento con respecto a la posición de reposo (pág. 512)

nonlinear graph / gráfica no lineal una gráfica en que los datos trazados o mostrados forman una línea curva (pág. 348)

nonmetals / no metales elementos que son malos conductores del calor y la corriente eléctrica (pág. 136)

nonrenewable energy resource / recurso energético no renovable una fuente de energía que existe en cantidades limitadas y que una vez utilizada no puede ser reemplazada salvo con el transcurso de millones de años (pág. 462)

nuclear energy / energía nuclear la energía que se encuentra almacenada en los núcleos atómicos (pág. 452)

nuclear radiation / radiación nuclear partículas y ondas electromagnéticas con carga emitidas desde el núcleo de los radioisótopos (pág. 293)

nucleic acid / ácido nucleico un polímero grande con nitrógeno que se encuentra principalmente en el núcleo de las células (pág. 279)

nucleus / núcleo masa densa con carga positiva que se encuentra ubicada en el centro de un átomo (pág. 105)

O

observation / observación información que se obtiene a través de los sentidos (pág. 8)

Ohm's law / ley de Ohm la relación entre voltaje, corriente y resistencia $V = IR$ (pág. 607)

opaque / opaco la descripción de un material que absorbe o refleja toda la luz que incide sobre él de modo que no puede verse nada a través del mismo (pág. 547)

orbital / orbital región de espacio alrededor del núcleo en donde es posible encontrar un electrón (pág. 117)

organic compounds / compuestos orgánicos compuestos que contienen carbón e hidrógeno, a menudo se combinan con algunos otros elementos tales como el oxígeno o nitrógeno (pág. 262)

output arm / brazo de salida la distancia entre el fulcro en una palanca y la fuerza desarrollada (pág. 428)

output distance / distancia de salida distancia a través de la cual actúa una fuerza desarrollada de una máquina (pág. 420)

output force / fuerza desarrollada fuerza que ejerce una máquina (pág. 420)

oxidation-reduction (redox) reaction / reacción de oxidación-reducción (redox) una reacción química en la que hay transferencia de electrones entre los reactantes (pág. 204)

P

parallel circuit / circuito en paralelo un circuito eléctrico con dos o más pasos a través de los que puede fluir carga (pág. 610)

pascal (Pa) / pascal (Pa) unidad de presión del SI que equivale a 1 newton por metro cuadrado (N/m^2) (pág. 391)

period / período hilera en una tabla periódica de elementos (pág. 131); el tiempo que se necesita para tener un ciclo completo de movimiento periódico (pág. 504)

periodic law / ley periódica el patrón de repetición de propiedades que muestran los elementos en la tabla periódica (pág. 131)

periodic motion / movimiento periódico todo movimiento que se repite a intervalos regulares (pág. 504)

periodic table / tabla periódica una organización de elementos en columnas basada en una serie de propiedades que se repiten de hilera en hilera (pág. 127)

pH / pH una medida de la concentración del ión de hidronio que tiene una solución (pág. 247)

Spanish Glossary

phase change / cambio de fase un cambio físico reversible que ocurre cuando una sustancia cambia de un estado de materia a otro (pág. 84)

phosphor / fósforo material sólido que emite luz por fluorescencia (pág. 559)

photoelectric effect / efecto fotoeléctrico la emisión de electrones de un metal causada por la luz que llega hasta un metal (pág. 537)

photon / fotón paquete de energía electromagnética (pág. 537)

photosynthesis / fotosíntesis proceso en que las plantas combinan químicamente dióxido de carbono y agua para formar carbohidratos, proceso que requiere luz y clorofila (pág. 282)

physical change / cambio físico un cambio que ocurre cuando algunas propiedades de un material cambian, pero las sustancias del material permanecen constantes (pág. 51)

physical property / propiedad física toda característica de un material que se puede observar o medir sin cambiar la composición de las sustancias del material (pág. 45)

physics / física el estudio de materia y energía y las interacciones entre las dos a través de fuerzas y movimiento (pág. 4)

pigment / pigmento un material que absorbe selectivamente ciertos colores de luz y refleja otros colores (pág. 553)

pitch / tono frecuencia de un sonido como lo percibe quien lo escucha (pág. 515)

plane mirror / espejo plano espejo con superficie plana (pág. 571)

plasma / plasma el estado de la materia en el que los átomos han sido despojados de sus electrones (pág. 315)

polar covalent bond / enlace polar covalente enlace covalente en el que los electrones no se comparten por igual (pág. 168)

polarized light / luz polarizada tipo de luz que tiene luz con ondas que vibran en un solo plano (pág. 548)

polyatomic ion / ión poliatómico un grupo de átomos con enlaces covalentes de átomos que tiene carga positiva o negativa y actúa como unidad (pág. 172)

polymer / polímero una molécula de gran tamaño que se forma cuando muchas moléculas pequeñas están unidas entre sí por enlaces covalentes (pág. 275)

potential difference / diferencia potencial voltaje, es decir, la diferencia de energía eléctrica potencial entre dos puntos de un campo eléctrico (pág. 606)

potential energy / energía potencial energía que se almacena como consecuencia de la posición o forma (pág. 448)

power / potencia tasa de realizar trabajo (pág. 414)

precipitate / precipitado un sólido que se forma y se separa de una mezcla líquida (pág. 57)

precision / precisión medida de cuán exacta es una medición (pág. 19)

pressure / presión resultado de una fuerza distribuida sobre un área (págs. 75, 390)

primary colors / colores primarios tres colores específicos que se pueden combinar en intensidades variadas para crear millones de colores (pág. 552)

products / productos sustancias nuevas que se forman como consecuencia de una reacción química (pág. 192)

projectile motion / movimiento de proyectil la trayectoria curvada de un objeto en caída libre después de haber recibido una velocidad horizontal inicial (pág. 362)

protein / proteína polímero grande que se forma cuando los aminoácidos se unen entre sí (pág. 280)

proton / protón una partícula subatómica con carga positiva que se encuentra en el núcleo de un átomo (pág. 108)

pulley / polea una máquina simple con una cuerda que pasa por el canal de una rueda (pág. 432)

pupil / pupila abertura que permite la entrada de luz en el ojo (pág. 589)

pure substance / sustancia pura material que siempre tiene exactamente la misma composición; elemento o compuesto (pág. 39)

Q

quark / quark partícula subatómica que según las teorías se encuentra entre las unidades básicas de la materia (pág. 305)

R

radiation / radiación transferencia de energía por ondas que se mueven en el espacio (pág. 481)

radioactivity / radiactividad proceso en el que un núcleo atómico inestable emite partículas con carga y energía (pág. 292)

radioisotope / radioisótopo isótopo con núcleo inestable (pág. 292)

rarefaction / rarefacción área de una onda longitudinal en que las partículas del medio se esparcen (pág. 502)

ray diagram / diagrama de rayo diagrama que muestra cómo los rayos de luz cambian de dirección cuando chocan contra los espejos y pasan a través de los lentes (pág. 570)

reactant / reactante una sustancia que sufre cambios durante una reacción química (pág. 192)

reaction rate / velocidad de reacción velocidad con que los reactantes se transforman en productos en un tiempo determinado (pág. 212)

reactivity / reactividad propiedad que describe con qué facilidad una sustancia se combina químicamente con otras sustancias (pág. 55)

real image / imagen real copia de un objeto que se forma en el punto en que los rayos de luz se encuentran (pág. 572)

reflecting telescope / telescopio reflector telescopio que utiliza espejos y lentes convexas para reunir y enfocar luz (pág. 581)

reflection / reflexión la interacción que se produce cuando una onda rebota contra una superficie que no puede atravesar (pág. 508)

refracting telescope / telescopio refractor telescopio que usa sólo lentes para reunir y enfocar luz (pág. 581)

refraction / refracción la curva de una onda al entrar en ángulo en un nuevo medio (pág. 508)

refrigerant / refrigerante fluido que se vaporiza y se condensa dentro de la tubería de una bomba de calor (pág. 490)

regular reflection / reflexión regular reflexión que se produce cuando ondas de luz paralelas chocan contra una superficie y todas se reflejan en la misma dirección (pág. 547)

relative motion / movimiento relativo movimiento en relación al marco de referencia (pág. 329)

renewable energy resource / recurso renovable de energía fuente de energía que se puede reemplazar en períodos relativamente cortos (pág. 463)

resistance / resistencia oposición al flujo de cargas eléctricas en un material (pág. 605)

resonance / resonancia la respuesta de una onda estacionaria a otra onda de la misma frecuencia, con gran incremento de amplitud de la onda estacionaria (pág. 521)

responding variable / variable respuesta variable que cambia en respuesta a un cambio en la variable manipulada (pág. 8)

resultant vector / vector resultante la suma vectorial de dos o más vectores (pág. 331)

retina / retina superficie interna de la parte posterior del ojo, que contiene terminales nerviosas sensibles a la luz (pág. 589)

reversible reaction / reacción reversible una reacción química en la que la conversión de reactantes en productos y la conversión de productos en reactantes se produce al mismo tiempo (pág. 217)

rods / bastoncillos neuronas sensibles a la luz en la retina que detectan luz de baja intensidad y distinguen blanco, negro y gris (pág. 589)

rolling friction / fricción de rodamiento fuerza de fricción que actúa sobre objetos rodantes y que se produce debido al cambio de forma en el punto de contacto de rodamiento (pág. 360)

S

salt / sal compuesto iónico que se forma cuando un ácido reacciona con una base (pág. 244)

saturated hydrocarbon / hidrocarburo saturado un hidrocarburo que tiene todos sus enlaces simples (pág. 264)

saturated solution / solución saturada una solución que contiene la cantidad de soluto que el solvente puede contener a una cierta temperatura (pág. 236)

scattering / dispersión proceso en el que la luz cambia de dirección cuando atraviesa un medio (pág. 549)

science / ciencia sistema de conocimientos sobre el mundo natural y los métodos que se usan para encontrar esos conocimientos (pág. 3)

scientific law / ley científica una afirmación que resume un patrón que se encuentra en la naturaleza (pág. 9)

scientific method / método científico un plan organizado que se utiliza para recoger, organizar y transmitir información (pág. 7)

scientific notation / notación científica una forma de expresar un valor como el producto de un número entre 1 y 10 y una potencia de 10 (pág. 14)

scientific theory / teoría científica una explicación bien comprobada que corresponde a un conjunto de observaciones o resultados experimentales (pág. 9)

screw / tornillo plano inclinado envuelto alrededor de un cilindro (pág. 431)

secondary color / color secundario color nuevo que resulta cuando se combinan dos colores primarios (pág. 552)

semiconductor / semiconductor un sólido cristalino que conduce corriente eléctrica sólo bajo ciertas condiciones (pág. 621)

series circuit / circuito en serie circuito eléctrico con un sólo trayecto a través del cual puede fluir la carga (pág. 610)

significant figures / cifras significativas todos los dígitos que se miden directamente en una medición, más el último dígito, que es aproximado (pág. 19)

single-replacement reaction / reacción de sustitución simple una reacción química en la que un elemento toma el lugar de otro en un compuesto (pág. 202)

sliding friction / fricción de deslizamiento una fuerza de fricción que se opone al movimiento de un objeto a medida que se desliza sobre una superficie (pág. 359)

Spanish Glossary

slope / pendiente línea inclinada que equivale a la proporción de un cambio vertical con el correspondiente cambio horizontal (págs. 23, 334)

solar energy / energía solar luz solar que se convierte en energía utilizable (pág. 464)

solenoid / solenoide una bobina de alambre conductor que produce un campo magnético (pág. 637)

solid / sólido estado de la materia en el que los materiales tienen una forma definida y un volumen definido (pág. 69)

solubility / solubilidad cantidad máxima de soluto que se disuelve normalmente en una cierta cantidad de solvente a cierta temperatura (pág. 235)

solute / soluto una sustancia cuyas partículas se disuelven en una solución (pág. 229)

solution / solución una mezcla que se forma cuando se disuelven sustancias y forman una mezcla homogénea (pág. 42)

solvent / solvente una sustancia en la que se disuelve un soluto (pág. 229)

sonar / sonar técnica que sirve para determinar la distancia a un objeto bajo el agua (pág. 516)

sound wave / onda sonora onda longitudinal que consiste en compresiones y rarefacciones y que viaja a través de un medio (pág. 514)

specific heat / calor específico cantidad de calor que se necesita para elevar la temperatura de un gramo de material un grado Celsius (pág. 476)

speed / rapidez proporción de la distancia a que se mueve un objeto con respecto a la cantidad de tiempo en que se mueve el objeto (pág. 332)

standing wave / onda estacionaria onda que parece quedarse en un lugar y no moverse a través de un medio (pág. 512)

static electricity / electricidad estática estudio del comportamiento de las cargas eléctricas y de la manera en que la carga se transfiere entre objetos (pág. 602)

static friction / fricción estática fuerza de fricción que actúa sobre los objetos que no se mueven (pág. 359)

strong nuclear force / fuerza nuclear fuerte una fuerza potente de atracción que une protones y neutrones en el núcleo (págs. 308, 379)

sublimation / sublimación cambio de fase en que una sustancia cambia de estado sólido a gaseoso o vapor sin pasar por el estado líquido primero (pág. 91)

substance / sustancia materia que siempre tiene exactamente la misma composición; elemento o compuesto (pág. 39)

substituted hydrocarbon / hidrocarburo sustituido hidrocarburo en el que uno o más átomos de hidrógeno han sido reemplazados o sustituidos (pág. 272)

superconductor / superconductor un material con resistencia casi cero al ser enfriado a temperaturas bajas (pág. 605)

supersaturated solution / solución supersaturada una solución que contiene más cantidad de soluto que el solvente puede retener normalmente a una determinada temperatura (pág. 236)

surface wave / onda superficial onda que viaja a lo largo de una superficie y que separa dos medios (pág. 503)

suspension / suspensión una mezcla heterogénea que se separa con el tiempo en capas (pág. 43)

synthesis reaction / reacción de síntesis reacción química en la que dos o más sustancias reaccionan para formar una sola sustancia (pág. 200)

T

technology / tecnología uso del conocimiento científico para resolver problemas prácticos (pág. 3)

telescope / telescopio un instrumento óptico que usa lentes (o lentes y espejos) para recoger y enfocar luz desde objetos lejanos (pág. 580)

temperature / temperatura es una medición de cuán caliente o frío está un objeto si se lo compara con un punto de referencia (pág. 475)

terminal velocity / velocidad terminal velocidad constante de un objeto en caída cuando la fuerza de resistencia del aire es igual a la fuerza de gravedad (pág. 361)

thermal conductor / conductor térmico un material que conduce bien la energía térmica (pág. 480)

thermal energy / energía térmica la energía potencial y cinética total relacionada con el movimiento de todas las partículas de un objeto (pág. 451)

thermal expansion / expansión térmica aumento de volumen de un material cuando incrementa su temperatura (pág. 476)

thermal insulator / aislante térmico material que no conduce bien la energía térmica (pág. 480)

thermodynamics / termodinámica estudio de las conversiones entre energía térmica y otras formas de energía (pág. 482)

thermogram / termograma un dibujo o imagen con código de colores que utiliza variaciones en la radiación infrarroja y que sirve para mostrar los cambios en la temperatura (pág. 543)

thermometer / termómetro un instrumento que sirve para medir la temperatura (pág. 20)

total internal reflection / reflexión interna total la reflexión completa de un rayo de luz que regresa a su medio original cuando el ángulo de incidencia es mayor que el ángulo crítico de refracción (pág. 578)

transformer / transformador un dispositivo que aumenta o disminuye el voltaje de dos circuitos CA conectados (pág. 644)

transistor / transistor un componente en estado sólido que tiene tres capas de material semiconductor y que sirve para encender o apagar corriente o para incrementar la fuerza de señales electrónicas (pág. 621)

transition metals / metales de transición elementos que forman un puente entre los elementos que se encuentran en el lado izquierdo y derecho de la tabla periódica (pág. 136)

translucent / translúcido descripción de un material que dispersa luz que pasa a través del mismo (pág. 547)

transmutation / transmutación la conversión de un elemento en otro por medio de una reacción nuclear (pág. 303)

transparent / transparente descripción de un material que deja pasar la mayor parte de la luz que incide sobre él (pág. 546)

transuranium elements / elementos del grupo transuranio elementos que tienen números atómicos mayores que 92 (pág. 304)

transverse wave / onda transversal onda que hace vibrar a un medio en ángulos rectos en la dirección en que viaja la onda (pág. 50)

trough / valle punto más bajo de una onda transversal (pág. 501)

turbine / turbina un dispositivo con paletas en forma de ventilador que giran cuando son impulsadas, por ejemplo, por agua o vapor (pág. 646)

U

unsaturated hydrocarbon / hidrocarburo no saturado hidrocarburo que contiene uno o más enlaces dobles o triples (pág. 265)

unsaturated solution / solución no saturada una solución en que puede disolverse más soluto a una determinada temperatura (pág. 236)

V

valence electron / electrón de valencia electrón que se encuentra en el nivel energético más alto ocupado que tiene un átomo (pág. 139)

vaporization / vaporización cambio de fase en que una sustancia cambia de estado líquido a gaseoso (pág. 88)

vapor pressure / presión de vapor presión que producen las colisiones o choques de partículas en un vapor dentro de las paredes de un contenedor (pág. 89)

vector / vector una cantidad que tiene una dirección asociada con la misma (pág. 330)

velocity / velocidad la rapidez y la dirección en la que se mueve un objeto y se mide según un punto de referencia (pág. 336)

virtual image / imagen virtual una copia de un objeto que se forma en el punto desde donde parece venir la luz (pág. 571)

viscosity / viscosidad la tendencia que tiene un líquido a dejar de fluir; resistencia a fluir (pág. 45)

vitamin / vitamina un compuesto orgánico que no producen los organismos vivos pero lo necesitan en pequeñas cantidades (pág. 284)

voltage / voltaje diferencia potencial, la diferencia de energía eléctrica potencial entre dos puntos en un campo eléctrico (pág. 606)

volume / volumen la cantidad de espacio que ocupa un objeto (pág. 16)

W

waste heat / calor perdido energía térmica descargada en un área a una temperatura más baja que no se convierte en trabajo útil (pág. 483)

watt (W) / vatio (W) unidad de potencia del SI que equivale a un julio por segundo (pág. 415)

wavelength / longitud de onda la distancia entre un punto de la onda y el mismo punto en el siguiente ciclo de la onda (pág. 505)

weak nuclear force / fuerza nuclear débil fuerza de atracción potente que actúa sobre un alcance corto o a corta distancia (pág. 380)

wedge / cuña objeto en forma de V que tiene lados en forma de dos planos inclinados, el uno hacia el otro (pág. 431)

weight / peso fuerza de gravedad que actúa sobre un objeto (pág. 367)

wheel and axle / rueda y eje una máquina simple que está formada por dos discos o cilindros rígidamente unidos y cada uno tiene un radio diferente (pág. 430)

work / trabajo el producto de la distancia y fuerza en la dirección en que se mueve un objeto (pág. 412)

work input / trabajo de entrada trabajo que realiza una máquina cuando la fuerza aplicada actúa a través de la distancia de entrada (pág. 419)

work output / trabajo de salida trabajo que realiza una máquina cuando la fuerza desarrollada actúa a través de la distancia de salida (pág. 420)

Index

The page on which a term is defined is indicated in **boldface** type.

Index

Index

fluid, 360, 426
  heat produced by, 474
  mechanical advantage and,
    422–423, 424
  mechanical efficiency and, 425
  rolling, 360
  static, 359
  sliding, 359
Frisch, Otto, 309
frost, 91, 249, 608
fulcrum, **428**
Fulton, Robert, 422
functional groups, **272**–274
fuse, **612**
fusion, **315**, 459

galaxies, 452
Galilei, Galileo, 363
gallium, 129
galvanometers, **638**
gamma decay, 293, 294–296
gamma particles, 294–296
gamma rays, **294**, 297, 307, 540, 543, 545
gas(es), **70,** 135
  behavior of, 72–73, 75–83
  as indicator of chemical change, 57
  kinetic theory and, 72, 73, 479
  natural, 266, 267, 462
  noble (Group 8A), 145, 158, 167
  radon, 296
  thermal conduction in, 479
gas laser, 560–561
gas law(s), 75–83
  Boyle's law, 78, 79, 80
  Charles's law, 78, 80
  combined, 80–81
gas pressure, 76
  factors affecting, 76–77
gas welding, 178
gasoline, 267, 273
gears
  bicycle, 436–437
  in nanotechnology, 106
Geiger counters, 297
gemstones, 575
  synthetic ruby, 163
generators, electric, **643**–644, 648–649
  AC generators, 643–644
  DC generators, 644
  energy sources for, 646
geology, **4**
geothermal energy, **464**
germanium, 129, 136, 142
glare, 549
glass, 569
  manufacturing, 137
  shatterproof, 142
global positioning system (GPS), 340–341
glucose, tagged, 306
glycine, 280
gold, 39, 179
  alloys of, 178
  jewelry, 46, 178
  melting and boiling points, 47
  reactivity, 135
  symbol for, 40
Goldberg, Rube, 427
gold foil experiment, 104
Go Online, 672

NSTA SciLinks (at www.SciLinks.org),
  5, 23, 42, 55, 77, 88, 104, 109, 116,
  128, 131, 159, 167, 174, 193, 200,
  205, 213, 217, 232, 242, 247, 266,
  276, 300, 310, 329, 333, 345, 358,
  368, 373, 381, 391, 396, 403, 413,
  418, 422, 429, 449, 455, 477, 482,
  501, 507, 510, 533, 551, 572, 605,
  611, 638, 644
PlanetDiary (at PHSchool.com) 15,
  294
Science News articles (at
  PHSchool.com), 9, 50, 73, 140, 180,
  198, 283, 464, 490, 517, 561, 581
PHSchool.com, 27, 30, 35, 59, 64, 93,
  96, 122, 154, 185, 188, 224, 258, 281,
  288, 302, 317, 320, 325, 349, 352,
  383, 386, 408, 439, 442, 467, 470,
  496, 513, 528, 566, 579, 593, 596,
  608, 626, 649, 652
gramophone, 518
graph(s), 22, 23–24, 671
  bar, 24, 671
  circle, 24, 671
  distance-time, 334, 348
  line, 23, 347, 671
  of motion, 334, 346–348
  nonlinear, 348
  speed-time, 347
graphite, 263
gravitation, law of universal, 9, 380–382
gravitational force, **380**
  compared to electric force, 601
gravitational potential energy, **449,** 456
gravity, **361**–362, 380–382
  acceleration and, 343, 361
  dependence on mass and distance, 381
  falling objects and, 360–361
Greek models of atoms, ancient, 100
ground state, of atoms, **118**
grounding, **613**
groundwater, 53
groups, in periodic table, **131**

Hahn, Otto, 309, 313
half-life, **299**–300, 301, 306, 312
Hall, Charles, 178
halocarbons, 272, 273
halogens (Group 7A), **144**
  molecules of, 166
hardness, 47
hearing, 517
heart, 251
heat, **474,** 479–481
  conduction, 479–480
  convection, 480–481
  conversions of. See thermodynamics.
  flow of, 474, 482, 490, 492
  measuring changes in, 478
  uses of, 486–492
  waste, 483
  work and, 474
heat conductors, comparing 46
heat engines, 483, 486–488
  external combustion engine, 486
  hybrid cars, 487–488
  internal combustion engine, 487

heat exchanger, 271
heating systems, 489–490
heat of fusion, **86**
heat of solution, **232**
heat of vaporization, **88**
heat pumps, 490
heat sink, 615
heavy water, 112
helium, 70, 72, 145
hemoglobin, 147, 218, 268, 280
Héroult, Paul, 178
Herschel, William, 539, 540
hertz (Hz), **504**
heterogeneous mixture, **41**
history. See Science and History.
HIV testing, 253
homogeneous mixture, **42**
Hoover Dam, 463
horsepower, **416**
hot-air balloons, 82–83
hot-water heating, 489
hybrid automobiles, 488
hydraulic systems, **395**
hydrazine, 194
hydrocarbons, **264**–269
  fossil fuels, 267–271, 281, 462, 466
  saturated, 264
  substituted, 272–274
  unsaturated, 266
hydrochloric acid, 199, 240, 241, 245, 254
hydroelectric energy, **463**
hydrogen
  atomic structure in, 110, 131
  as essential element, 146, 147
  as fuel, 139, 464
  isotopes of, 112, 315
  molecular models, 166
  in periodic table, 139
  melting and boiling points, 47
  reaction with chlorine, 168
hydrogen bonding, 169
hydrogen carbonate, 251
hydrogen chloride, 168, 230, 241, 248
hydrogen fuel cell, 608
hydronium ions, 241, 245, 246
hydroxide ions, 248, 273
hypothesis, **8**–9

icebergs, 84
ideal mechanical advantage (IMA),
  423, 425
  of inclined plane, 430
  of lever, 428
  of pulleys, 432
  of screws, 430
  of wedges, 430
  of wheel and axle, 430
image(s), **547**
  real, 572
  virtual, 571, 573, 576
incandescent light, **558,** 559
incidence, angle of, 570
incident ray of light, 575
inclined plane, 427, 430, **431**
incomplete combustion, 268
index of refraction, 574–**575**
indicators, **241,** 243, 254–255

induction, **603**
  electromagnetic, 642
Industrial Revolution, innovations during, 422–423
inertia, **364**–365, 381, 382
  mass and, 369
infrared radiation, 540, 543, 556–557
inner ear, 517
input arm, of lever, **428**
input distance, **419**
input force, **419**
instantaneous acceleration, 348
instantaneous speed, **334**
insulators
  electrical, **605**
  thermal, **480**
integrated circuits, 183, **622**
intensity
  of electromagnetic waves, **538**
  sound, **515**
interference, **510**–511
internal combustion engine, **487**
International Union of Pure and Applied
  Chemistry (IUPAC), 170
Internet links, *See* Go Online.
inverse proportion, **23**–24
iodine, 36, 144, 147
  molecules of, 166
iodine-131, 299, 306
ionic bonds, 159, **160**–164
  electron configurations and, 158
  electron transfer and, 159
  formation of, 160–161
  ionization energy and, 161
ionic compounds, 161–164, 171–174
  binary, 171
  dissociation of, 229
  writing formulas for, 173, 174
ionization, **230**
  and lightning, 603
  of molecular compounds, 230
  by nuclear radiation, 296
ionization energy, 161
ions, **159**, 160
  formation of, 159–160
  hydronium, 241, 245, 246
  hydroxide, 248, 273
  metal, 172, 605
  names of, 171–173
  polyatomic, 172, 173
  size of, 160
iris, **589**
iron, 19, 58, 110
  as essential element, 147
  as ferromagnetic material, 633
  rusting of, 142
  in steel, 180
isobutane, 265
isomers, **265**
isotopes, **112**
  atomic mass and, 134
  of chlorine, 134
  radioisotopes, 293
Issues in Science, 59, 281, 302, 513, 579, 608

Joule, James Prescott, **414**, 482
joule (J), **414**, 476
journals, scientific, 25

karats, and purity of gold, 178
Keck telescopes, 580
Kelvin (K) scale, 20, 475
  gas laws and, 78, 80
kilometers (km), 329
kilopascal (kPa), 75
kilowatt-hours, 612
kilowatts, 611
kinetic energy, 6, **71**, **447**–448, 456–457
  in crystal lattices, 164
  temperature and, 475
kinetic theory, **71**
  of gases, 73
  of matter, 9
knowledge, scientific, 3
krypton, 145, 561

laboratory balance, 675
labs. *See* Contents, xii–xv.
Land, Edwin H., 583
Landsteiner, Karl, 252
lanthanide series, 136
lapis lazuli, 555
laser, **560**–561
laser surgery, 591
latitude and longitude system, 339
lattice
  crystal, 162–163, 164
  metal, 177
lauric acid, 92
Lavoisier, Antoine, 126, 196
laws, scientific, 9
lead, 142
  compounds of, 203
  dangers of, 148
Le Châtelier, Henri-Louis, 218, 266
Le Châtelier's principle, 218–219
LEDs. *See* light-emitting diodes.
length, **16**
lens(es), 574–**576**, 577–578
  concave, 576
  convex, 576–577
  of eye, 589, 591
levers, 427, **428**–429
Leyster, Judith, 557
Libby, W. F., 313
life science, 4
lift, **396**–397, 398–399
light, 546–549. *See* also color.
  bulbs, 145, 176, 558
  coherent, 560
  energy levels and, 116
  fluorescent, 559
  incandescent, 558, 559
  incident ray of, 575
  index of refraction, 574–575
  laser, 560–561
  neon lights, 145, 561
  polarization of, 548–49
  reflection of, 135, 547
  refraction of, 548
  scattering of, 43, 44, 549
  sodium-vapor, 562
  speed of, 14, 15, 310, 459, 534, 574
  tungsten-halogen, 562
  visible, 452, 540, 543
light-emitting diodes (LEDs), 129, 183, 621
lighthouses, 170, 577
light microscopes, 584

lightning, 452, 600, 603
lime (quicklime), 170, 204
  in glass-making, 137
limestone, 141, 270
  reaction with hydrochloric acid, 199
line, slope of, 334
linear graphs, 23, **347**
Lippershey, Hans, 581
liquid(s), **69**, 135
  behavior of, 73
  conduction in, 479
  kinetic theory and, 73
  viscosity of, 45
liquid crystal display (LCD), 620
lithium, 140
  atomic structure and, 118, 131
litmus paper, 241, 243
longitude, 339
longitudinal waves, **502**, 505, 507
lost wax casting, 49
loudness, **515**
loudspeakers, 518–519, 639
Lowell, Francis, 422
luminous, **558**
lungs, 77, 251
lye, 240, 242

McCormick, Cyrus, 423
Machines, **417**
  compound, 435
  efficiency of, 425–426
  inclined plane, 427, 430
  levers, 427, 428–429
  mechanical advantage, 421–424, 438–439
  pulley, 427, 432–434
  screw, 427, 431
  simple, 427–433
  wedge, 427, 431
  wheel and axle, 427, 430
  work and, 417–420
macula, 591
magnesium, 135, 138, 141
  alloys of, 181
  electron dot diagram, 166
  as essential element, 146
  reaction with oxygen, 101
magnesium chloride, 161, 231
magnetic resonance imaging (MRI), 640–641
magnetism, 628–653
  Earth's magnetic field, 632
  electromagnets, 637–638
magnetic domains, **632**–633
magnetic materials, 632–633
magnetic field, **533**, **631**–632, 637
magnetic forces, 379, **630**
magnetic poles, **630**
magnetite, 630
magnetophone, 518
magnetosphere, **632**
malleability, **46**, 135–137
manipulated variable, **8**, 23
Marsden, Ernest, 104
Mars, 2
mass, **16**, **365**
  compared to weight, 368–369
  conservation of, 191, 193

Index

Index

Index

Acknowledgments

Staff Credits

The people who made up the Prentice Hall Physical Science: Concepts in Action team—representing design services, editorial, editorial services, market research, marketing services, education technology, production services, project office, and publishing processes—are listed below. Bold type denotes the core team members.

Leann Davis Alspaugh, Neil Benjamin, **Barbara Bertell,** Suzanne Biron, Diane Braff, Kristen Cetrulo Braghi, Kenneth Chang, Jonathan D. Cheney, **Todd Christy,** Bob Craton, Kathleen J. Dempsey, **Frederick Fellows,** Jonathan Fisher, Kathryn Fobert, Paul Gagnon, Julia Gecha, Robert Graham, Ellen Welch Granter, Susan Hutchinson, **Judie Jozokos,** Kelly Kelliher, Dotti Marshall, Tim McDonald, Terri Mitchell, **Jen Paley, Caroline M. Power,** Siri Schwartzman, Malti Sharma, Emily Soltanoff, Jennifer Teece

Additional Credits

Ann Bekebrede, Frances Jenkins, Matt Walker

[DK] The DK Designs team who contributed to Prentice Hall Physical Science: Concepts in Action were as follows: Samantha Borland, Marian Broderick, Carole Curcie, Richard Czapnik, Nigel Duffield, Cynthia Frazer, James A. Hall, Rose Horridge, Heather Jones, Anthony Limerick, David Lloyd, Marie Osborn, Leyla Ostovar, Ralph Pitchford, Pamela Shiels, Andrew Szudek

Illustration

Leann Davis Alspaugh: 223; DK Picture Library: 487, 517, 581, 584, 621, 662; Paul Gagnon: 4; Gene Givan: 234, 272, 289; Ellen Welch Granter: 16, 17, 22b, 23, 24b, 92, 134b, 150, 208l, 208r, 215, 221, 469, 470, 542, 543, 558, 559, 563, 564, 566, 567r, 775; Graph/fix: Bruce Cowie: 130b, 358, 361, 396, 413, 418, 431, 480, 481, 482, 491b, 512, 571; J/B Woolsey Associates: 131, 132–133, 134t, 140, 141, 142, 143, 144, 145, 153, 155, 161t; George Kelvin: 259, 343, 601, 605, 606, 609, 632, 633, 636, 638, 639, 643, 647; George Ladas: 336, 337, 343; Matt Mayerchak: 2, 7, 14, 22t, 100t, 108, 113, 126, 130t, 139, 152, 158, 165, 170, 176, 186, 192, 199, 206, 212, 216, 222, 292, 298, 303, 308t, 318, 356, 363, 372, 378, 384, 390, 394, 400t, 406r, 412t, 417, 421t, 427, 440, 446, 453, 462, 468, 474, 479, 486t, 494, 500, 504t, 508, 514t, 526, 570t, 574, 580, 588, 594; Morgan-Cain & Associates: 20, 29, 30, 31, 65, 85b, 88, 97, 123l, 123r, 127, 159t, 159b, 160, 161b, 162, 164, 166t, 166b, 168t, 168b, 169, 171, 172t, 172b, 173, 175, 177, 187, 188l, 188r, 224, 225, 229, 230, 231, 237, 263, 264, 294–295, 296, 299t, 308l, 309, 310, 311, 319, 320, 321, 359, 368, 376, 380, 381, 382, 385, 387, 391, 395b, 397, 400b, 401, 406l, 407, 408, 409, 419, 428, 441, 442, 443l, 471, 475t, 475b, 478, 486b, 489, 490, 492, 496, 497, 501, 502, 503, 504b, 505, 507, 509t, 511, 516, 527, 528, 529, 570l, 572bl, 572br, 573tl, 573tr, 575t, 576l, 576r, 577t, 577m, 577b, 578, 584b, 585, 589, 590, 592, 595, 596l, 596r, 597, 656, 657, 663, 665, 666, 671, 673; Jen Paley: 24t, 26, 28, 38, 41, 42, 45, 47, 54, 60, 62, 64, 68, 71, 72t, 75, 78l, 84, 94, 96, 109, 112, 117, 119, 120, 154, 167, 184, 189, 197, 293, 299b, 357, 377, 383, 386, 392, 395t, 405, 421b, 433, 438, 439, 443r, 463, 476, 479b, 491t, 493, 509b, 514b, 515, 532, 539, 546, 550, 567l, 575b, 663ml, 663tr, 663mr, 668tl, 668bl, 668mr, 668br; Precision Graphics: 44, 46, 69, 70, 72, 77, 78r, 89, 95, 100b, 102, 103, 104, 121, 122, 193, 194, 207, 217, 230, 258, 262, 264, 265, 266, 267, 273, 274, 276, 279, 282, 331, 430, 432, 533, 534, 536, 537, 538, 540, 541, 548; www.TrevorJohnston.com: 8, 85t

Cover design Maria Keogh/Kokopelli Design Studio, Inc.;

Cover photo Tom Sanders/Image State

Photo research Paula Wehde

Dorling Kindersley picture research done in London, England by Cynthia Frazer and Marie Osborn; Dorling Kindersley illustrations done by Richard Bonson, KJA. Artists.com, and Martin Sanders in London, England

Photographs

Every effort has been made to secure permission and provide appropriate credit for photographic material. The publisher deeply regrets any omission and pledges to correct errors called to its attention in subsequent editions.

Unless otherwise acknowledged, all photographs are the property of Pearson Education, Inc.

Photo locators denoted as follows: Top (T), Center (C), Bottom (B), Left (L), Right (R), Background (Bkgd)

i, ii, Tom Sanders; **iv** (B) ©Fukuhara Inc./Corbis; **vi** (TL) Photo Researchers, Inc.; **vii** (B) Alain Nogues/Corbis; **viii** (B) Donald Miralle/Staff/Getty Images; **x** (B) ©Galen Rowell/Corbis; **xi** (TR) Roger Ressmeyer/Corbis; **xiii** (B) Breck P. Kent Natural History Photography; **xv** (B) Colin Keates/DK Images; **xviii** (C) Rosenfeld Images Ltd./Photo Researchers, Inc.

2 Jeff Gentner/©AP Images, (BC) Photo Researchers, Inc., (TR) Rosenfeld Images Ltd./Photo Researchers, Inc., (BL) Science Photo Library/Photo Researchers, Inc.; **3** (B) ©AP Images, (TL) Courtesy of AT&T Archives and History Center, Warren, NJ, (B) M_G/Shutterstock, (TR, C) Ryan McVay/Getty Images; **4** (T) ©Emi Allen/SuperStock, (BCL) ©Paul Seheult/Corbis, ©PHOTOTAKE Inc/Alamy Images, (TCR) AGStockUSA, (TR) John W. Bova/Photo Researchers, Inc., (L) Kevin Fleming/Corbis, (BR) Leland Bobbé/Corbis, (C) NASA, NASA/Photo Researchers, Inc.; **5** (B) Richard Berenholtz/Corbis; **6** Dennis MacDonald/PhotoEdit, Inc.; **7** (BR, B) Dennis MacDonald/PhotoEdit, Inc., (TR) Rosenfeld Images Ltd./Photo Researchers, Inc.; **9** (BR) Colin Cuthbert/Newcastle University/Photo Researchers, Inc.; **10** (T) ©The Boeing Company; **11** (TR) Steve Chenn/Corbis; **12** (BL) Jeremy Sutton Hibbert/Rex Features, Limited, (R) Rex Features, Limited; **13** (CR, BR) ©DK Images, (CC) Anna Clopet/Corbis; **14** (BL) Frank Zullo/Photo Researchers, Inc., (TR) Rosenfeld Images Ltd./Photo Researchers, Inc.; **16** (TL) Will Hart/PhotoEdit, Inc.; **17** (TR, T) ©Don Farrall/Getty Images, (B) C Squared Studios/Getty Images; **18** Jonathan Nourok/PhotoEdit, Inc.; **19** (CR) ©DK Images, (B) Tom Pantages; **21** (L) David Young-Wolff/PhotoEdit, Inc., (TR) Sally and Richard Greenhill Photo Library; **22** (TR) Rosenfeld Images Ltd./Photo Researchers, Inc.; **25** (TR) ©AP Images, (TL) Layne Kennedy/Corbis; **32** ©R. Wallace/Stock Photos/Corbis; **34** (TR) Gabe Palmer/Corbis, (CL) Mark Richards/PhotoEdit, Inc., (BR) Scott Speakes/Corbis, (BR) Tom Stack & Associates, Inc.; **35** (BR) Bill Aron/PhotoEdit, Inc., (TR) Peter Beck/Corbis, (BL) Reuters/Corbis, (TL) The Image Works, Inc.; **36** Peter Menzel/Stock Boston; **38** (T) Peter Menzel/Stock Boston, (BL) Phil Banko/Corbis; **39** (BR) ©Lester V. Bergman/Corbis, (R, L, BC) Charles D. Winters/Photo Researchers, Inc.; **40** (CL) Bill Aron/PhotoEdit, Inc., (TL) Dave King/Courtesy of The Science Museum, London/©DK Images, (BL) Mark A. Schneider/Photo Researchers, Inc.; **41** (BL) E. R. Degginger/Photo Researchers, Inc.; **42** (CL) Fukuhara, Inc./Corbis; **43** (TR) Danylchenko Iaroslav/Shutterstock, (TC) Dennis MacDonald/PhotoEdit, Inc., (BL) Grafton Marshall Smith/Corbis; **44** (TL) Rachel Epstein/PhotoEdit, Inc.; **45** (TBR) E. J. Tarbuck, (T) Peter Menzel/Stock Boston, (B) Ross Durant Photography/Getty Images; **46** (B) Araldo de Luca/Corbis; **47** (TR) Jeffrey Greenberg/Photo Researchers, Inc.; **48** (B) Ric Ergenbright/Corbis; **49** (CR) Bridgeman Art Library, (TR) David Samuel Robbins/Himalayan Odyssey Tours; **50** (T) Eda Rogers; **51** (TR) Nancy Ney/Corbis, (C) Paul A. Souders/Corbis; **54** (BL) Michelle Garrett/Corbis, (T) Peter Menzel/Stock Boston; **55** (B) Chinch Gryniewicz/Ecoscene/Corbis; **57** (TL) Grant Smith/Corbis, (TR) Pat Bruno/Positive Images, (BL) Phil Degginger/Alamy Images, (BR) Souders Studios/Getty Images; **58** (T) ©Mike Rex/Alamy Images; **59** ©Richard Schultz/Corbis; **63** (CR) C.C. Lockwood/Photoshot; **64** (TR) ©IndexStock/SuperStock; **66** Charles Mauzy/Corbis; **68** (T) Charles Mauzy/Corbis; **69** (BR) Charles D. Winters/Photo Researchers, Inc., (TR) Clive Streeter/DK Images; **71** (BR) Chris Mooney/Getty Images; **72** (TR) Charles Thatcher/Getty Images; **73** (BR) Photo(s) by Jim Whitmer; **74** (TR, TC) Michael Cogliantry/Getty Images; **75** (T) Charles Mauzy/Corbis, (B) Zen Shui/SuperStock; **76** Tony Freeman/PhotoEdit, Inc.; **81** (T) Pat Lanza/Photoshot; **84** (B) ©Mlenny Photograhy/Alexander Hafemann/iStockphoto, (T) Charles Mauzy/Corbis; **86** (BL) AGStockUSA, (TR) Galen Rowell/Corbis; **87** (T) Matthew Stockman/Getty Images; **89** (BR) Dave King/Courtesy of The Science Museum, London/©DK Images, (TR) Steve & Dave Maslowski/Photo Researchers, Inc.; **90** fotosav/Shutterstock; **91** Margo Wright/Courtesty Tinker Take-Off; **98** News & Media Relations, Rice University; **100** (T) News & Media Relations, Rice University; **101** (BR) Clive Streeter/©DK Images, (T) Stephen Frisch/Stock Boston; **102** (BL) Clive Streeter/DK Images; **103** (B) Mary Kate Denny/PhotoEdit, Inc.; **105** (TR) Bettmann/Corbis; **108** (BL) Michael Powers/Stock Boston, (T) News & Media Relations, Rice University; **110** (B) ©Joel Arem/Photo Researchers, Inc., (TL) Charles D. Winters/Photo Researchers, Inc., (C) Russell Lappa/Photo Researchers, Inc.; **111** (TR) Science Museum/Science & Society Picture Library; **113** (B) Bohdan Hrynewych/Stock Boston, (T) News & Media Relations, Rice University; **116** Chris Curtis/Shutterstock; **118** (TL) William Sallaz/Duoma/Corbis; **119** (TR) Jerry Mason/Photo Researchers, Inc.; **120** ©Joel Arem/Photo Researchers, Inc.; **124** Wolfgang Kaehler/Corbis; **126** (BL) Michael Newman/PhotoEdit, Inc., (TR) Wolfgang Kaehler/Corbis; **129** (TR) Alan Schein Photography/Corbis, (C) Kenneth Eward/Photo Researchers, Inc.; **130** (B) Pedro Sousa/Alamy, (TR) Wolfgang Kaehler/Corbis; **135** (BR) David Parker/Photo Researchers, Inc., (BL) Science Photo Library/Photo Researchers, Inc.; **136** (T) Comstock Images/Getty Images, (B) Jonathan Nourok/PhotoEdit, Inc.; **138** (TR) ©David R. Frazier/Photo Researchers, Inc., ©PHOTOTAKE Inc/Alamy Images, (TL) ©sciencephotos/Alamy Images, (CR, CL) Charles D. Winters/Photo Researchers, Inc., (TC) Dave King/ Courtesy of The Science Museum, London/©DK Images, (CB) Fundamental Photographs, (TRL) Richard Megna/Fundamental Photographs, (TCL) Science Photo Library/Photo Researchers, Inc.; **139** (B) Mike Fiala/Getty Images, (TR) Wolfgang Kaehler/Corbis; **140** (TR) Richard Megna/Fundamental Photographs; **141** (L, BL) ©inga spence/Alamy Images, (C) ©Stefano Scata/Getty Images, (R) Gina Sanders/Shutterstock; **142** (TR) ©Michael Ventura/Alamy Images, (BL) Dana White/PhotoEdit, Inc.; **143** (TR) David Nunuk/Science Photo Library/Photo

Researchers, Inc.; **144** (TL) ©PHOTOTAKE Inc/Alamy Images, (TR) Elena Rooraid/ PhotoEdit, Inc., (B) Pearson Education/Prentice Hall College; **145** (T) Raymond Gendreau/Getty Images; **147** (TR) ©DK Images, (BR) Martin Brigdale/©DK Images, (BL) Philip Dowell/©DK Images, (CC) Roger Phillips/©DK Images, (CL) Stephen Hayward/©DK Images, (CR) Steve Gorton/©DK Images; **156** George D. Lepp/Corbis; **158** (TR) George D. Lepp/Corbis, (BL) Horie Corporation; **161** (BR) Galen Rowell/Corbis; **162** (TR) ©M. Claye/Jacana Scientific Control/Photo Researchers, Inc.; **163** (TCR) Colin Keates/©DK Images, (TR) Colin Keates/The Natural History Museum, London/©DK Images; **165** (B) Charles Gupton/Stock Boston, (TR) George D. Lepp/Corbis; **166** (TL) Mark M. Lawrence/Corbis; **170** (T) George D. Lepp/Corbis, (BL) Jennifer Cheung; **171** (TR, TL) Thomas Markusen/ Markusen Metal Studios Ltd.; **172** (TL) ©Matthias Kulka/Corbis; **176** (BL) Andrew Syred/Photo Researchers, Inc., (T) George D. Lepp/Corbis; **178** (BC) ©Dave King/ Motoring Picture Library. National Motor Museum, Beaulieu/DK Images, (CR) Hulton Archive/Getty Images; **179** (L) Bettmann/Corbis, (CR) George Hall/Corbis, (C) John Carter/Photo Researchers, Inc.; **180** (TL) ©SuperStock/AGE Fotostock, (TR) Paul Conklin/PhotoEdit, Inc.; **181** (T) ©age fotostock//SuperStock; **182** (BL) ©DK Images, (BC) Colin Keates/©DK Images; **183** (TC) ©Clive Streeter/Courtesy of The Science Museum, London/DK Images, (TR) Clive Streeter/©DK Images, (TR) Jan Hinsch/Science Photo Library/Photo Researchers, Inc., (C) Matthew Ward/©DK Images, (BL) Tony Craddock/Photo Researchers, Inc.; **188** (T) Honda, ho/©AP Images; **190** John Warden/Superstock; **192** John Warden/Superstock; **192** (BL) ©Charles O'Rear/Corbis; **194** (TL) Stock Connection; **197** John E. Kelly/Getty Images; **199** John Warden/Superstock; **199** (BR) David Bartruff/Stock Boston; **200** (TL) Tom Pantages; **201** (TR) Don Johnston/Getty Images; **202** (TR) Clive Steeter/ ©DK Images, (TC, BL) Clive Streeter/©DK Images; **203** (TR) Richard Megna/Fundamental Photographs; **204** (TL) Charles D. Winter/Photo Researchers, Inc., (B) Richard Megna/Fundamental Photographs; **206** John Warden/Superstock; **206** (BL) Bill Bachmann/PhotoEdit, Inc.; **209** (TR) Richard Megna/Fundamental Photographs; **210** (R) Francis Specker/©AP Images, (BL) Ted Soqui/Getty Images; **211** (BC) Mike Stewart/Corbis, (CR) Paul A. Souders/Corbis, (T) PAUL CROCK/AFP/ Getty Images; **212** John Warden/Superstock; **212** (BL) Will Hart; **213** (BR) Steven Martine/©AP Images; **214** (BL) ©DK Images; **216** John Warden/Superstock; **216** (B) David Sailors Photography, (B) David Sailors/Corbis; **218** (B) Edgar Fahs Smith Collection/Rare Book and Manuscript Library, University of Pennsylvania, (T) Getty Images; **219** (TR) UpperCut Images/Alamy; **219** (TR) Ken Graham/Accent Alaska; **226** Claus Meyer/Minden Pictures; **228** (T) Claus Meyer/Minden Pictures, (B) Sea Images/PhotoLibrary Group, Inc.; **229** (TR) Chris Collins/Corbis; **230** (TL) Eric Kamp/PhotoLibrary Group, Inc.; **231** (TR) Annie Griffiths Belt/Corbis; **233** (TR) Dick Makin Imaging; **235** (T) Claus Meyer/Minden Pictures; **236** (R) Fundamental Photographs, (TL) Jules Frazier/Getty Images, (C, BL) Richard Megna/Fundamental Photographs; **237** (BR) Mark Hanauer/Corbis; **238** (BR) Steve Gorton/©DK Images; **239** (TR) Bill Varie/Corbis; **240** (T) Claus Meyer/Minden Pictures, (B) Russ Lappa; **241** (BR) Paul Silverman/Fundamental Photographs; **242** Charles Gullung/Corbis; **243** (B) Bob Krist/Corbis, (T) PictureNet/Corbis; **244** (BL) James L. Amos/Corbis; **246** (T) Claus Meyer/Minden Pictures, (B) The Image Works, Inc.; **249** (TR) David Young-Wolff/Getty Images; **256** (R) Fundamental Photographs, (L, C) Richard Megna/Fundamental Photographs; **260** Arnulf Husmo/Getty Images; **262** (T) Arnulf Husmo/Getty Images, (B) Mark A. Johnson/Corbis; **264** (TL) Javier Larrea Roa/AGE Fotostock; **266** (BL) C. Marvin Lang/University of Wisconsin at Stevens Point, (T) Dmitry Kosterev/Shutterstock, (C) Jupiterimages/Thinkstock; **267** (B) ©David Lyons/Alamy Images, (T) Davis Muench/Corbis; **268** (TL) Barry Rowland/AGE Fotostock; **269** (T) Spencer Platt/Getty Images; **272** (T) Arnulf Husmo/Getty Images; **274** (TR) Hisham Ibrahim/Getty Images; **275** (T) Arnulf Husmo/Getty Images, (B) Digital Vision/Getty Images; **276** (B) ©David Lyons/Alamy Images, (TC) Andy Crawford/©DK Images, (TR) Michael Conroy/©AP Images, (TL) Michael Pole/ Corbis; **277** (B) ©DK Images, (CR) Simon Belcher/Alamy, (TR) The Advertising Archive; **278** ©Bichon/photocuisine/Corbis; **279** (BL) Stephen Simpson/Getty Images; **280** (L) Andrew Whittuck/DK Images; **281** Scott Camazine/Photo Researchers, Inc., (TL) Yogi, Inc./Corbis; **282** (B) Aldo Torelli/Getty Images, (T) Arnulf Husmo/Getty Images; **283** (TR) Jane Sapinsky/SuperStock; **284** (TL) Michael P. Gadomski/Photo Researchers, Inc.; **287** (CR) Shannon Fagan/Corbis; **290** CERN/ Photo Researchers, Inc.; **292** (BL) ©The Granger Collection, NY, (TR) CERN/Photo Researchers, Inc., (BC) Jean-Loup Charmet/Science Photo Library/Photo Researchers, Inc.; **293** (TR) Francois Gohier/Photo Researchers, Inc.; **296** (TL) Roberto de Gugliemo/Photo Researchers, Inc.; **298** (TR) CERN/Photo Researchers, Inc., (BL) Kenneth Garrett; **301** ©The Trustees of The British Museum; **302** (T) Creatas/©Punchstock; **303** (TR) CERN/Photo Researchers, Inc., (BR) David Lees/ Corbis; **304** NASA; **305** (T) David Parker/Science Photo Library/Photo Researchers, Inc.; **306** (TL, R) Roger Ressmeyer/Corbis; **308** (TR) CERN/Photo Researchers, Inc.; **309** (BR) ©AP Images; **311** (BR) Matthew McVay/Getty Images; **312** (BR) Hulton Archive/Getty Images, (BL) Photo Researchers, Inc., (BC) Physics Today Collection/American Institute of Physics/Photo Researchers, Inc.;

313 (TC, BL) Science Source/Photo Researchers, Inc., (R) Idaho National Laboratory; **314** Patrick Landmann/Photo Researchers, Inc.; **315** (TR) Roger Ressmeyer/Corbis; **322** Jon Arnold/Getty Images; **324** (TR) Michael J. Doolittle/The Image Works, Inc., (L) Reuters/Corbis, (BR) Robert Brenner/PhotoEdit, Inc.; **325** (TR) ©Syracuse Newspapers/Suzanne Dunn/The Image Works, Inc., (BL) Adam Woolfitt/Corbis, (C) Jonathan Hillyer/Esto, (BR) Lou Jones/Getty Images; **326** ©Duomo/Corbis; **328** (TR) ©Duomo/Corbis, (BL) Tony Freeman/PhotoEdit, Inc.; **329** (T) Pedro Coll/AGE Fotostock; **332** (T) ©Duomo/Corbis, (B) Dennis O'Clair/Getty Images; **334** (TR) Leonard Lessin/Peter Arnold, Inc., (T) Steve Krongard/Getty Images; **335** (T) Melissa Carroll/iStockphoto; **336** (T) ©Randy Wells/Corbis, (BL) Sharon Green/Corbis; **338** (CR) ©DK Images, (R) Joel W. Rogers/Corbis, (BL) Stephen Oliver/©DK Images; **340** (TR) ESA/CE/EUROCONTROL/ Photo Researchers, Inc.; **341** (TL) Cen Lu/AGE Fotostock, (TL) dyoma/Shutterstock, (CR) Niels Poulsen DK/Alamy Images, (TR) Stephen Oliver/©DK Images; **342** (T) ©Duomo/Corbis, (BL) David Young-Wolff/PhotoEdit, Inc.; **344** (TL) Barnabas Kindersley/©DK Images, (B) Lester Lefkowitz/Corbis; **345** (TR) Benjamin Rondel/Corbis; **347** (T) Karl Weatherly/Getty Images, (B) Michael Newman/ PhotoEdit, Inc.; **355** Bob Martin/Getty Images; **356** (BL) ©AP Images, (TR) Bob Martin/Getty Images; **357** (R, L) David Young-Wolff/PhotoEdit, Inc.; **358** (T) David Young-Wolff/PhotoEdit, Inc.; **361** (TR) James Steinberg/Photo Researchers, Inc., (BR) Nicholas Bergkessel, Jr./Photo Researchers, Inc.; **362** (R) Fundamental Photographs, (TC) Peticolas/Megna/Fundamental Photographs; **363** (C) ©Bettmann/Corbis, (B) ©The Granger Collection, NY, (TR) Bob Martin/Getty Images; **364** (TL) Bettmann/Corbis, (BR, BL) Insurance Institute for Highway Safety, (CL) Sheila Terry/Science Photo Library/Photo Researchers, Inc.; **365** (BR, BL) Insurance Institute for Highway Safety; **366** (C) ©Mercedes Benz/©DK Images; **369** (TR) ©AP Images, (TL) Bettmann/Corbis; **370** (R) Steve Fitchett/Getty Images; **371** (TR, CR, BL) David Wootton Photography; **372** (TR) Bob Martin/Getty Images, (BL) Joe McBride/Getty Images; **373** (R) Duomo/Corbis; **374** (T) ©Doug Martin/ Photo Researchers, Inc., (CR) Corbis, (L) Mary Evans Picture Library; **375** (BL) Bettmann/Corbis, (BR) Joyrides/Joe Schwartz, (CC) Macduff Everton/Corbis; **378** (TR) Bob Martin/Getty Images, (BL) Ludek Press/Science Photo Library/Photo Researchers, Inc.; **379** (BR) Michelle D. Bridwell/PhotoEdit, Inc., (TR) Tony Anderson/Getty Images; **388** ©Guy Grenier/Masterfile Corporation; **390** (T) ©Guy Grenier/Masterfile Corporation, (B) Aaron Haupt/Stock Boston, (C) Jonathan Nourok/PhotoEdit, Inc.; **391** (BR) Charles D. Winter/Photo Researchers, Inc.; **392** ©sciencephotos/Alamy Images; **394** (T) ©Guy Grenier/Masterfile Corporation; **395** (BL) moodboard/SuperStock; **396** (T) Firefly Productions/Corbis; **398** (R) Cameron Heryet/Getty Images; **400** (T) ©Guy Grenier/Masterfile Corporation; **402** (BL) Steve Kaufman/Corbis; **404** (T) Layne Kennedy/Corbis; **406** (TL) ©sciencephotos/Alamy Images; **410** Paul Chesley/Getty Images; **412** (TR) Paul Chesley/Getty Images, (BL) Reuters/Corbis; **414** (B) ©David Grossman/The Image Works, Inc., (TL) Dennis MacDonald/PhotoEdit, Inc.; **416** (T) Kevin Fleming/Corbis, (CL) Tony Freeman/PhotoEdit, Inc.; **417** (R) Gabe Palmer/ Palmer Kane Studio, (TR) Paul Chesley/Getty Images; **418** (T) Tony Freeman/ PhotoEdit, Inc.; **420** (TL) Kevin Fleming/Corbis; **421** (TR) Paul Chesley/Getty Images; **422** (BL) ©Bettmann/Corbis, (BC) North Wind Picture Archives, (BR) Science & Society Picture Library; **423** (BR) Lambert/Stone/Getty Images, (CL, CC) Science & Society Picture Library; **424** (BL) Wolfgang Deuter/Corbis; **426** (TL) Michael Rosenfeld/Getty Images; **427** (B) ©Rube Goldberg Inc., (TR) Paul Chesley/ Getty Images; **428** (C) Richard Hutchings/PhotoEdit, Inc., (TR) Rob Crandall/The Image Works, Inc.; **430** (BL) Neil Beer/Corbis; **431** (TR) Michael Thompson/Animals Animals/Earth Scenes; **432** (TL) H. David Seawell/Corbis; **435** (TR) ©Fukuhara Inc./Corbis; **436** (T) DK Images; **437** (CR) John Kelly/Getty Images; **439** (TR) Getty Images; **444** David A. Northcott/Corbis; **446** (TR) David A. Northcott/Corbis, (BL) Galen Rowell/Corbis; **447** (TR) David R. Frazier/Photo Researchers, Inc., (C) Michael Pohuski/Getty Images, (B) Mike Powell/Getty Images; **448** (BL) Adamsmith/ Getty Images; **449** ©Flirt/SuperStock; **450** (TR) CSA Images, (TL) Mark Thompson/ Getty Images; **451** (R) Dawson Jones/Stock Boston, (T) Tom Stewart/Corbis; **452** (B) ©Myron Jay Dorf/Corbis, (B) ©Warren Faidley/Corbis; **453** (B) American Museum of Natural History , (TR) David A. Northcott/Corbis; **454** (T) Myron Jay Dorf/Corbis; **455** (T) Donald Miralle/Staff/Getty Images; **456** (TL) John W. Bova/ Photo Researchers, Inc., (B) Phil Degginger/Getty Images; **457** (TR) Gilbert Iundt/ TempSport//Corbis; **459** (T) Topham/The Image Works, Inc.; **460** (R) ©Robin Smith/Getty Images; **461** (B) Detroit Publishing Co./Library of Congress, (CL) Premier Rides; **462** (TR) David A. Northcott/Corbis, (B) George Hunter/ Getty Images; **463** (TR) David Parker/Science Photo Library/Photo Researchers, Inc.; **464** (B) ©Visions of America/Joe Sohm/Getty Images, (T) Charles Krebs/Corbis; **465** (TR) Dave King/©DK Images; **466** John Elk/ Stock Boston; **472** ©W.A. Sharman; Milepost 92 1/2/Corbis; **474** (BL) ©The Granger Collection, NY, (TR) ©W.A. Sharman; Milepost 92 1/2/Corbis; **475** (B) Duncan Smith/Corbis, (TR) Jonelle Weaver/Getty Images; **479** (TR) ©W.A. Sharman; Milepost 92 1/2/Corbis, (BR) Alfred Pasieka/Photo Researchers, Inc.; **480** (BL) Eastcott/Momatiuk/Stock

Boston, (T) Penina/Getty Images, (BR) Steve Cohen/Getty Images; **481** Philip Lewis/Alamy Images; **482** Johner Images/Alamy; **483** Geoffrey Wheeler/National Institute of Standards and Technology; **484** (C) BRE Global Limited; **486** (T) ©W.A. Sharman; Milepost 92 1/2/Corbis; **491** (B) David Young-Wolff/PhotoEdit, Inc.; **495** Insadco Photography RF/AGE Fotostock; **498** Peter Sterling/Getty Images; **500** (B) M. Timothy O'Keefe/Photoshot, (T) Peter Sterling/Getty Images; **504** (T) Peter Sterling/Getty Images; **508** JoLin/iStockphoto, (T) Peter Sterling/Getty Images; **509** (BL) Tom Stack & Associates, Inc.; **510** (TL) Fundamental Photographs, (TR) Richard Megna/Fundamental Photographs; **512** (TL, CL) Richard Megna/Fundamental Photographs; **513** (TL) ©Stephen Frink; **514** (T) Peter Sterling/Getty Images; **515** (B) C Squared Studios/Getty Images, (T) Martin Fox/PhotoLibrary Group, Inc.; **516** (TL) Darryl Torckler/Getty Images; **518** (BR) Clive Streeter/©DK Images, (BC) Dave King/DK Images, (BL) The Science Museum, London/DK Images; **519** (BL) Bettmann/Corbis, (CC) Corbis, (TC) Paul Fleet/Alamy; **520** (TR) ©DK Images, (CC) DK Images; **521** (TR) Talaske, Inc.; **522** (B) Randy Jolly/Corbis; **523** (BL) Alan Thornton/Getty Images; **530** (Bkgrd,) Andrew Woodley/Alamy Images; **532** (B) Rob Bartee/SuperStock; **536** (TL) Dave King/©DK Images; **539** (B) ©The Print Collector/Alamy Images; **541** (B) David Young-Wolff/Getty Images, (T) Robert E. Daemmrich/Getty Images; **542** Spencer Grant/PhotoEdit, Inc.; **543** (TR, TL) FLIR Systems, Inc; **544** (BL) David Arky/Corbis; **545** (T) WDCN/Univ. College London/Photo Researchers, Inc.; **546** (B) ©Stephen Frink; **547** (B) Arthur Morris/Corbis, (TL) C Squared Studios/Getty Images, (TR) Stockbyte/Getty Images; **548** (TL) ©Southern Illinois University/Photo Researchers, Inc.; **550** (BR) B Busco/The Image Bank/Getty Images, (BL) Jerome Wexler/Photo Researchers, Inc.; **551** (TL) Dave King/Courtesy of The Science Museum, London/©DK Images; **552** (BL) Leonard Lessin/Photo Researchers, Inc.; **554** (B) ©DK Images; **555** (T) ©DK Images, (BCR) Tate Enterprises, Ltd; **556** (CR, BL) Volker Steger/Photo Researchers, Inc.; **557** (TR) ©1996 Board of Trustees, National Gallery of Art, Washington, D.C. Gift of Mr. and Mrs. Robert Woods Bliss. Photograph by Lorene Emerson./Image ©2003 Board of Trustees, National Gallery of Art, Washington, (CL) ©National Gallery, London, (CC) RAPHAEL/©National Gallery, London; **558** (L, B) ©David R. Frazier/Photo Researchers, Inc., (T) Andrew Woodley/Alamy Images; **559** (TR) David Young-Wolff/PhotoEdit, Inc.; **560** (BC) ©DK Images, (C) Dave King/©DK Images; **562** (TL, CL) Tony Freeman/PhotoEdit, Inc.; **565** PhotoEdit, Inc.; **568** David Frates/Positive Images; **570** (B) Andrey Tarantin/Shutterstock, (TR) David Frates/Positive Images, (R) Kochneva Tetyana/Shutterstock; **571** (TR) Ariel Skelley/Corbis; **574** (TR) David Frates/Positive Images; **576** (BL) Darwin Dale/Photo Researchers, Inc.; **577** (BR) Peter Finger/Corbis; **579** (TL) Stockbyte/Getty Images; **580** (BL) ©Roger Ressmeyer/Corbis, (TR) David Frates/Positive Images; **582** (BR) Corbis, (L) Giraudon/Bridgeman Art Library, (CR) Science & Society Picture Library; **583** (CL) ©DK Images, (BC) Corbis, (R) Judith Collins/Alamy; **587** (TR) BSIP, Edwige/Photo Researchers, Inc., (TCR) Dave King/DK Images; **588** (BL) Dave Greenwood/Getty Images, (T) David Frates/Positive Images; **591** (B) ©DK Images, (TR, TCR) Paul Parker/Photo Researchers, Inc.; **598** Kent Wood/Photo Researchers, Inc.; **600** (TR) Kent Wood/Photo Researchers, Inc., (BL) Michael Newman/PhotoEdit, Inc.; **602** (BL) ©DK Images, (CL) Andy Crawford/©DK Images; **607** (R) Fundamental Photographs; **608** (TL) Grantpix/Photo Researchers, Inc.; **609** (B) Dennis MacDonald/PhotoEdit, Inc.; **612** (B) Russ Lappa; **613** (R) Fundamental Photographs, (T) Stockbyte/Getty Images; **614** (BL) bigfishphotoagent/Alamy Images, (C) Daisy Images/Alamy; **616** (TR) Lawrence Migdale/Photo Researchers, Inc., (CL) Matthew Klein, (BL) NASA; **617** (L) Richard Lam/©AP Images; **618** (BL) Ephraim Ben-Shimon/Corbis, (BR) Michael Matisse/Getty Images; **619** (TR) ©DK Images, (CR) DK Images, (B) Science & Society Picture Library; **620** (TR) Franka Bruns/©AP Images; **622** (T) Digital Vision/Getty Images; **626** ©Visions of America, LLC/Alamy, (CR) Getty Images; **628** Photoshot; **630** (TR) Photoshot, (BL) Reprinted by permission of Houghton Mifflin Company. All rights reserved.; **631** (T, C) Richard Megna/Fundamental Photographs, (CR, BR) Spencer Grant/Photo Researchers, Inc.; **634** (TR) Jose Luis Pelaez, Inc./Corbis; **635** (BR) Bettmann/Corbis, (TR) Photoshot; **638** (BR) Harvey Schwartz/PhotoLibrary Group, Inc.; **640** (B) ©DK Images; **641** (BL) Sovereign, ISM/Photo Researchers, Inc.; **642** JTB Photo Communications, Inc./Aflo Foto Agency, (TR) Photoshot; **644** (T) SuperStock; **645** (BR) Lloyd Cluff/Corbis; **646** (BL) A & C Wiley/Wales/PhotoLibrary Group, Inc., (TR) David Papazian/Corbis.

Periodic Table of the Elements

Key

6 — Atomic number
C — Element symbol
Carbon — Element name
12.011 — Atomic mass

Legend

Nonmetals — C, Li, B (Metalloids), Metals

Solid — Li, B
Liquid — Hg, Br
Gas — C, H
Not found in nature — Tc, Rf

1 / 1A	2 / 2A	3 / 3B	4 / 4B	5 / 5B	6 / 6B	7 / 7B	8 / 8B	9 / 8B	10 / 8B	11 / 1B	12 / 2B	13 / 3A	14 / 4A	15 / 5A	16 / 6A	17 / 7A	18 / 8A
1 **H** Hydrogen 1.0079																	2 **He** Helium 4.0026
3 **Li** Lithium 6.941	4 **Be** Beryllium 9.0122											5 **B** Boron 10.81	6 **C** Carbon 12.011	7 **N** Nitrogen 14.007	8 **O** Oxygen 15.999	9 **F** Fluorine 18.998	10 **Ne** Neon 20.179
11 **Na** Sodium 22.990	12 **Mg** Magnesium 24.305											13 **Al** Aluminum 26.982	14 **Si** Silicon 28.086	15 **P** Phosphorus 30.974	16 **S** Sulfur 32.06	17 **Cl** Chlorine 35.453	18 **Ar** Argon 39.948
19 **K** Potassium 39.098	20 **Ca** Calcium 40.08	21 **Sc** Scandium 44.956	22 **Ti** Titanium 47.90	23 **V** Vanadium 50.941	24 **Cr** Chromium 51.996	25 **Mn** Manganese 54.938	26 **Fe** Iron 55.847	27 **Co** Cobalt 58.933	28 **Ni** Nickel 58.71	29 **Cu** Copper 63.546	30 **Zn** Zinc 65.38	31 **Ga** Gallium 69.72	32 **Ge** Germanium 72.59	33 **As** Arsenic 74.922	34 **Se** Selenium 78.96	35 **Br** Bromine 79.904	36 **Kr** Krypton 83.80
37 **Rb** Rubidium 85.468	38 **Sr** Strontium 87.62	39 **Y** Yttrium 88.906	40 **Zr** Zirconium 91.22	41 **Nb** Niobium 92.906	42 **Mo** Molybdenum 95.94	43 **Tc** Technetium (98)	44 **Ru** Ruthenium 101.07	45 **Rh** Rhodium 102.91	46 **Pd** Palladium 106.4	47 **Ag** Silver 107.87	48 **Cd** Cadmium 112.41	49 **In** Indium 114.82	50 **Sn** Tin 118.69	51 **Sb** Antimony 121.75	52 **Te** Tellurium 127.60	53 **I** Iodine 126.90	54 **Xe** Xenon 131.30
55 **Cs** Cesium 132.91	56 **Ba** Barium 137.33	71 **Lu** Lutetium 174.97	72 **Hf** Hafnium 178.49	73 **Ta** Tantalum 180.95	74 **W** Tungsten 183.85	75 **Re** Rhenium 186.21	76 **Os** Osmium 190.2	77 **Ir** Iridium 192.22	78 **Pt** Platinum 195.09	79 **Au** Gold 196.97	80 **Hg** Mercury 200.59	81 **Tl** Thallium 204.37	82 **Pb** Lead 207.2	83 **Bi** Bismuth 208.98	84 **Po** Polonium (209)	85 **At** Astatine (210)	86 **Rn** Radon (222)
87 **Fr** Francium (223)	88 **Ra** Radium (226)	103 **Lr** Lawrencium (262)	104 **Rf** Rutherfordium (261)	105 **Db** Dubnium (262)	106 **Sg** Seaborgium (263)	107 **Bh** Bohrium (264)	108 **Hs** Hassium (265)	109 **Mt** Meitnerium (268)	110 **Ds** Darmstadtium (269)	111 **Rg** Roentgenium (272)	112 **Cn** Copernicium (277)	*113 **Uut** Ununtrium (284)	*114 **Uuq** Ununquadium (289)	*115 **Uup** Ununpentium (288)	*116 **Uuh** Ununhexium (293)		118 *Uuo Ununoctium (299)

*Name not officially assigned

Lanthanide Series

57 **La** Lanthanum 138.91	58 **Ce** Cerium 140.12	59 **Pr** Praseodymium 140.91	60 **Nd** Neodymium 144.24	61 **Pm** Promethium (145)	62 **Sm** Samarium 150.4	63 **Eu** Europium 151.96	64 **Gd** Gadolinium 157.25	65 **Tb** Terbium 158.93	66 **Dy** Dysprosium 162.50	67 **Ho** Holmium 164.93	68 **Er** Erbium 167.26	69 **Tm** Thulium 168.93	70 **Yb** Ytterbium 173.04

Actinide Series

89 **Ac** Actinium (227)	90 **Th** Thorium 232.04	91 **Pa** Protactinium 231.04	92 **U** Uranium 238.03	93 **Np** Neptunium (237)	94 **Pu** Plutonium (244)	95 **Am** Americium (243)	96 **Cm** Curium (247)	97 **Bk** Berkelium (247)	98 **Cf** Californium (251)	99 **Es** Einsteinium (252)	100 **Fm** Fermium (257)	101 **Md** Mendelevium (258)	102 **No** Nobelium (259)